D1257187

Treatment of Mental Illness and Behavioral Disorder in the Mentally Retarded

Proceedings of the International Congress
May 3-4, 1990
Amsterdam, The Netherlands

EDITED BY:
Anton Došen, M.D.
Adriaan van Gennep, Ph.D.
Gosewijn J. Zwanikken, M.D.

Logon Publications
Leiden - The Netherlands
1990

CIP-GEGEVENS KONINKLIJKE BIBLIOTHEEK, DEN HAAG

Treatment

Treatment of mental illness and behavioral disorder in the mentally retarded : proceedings of the 1990 international congress Amsterdam, the Netherlands / ed. by: A. Došen, A. van Gennep, G.J. Zwanikken.
– Leiden : Logon
Met lit. opg.
ISBN 90-73197-02-3 geb.
SISO 607 UDC 616.89-08-056.36(042.3)
Trefw.: gedragsstoornissen : geestelijk gehandicapten / psychische stoornissen : geestelijk gehandicapten.

Printed in the Netherlands by ICG Printing bv, Dordrecht

Contents

page

Preface 8

Authors 9

The International Congress on Treatment of Mental Illness and Behavioral Disorder in the Mentally Retarded 13

Introductory Address
A. Došen 19

Section I: Plenary lectures

1. Mental illness in the mentally retarded: diagnostic issues and treatment considerations
   F.J. Menolascino 21
2. Developmental-Dynamic Relationship Therapy
   A. Došen 37
3. Toward a psychology of interdependence: a preliminary study of the effect of Gentle Teaching in 15 persons with severe behavioral disorders and their caregivers
   J.J. McGee 45
4. Individual psychoanalytic psychotherapy with severely and profoundly mentally handicapped patients
   V. Sinason 71
5. Group analytic therapy with people with mental handicap
   S.C. Hollins 81
6. Psychotropic drug therapy prescribing principles for mentally retarded persons
   R. Sovner 91
7. Treatment of anti-social behaviour
   K.A. Day 103
8. Mental health services for mentally ill/mentally retarded persons: a community mental health center model
   R.J. Fletcher 123

Section II: workshop and paper presentations

Psychodynamic therapies

9. Grief therapy for people with mental handicap
   S.C. Hollins 139

page

10. Therapy for people with dual diagnosis: treating the behaviours or the whole person?
N.T. Baum 143
11. Portrait of small therapy group with violin
A. Stammler 157
12. Some trends in psychoanalysis and their relevance for treating people with mental retardation
R. Ruth 167

Play therapy
13. Indications and goals for play therapy with the mentally retarded
J. Hellendoorn 179

Developmentally-dynamic relationship therapy
14. Treatment of psychiatric disorders and behavioral problems in mentally handicapped persons: working with relationship therapy and gentle teaching in an institutional setting
J. van Loon 189
15. Counseling of mentally retarded children with emotional and behavioural problems in a day care centre: a report of practice
J. Vonk & C. Egberts 201

Ericksonian therapy
16. Ericksonian approaches: hypnotherapeutic, systemic and strategic ideas
E. Hohn 209

Integrative approach
17. Diagnosing and treating psychopathology in clients with dual diagnosis: an integrative model
A. Pfadt 217

Systems-theoretic approaches
18. Systemic family therapy and mental retardation
K. Hennicke & C. Bradl 225
19. Treatment of severe behaviour disorder in the mentally retarded from a systems approach
J. Griffioen, S. de Graaff & J.F. Gehrels 233
20. Family based intervention: a model for in-home treatment of individuals with dual diagnosis
K.R. Mirick 241

page

Re-education, educational and socio-therapy
21. Cognitive re-education of mentally retarded persons as an instrument for social integration: an Italian experience
L. Moderato 249
22. An educational approach to behavioural disorders
G.H. van Gemert 255
23. Treatment of persons with a mental handicap: trends in orthopedagogy
A. van Gennep 269

Pharmacotherapy
24. Self-injurious behaviour in the mentally retarded and treatment by opiate antagonists
H. Kars & W.M.A. Verhoeven 279
25. Treatment of autistic disorders in the mentally retarded with the adrenocorticotrophic hormone (4-9) analog ORG 2766
J.K. Buitelaar 285
26. Pharmacotherapy and art therapy in the management of challenging behaviour
S.R. Sadik 291
27. Psychotropic drug use in mentally retarded adults: prevalence and risk factors
W. Meins 299

Behavioral modification
28. Behaviour treatment and behaviour therapy within the limits of the Dutch care for the mentally retarded
G. van Osch 307

Treatment of behavioral problems in the mildly mentally retarded
29. Training of social skills with mildly mentally retarded people with severe behaviour disorders
A.L. Le Grand 315
30. Clinical treatment of behavioral problems in mildly mentally retarded persons with severe personality disorders
G.J.C.M. Verberne 325

Treatment of behavioral problems in the severely mentally retarded
31. Effects of Gestalt therapy and drug therapy in hyperactive severely mentally retarded children
L. Igric, N. Sikic & D. Burusic 339

page

32. Running program for severely mentally retarded men with behaviour disorders
W. Blesch & A. Metzger 351

Treatment of the multiply handicapped mentally retarded
33. Psychotherapy of multiply handicapped persons
C.J.M. Lindner-Middendorp 355

Treatment of angry and aggressive behavior
34. Anger management training
B.A. Benson 361
35. Aggressive behaviour among people with learning difficulties – the nature of the problem
P. Harris & O. Russell 367

Treatment of sex offenders
36. Treatment of sexually deviant behaviour in mildly mentally retarded adults
G.J.C.M. Verberne 375
37. A model for staff training and clinical treatment for the mentally retarded sex offender
D. Cox-Lindenbaum 387

Assessment and treatment
38. Comparison of maladaptive behaviour between mentally handicapped adults with and without epilepsy
S. Deb & D. Hunter 395
39. A behavioral methodology for diagnosing affective disorders in individuals with mental retardation
R. Sovner & M. Lowry 401
40. Temperament research with mentally retarded people in the Netherlands
J.B. Blok 413

Multi-disciplinary teamwork on treatment
41. From punishment and treatment to living and residing as normal as possible: a case study
G. van Hove 421
42. Psychiatric disorders in mentally retarded patients and their treatment in a medium secure unit
M. Isweran & N. Brener 429
43. Challenging behaviours: problems: provisions and "solutions"
J. Dockrell, G. Gaskell & H. Rehman 437

page

44. Residential treatment of mildly mentally retarded children and adolescents with behaviour disorders, educational problems and social-affective problems
J.S.T. Niessen 445
45. Aspects of integrative and dialogical co-operation between therapeutic pedagogues and psychotherapists in working with the mentally retarded
W. Reukauf & H.S. Herzka 451

Foster care of the mentally retarded
46. Mental retardation, emotional and behavioural disorders and foster care: a useful combination?
J. Prins 459

Pre-therapy
47. Psychotherapy with a retarded, schizo-affective woman: an application of Prouty's pre-therapy
D. van Werde 469

Community based models of mental health care for the mentally retarded
48. Diagnostic and treatment issues for adults in community care
N. Bouras & C. Drummond 479
49. A network of services for the mental health care of the mild and moderately mentally retarded in south-east Noord-Brabant/The Netherlands
J.J.M. Gielen 485

Preface

On Thursday and Friday, May 3rd-4th 1990, the International Congress on Treatment of Mental Illness and Behavioral Disorder in the Mentally Retarded was held in the buildings of the Free University, Amsterdam, the Netherlands. About 400 professionals from fifteen different countries all over the world gathered to learn about recent developments in research and practice and to discuss their own ideas and experiences in an international forum.

The large number of abstracts submitted to the Congress Commitee and the diversity in approaches and opinions represented therein indicate that many professionals in the field of mental retardation are actively engaged in the search for new methods for treatment of mental illness and behavioral disorders and are highly committed to the care for mental health in the mentally retarded.

This volume contains the texts of all invited lectures, delivered in plenary session, as well as a large number of the short papers and workshops that were accepted by the Congress Committee for presentation in parallel sessions.

The Editors' objective was to keep the time span between the Congress and the publication of the Proceedings as short as possible, thus making the material presented at the Congress available to the participants as soon as possible. This could be achieved only by refraining from substantial editorial and corrective measures. As a consequence, the material in this volume represents a large variety in form, style and language level.

The Editors hope that the actuality, importance and urgency of the material presented here will outweigh the obvious shortcomings in style and language. We hope that this volume will contribute to quality of practical work of professionals in the field of mental retardation and will stimulate further research and development on treatment issues.

Amsterdam, June 1990

A. Došen
A. van Gennep
G.J. Zwanikken

Authors

N.T. Baum, Ph.D., Muki Baum Association, Downsview, Ontario, Canada

B.A. Benson, Ph.D., Department of Psychology, University of Illinois at Chicago, Chicago, Illinois, U.S.A.

W. Blesch, Centre for Mentally and Multiply Handicapped Persons *Anstalt Mosbach*, Mosbach, Germany

J.B. Blok, Ph.D., Institute for the Mentally Retarded *Stichting Haarendael*, Haaren, Netherlands.

N. Bouras, Ph.D., Division of Psychiatry, United Medical and Dental Schools, Guy's Hospital, London, U.K.

C. Bradl, Department of Child and Adolescent Psychiatry, *Rheinische Landesklinik*, Viersen, Germany.

N. Brener, Eric Shepherd Unit, Leavesden Hospital, Watford, U.K.

J.K. Buitelaar, Department of Child and Adolescent Psychiatry, Utrecht University Hospital, Utrecht, Netherlands.

D. Burusic, Centre for Rehabilitation *Stancic*, Zagreb, Yugoslavia.

D. Cox-Lindenbaum, ACSW, Ridgefield, Connecticut, U.S.A.

K.A. Day, Northgate Hospital, Morpeth, and Department of Psychiatry, Newcastle University, U.K.

S. Deb, M.D., Department of Mental Health, University of Aberdeen, Woodlands Hospital, Cults, Aberdeen, U.K.

J. Dockrell, Department of Social Psychology, London School of Economics, London, U.K.

A. Došen, M.D., Clinic for Psychiatric and Behavioral Disorders in the Mentally Retarded *Nieuw Spraeland*, Oostrum, Netherlands

C. Drummond, Division of Psychiatry, United Medical and Dental Schools, Guy's Hospital, London, U.K.

Ch. Egberts, *Stichting Werkgemeenschap Orthopedagogische Zorg*, Amsterdam, Netherlands.

R. Fletcher, ACSW, National Association for the Dually Diagnosed (NADD), Kingston, New York, USA

G. Gaskell, Department of Social Psychology, London School of Economics, London, U.K.

J.F. Gehrels, Community and Service Centre for Mentally Retarded Persons, *'s Heerenloo-Loozenoord*, Ermelo, Netherlands.

G.H. van Gemert, Ph.D., Department of Special Education, University of Groningen, Netherlands.

A. van Gennep, Ph.D., Department of Special Education, University of Amsterdam, Amsterdam, Netherlands

J.J.M. Gielen, Living Community for the Mentally Retarded *Eckartdal*, Eindhoven, Netherlands.

S. de Graaff, Community and Service Centre for Mentally Retarded Persons, *'s Heerenloo-Loozenoord*, Ermelo, Netherlands.

J. Griffioen, Community and Service Centre for Mentally Retarded Persons, *'s Heerenloo-Loozenoord*, Ermelo, Netherlands.

P. Harris, Norah Fry Research Centre, University of Bristol, Bristol, U.K.

J. Hellendoorn, Ph.D., Department of Special Education, University of Leiden, Netherlands.

K. Hennicke, M.D., Department of Child and Adolescent Psychiatry, *Rheinische Landesklinik*, Viersen, Germany.

H.S. Herzka, M.D., Department of Child and Adolescent Psychopathology, University of Zürich, Switzerland.

E. Hohn, Department of Child and Adolescent Psychiatry, *Rheinische Landesklinik*, Viersen, Germany.

S.C. Hollins, M.D., St. George's Hospital Medical School, University of London, U.K.

G. van Hove, Department of Special Education, University of Gent, Belgium.

D. Hunter, Department of Mental Health, University of Aberdeen, Woodlands Hospital, Cults, Aberdeen, U.K.

L. Igric, Faculty of Defectology, University of Zagreb, Yugoslavia.

M.S. Isweran, Eric Shepherd Unit, Leavesden Hospital, Watford, U.K.

H. Kars, Institute for Mental Retardation *Eemeroord*, Baarn, Netherlands.

A.L. Le Grand, Institute for the Mentally Retarded *Hoeve Boschoord*, Boschoord, Netherlands.

C.J.M. Lindner-Middendorp, Institute for the Mentally Retarded *Bartimeushage*, Doorn, Netherlands.

J. van Loon, Institute for the Mentally Retarded *De Sterre*, Clinge, Netherlands.

M. Lowry, Ph.D., Department of Psychology, Belchertown State School, Belchtertown, Massachusetts, U.S.A.

J.A. McGee, Ph.D., Department of Psychiatry, Creighton University, Omaha, Nebraska, U.S.A.

W. Meins, M.D., Psychiatric and Mental Hospital, University of Hamburg, Hamburg, Germany.

F.J. Menolascino, M.D., Department of Psychiatry, Creighton and Nebraska Universities, Omaha, Nebraska, U.S.A.

A. Metzger, Centre for Mentally and Multiply Handicapped Persons *Anstalt Mosbach*, Mosbach, Germany

K.R. Mirick, Family Consultant Program, Virginia Beach, Virginia, U.S.A.

L. Moderato, Bureau of Services for Handicapped Persons, Milano, Italy.

J.S.T. Niessen, Institute for the Mentally Retarded *De Reeve*, Kampen, Netherlands

G. van Osch, Institute for the Mentally Retarded *Hendrik van Boeijenoord*, Assen, the Netherlands.

A. Pfadt, Ph.D., New York State Institute for Basic Research in Developmental Disabilities, Staten Island, New York, U.S.A.

J. Prins, Department of Special Education, Free University, Amsterdam, Netherlands.

H. Rehman, Department of Social Psychology, London School of Economics, London, U.K.

W. Reukauf, Ph.D., Department of Child and Adolescent Psychopathology, University of Zürich, Switzerland.

O. Russell, Norah Fry Research Centre, University of Bristol, Bristol, U.K.

R. Ruth, Ph.D., Community Psychiatric Clinic, Gaithersburg, Maryland, U.S.A.

S.R. Sadik, M.D., Psychiatry of Mental Handicap, Medway Health Authority, Rochester, U.K.

N. Sikic, Centre for Rehabilitation *Stancic*, Zagreb, Yugoslavia.

V. Sinason, Tavistock Clinic, London, U.K.

R. Sovner, M.D., Lutheran Center for Mental Health and Mental Retardation, Brighton, Massachusetss, U.S.A.

A. Stammler, M.D., Paris, France.

G.J.C.M. Verberne, Clinic for Psychiatric and Behavioral Disorders in the Mentally Retarded *Nieuw Spraeland*, Oostrum, Netherlands

W.M.A. Verhoeven, M.D., Ph.D., Department of Biological Psychiatry, Psychiatric Hospital Venray, Netherlands.

J. Vonk, *Stichting Werkgemeenschap Orthopedagogische Zorg*, Amsterdam, Netherlands.

D. van Werde, Clinic *St. Camillus*, Gent, Belgium.

International Congress on Treatment of Mental Illness and Behavioral Disorder in the Mentally Retarded
May 3rd & 4th, 1990
Amsterdam, the Netherlands

Organization

* PAOS, the Netherlands Organziation for Postacademic Education in the Social Sciences
* Section on Mental Retardation of the World Psychiatric Association

Congress committee

* K.A. Day (United Kingdom)
* A. Došen (Netherlands) – Chairman
* A. van Gennep (Netherlands)
* F.J. Menolascino (United States)
* G.J. Zwanikken (Netherlands)

Congress co-ordinator

P. Engelen (PAOS, the Netherlands)

Members of congress committee and invited speakers

Prof.dr. J.A. Corbett, M.D., is Professor of Psychology at the University of Birmingham, Department of Mental Handicap, Lea Castle Hospital, Kidderminster, U.K.

Dr. K.A. Day is Consultant Psychiatrist at Northgate Hospital, Morpeth, Northumberland, and Senior Lecturer in the Department of Psychiatry, University of Newcastle-upon-Tyne, U.K.

Dr. A. Došen, M.D., is Consultant Psychiatrist and Director of Treatment at the Clinic for Psychiatric and Behavioral Disorders in the Mentally Retarded Nieuw-Spraeland in Oostrum, Netherlands

R. Fletcher, A.C.S.W., is Executive Director of the National Association for the Dually Diagnosed, Kingston, New York, USA

Prof.dr. A. van Gennep, Ph.D., is Professor of Special Education at the University of Amsterdam, Netherlands

Dr. S.C. Hollins, M.D., is Honorary Consultant and Senior Lecturer in the Psychiatry of Mental Handicap, St. George's Hospital Medical School, University of London, U.K.

Prof.dr. J.A. McGee is Associate Professor of Psychiatry, Creighton University, Omaha, Nebraska, USA

Prof.dr. F.J. Menolascino is Professor of Psychiatry and Chairman of the Department of Psychiatry, Creighton and Nebraska Universities, Omaha, Nebraska, USA

Mrs. V. Sinason is Principal Child Psychotherapist at the Tavistock Clinic, London, U.K.

Dr. R. Sovner, M.D., is Consultant Psychiatrist and Medical Director at the Lutheran Center for Mental Health and Mental Retardation, Brighton, Massachusetss, USA

Prof.dr. G.J. Zwanikken, M.D., is Professor of Psychiatry amd Chairman of the Department of Psychiatry, Catholic University of Nijmegen, Netherlands

Congress program

Invited lectures (plenary sessions)

F.J. Menolascino: Overview of psychiatric diagnosis and possibilities for treatment of the mentally retarded

S.C. Hollins: Psychoanalytic approach to treatment of groups of mentally retarded adults

R. Sovner: Overview of the use of psychotropic drug therapy in mentally retarded persons

A. Došen: Developmentally-Dynamic Relationship Therapy

V. Sinason: Individual psychoanalytic therapy of mentally retarded persons

J.J. McGee: Gentle Teaching: an approach to treatment of mentally retarded persons with severe behavioral disorders

J.A. Corbett: Treatment of self-injurious behaviour in mentally retarded persons

K.A. Day: Treatment of anti-social behaviour in mildly mentally retarded persons

R. Fletcher: A service-delivery model of mental health services for the mentally retarded with psychiatric disorders

Workshops and paper presentations (parallel session)

Psychotherapy in the mentally retarded
N.T. Baum (Canada): Therapy for people with dual diagnosis: treating the behaviours or the whole person?

Psychoanalytic therapy
V. Sinason (U.K.): Individual psychoanalytic therapy of mentally retarded persons
S.C. Hollins (U.K.): Grief therapy for people with mental handicap

Psychodynamic oriented treatment
R. Ruth (USA): Some trends in psychoanalysis and their relevance for treating people with mental retardation
M. Gardini, R. Tombolato, G. Ferrari, P. Nicoletti (Italy): Psychotic symptoms in mentally retarded children as an entrance door towards learning

Image Communication therapy
T. Maaskant & L. Schenk-de Jong (Netherlands): "The bear in the drying machine" and other stories: Hermeneutic Image Communication

Gentle teaching therapy
J. McGee (USA): Gentle teaching: treatment of mentally retarded persons with severe behavioural disorder

Developmentally-dynamic relationship therapy
M. Teuchies & J. van Loon (Netherlands): Relationship therapy and Gentle Teaching in the treatment of mentally handicapped people with psychiatric disorders and behavioural problems
J. Vonk & C. Egberts (Netherlands): Counseling mentally retarded children with emotional and behavioural problems in a day care center

Treatment of sex offenders
G.J.C.M. Verberne (Netherlands): Treatment of sexually deviant behaviour in mildly mentally retarded adults
D. Cox-Lindenbaum (USA): Staff training and clinical treatment for the mentally retarded sex offender

Integrative and systems-theoretic approaches
A. Pfadt (USA): Diagnosing and treating psychopathology in clients with dual diagnosis: an integrative perspective
S. de Graaff, J. Griffioen, J.F. Gehrels (Netherlands): Treatment of severe behaviour disorder in the mentally retarded from a systems approach

L. de Jaegher & F. Bovenlander (Netherlands): Treatment of behavioural disorders: an approach based on systems and communication theories

K. Mirick (USA): Family based intervention: a model for in-home treatment of individuals with dual diagnosis
D. Janotova (Czechoslovakia): Mentally retarded children and their families
K. Hennicke (West-Germany): Systemic family therapy and mental retardation
M. Isweran & N. Brener (U.K.): Psychiatric disorders in mentally retarded patients and their treatment in a medium secure unit
J. Prins (Netherlands): Mental retardation, emotional and behavioural disorders and foster care: a useful combination?

Self-enhancement therapy
K.A. Keuter (USA): Self-enhancement therapy group for the dually diagnosed

Educational approach
L. Moderato (Italy): Cognitive re-education as an instrument for social integration of mentally retarded persons
G.H. van Gemert (Netherlands): An educational approach to behavioural disorders: a case study
A. van Gennep (Netherlands): Treatment of persons with a mental handicap: trends in orthopedagogy.
J. Niesten & C.L.H. Lamberts (the Netherlands): Residential treatment of mildly mentally retarded children and young adults with behaviour disorders, educational problems and social-affective problems.
W. Reukauf & H.S. Herzka (Switzerland): Aspects of integrative and dialogical co-operation between therapeutic pedagogues and psychotherapists in working with the mentally retarded

Pharmacotherapy
R. Sovner (USA): The diagnosis and treatment of affective disorders in mentally retarded persons.
R. Cocchi (Italy): Pharmacotherapy in Down syndrome children
S.R. Sadik (U.K.): Pharamacotherapy and art therapy in the management of challenging behaviour in people with a mental handicap
W. Meins (West-Germany): Psychotropic drug use in mentally retarded adults: prevalence and risk factors

Symposium on mental retardation, mental illness and neuropeptides
J.M. van Ree (Netherlands): A preclinical perspective on treatment of behavour disorders in the mentally retarded with neuropeptides

H. Kars & W.M.A. Verhoeven (Netherlands): Self-injurious behaviour in the mentally retarded and treatment by opiate-antagonists
J.K. Buitelaar (Netherlands): Treatment of autistic disorders in the mentally retarded with the adrenocorticotrophic hormone (4-9) analog ORG 2766

Behavioural treatment
G. van Osch (Netherlands): Behaviour treatment and behaviour therapy within the Dutch system of care for the mentally retarded

Play therapy, music therapy
J. Hellendoorn (Netherlands): Indications and goals for play therapy with the mentally retarded
A. Stammler (France): Small therapy group with violin

Pre-therapy
D. van Werde (Belgium): Prouty's pre-therapy approach

Environmental adaptation
G. van Hove (Belgium): From punishment and treatment to living and residing as normal as possible: a case study
J. Dockrell, H. Rehman & G. Gaskell (U.K.): Can special units meet community needs? An evaluation of a unit for people with learning problems and challenging behaviour.
H. Groven (Netherlands): Therapy of profoundly retarded persons with persistent behaviour problems.

Community based models of mental health care for the mentally retarded
R. Fletcher: A service delivery model of mental health services for the mentally retarded with psychiatric disorders
N. Bouras & C. Drummond (U.K.): Diagnostic and treatment issues for adults in community care
J.J.M. Gielen (Netherlands): A network of services for the treatment of mentally ill/mentally retarded in the south-eastern region of the province of Noord-Brabant, the Netherlands

Treatment of behavioral problems in the mildly mentally retarded
K.A. Day (U.K.): The Northgate program for male mentally handicapped offenders.
A. Le Grand (Netherlands): Training of social skills with mildly mentally retarded people with severe behaviour disorders
G.J.C.M. Verberne (Netherlands): Clinical treatment of behavioural problems in mildly mentally retarded persons with severe personality disorders

Treatment of the severely and multiply handicapped mentally retarded
L. Igric & N. Sikic (Yugoslavia): The effects of Gestalt therapy and drug therapy in hyperactive severely mentally retarded children
A. Metzger & W. Blesch (West-Germany): Running program for severely mentally retarded men with behaviour disorders.
C. Lindner-Middendorp (Netherlands): Psychotherapy of multiply handicapped persons

Treatment of pervasive developmental disorder
M. Gardini (Italy): Hold the "black hole", "holding" left and right cerebral functions

Treatment of angry and aggressive behavior
B. Benson (USA): Anger management training

Assessment and treatment
S. Deb (U.K.): Psychopathology of people with mental handicap and epilepsy
T. Holland (U.K.): The nature of the eating disorder in the Prader-Willi syndrome
J.B. Blok (Netherlands): Temperament research with mentally retarded children in the Netherlands
G.H. Murphy (U.K.): Analysis of motivation and fire-related interests in people with a mild learning difficulty who set fires
P. Harris & O. Russell (UK): Aggressive behaviour among people with learning difficulties: the nature of the problem
D. Clarke, S. Bundey, J. Corbett, M. Kilpatrick & T. Webb (U.K.): A psychiatric and genetic study of Prader-Willi syndrome
D. Sansom & J. Corbett (U.K.): Behaviour problems in Rett syndrome
A. Xeromeritou (Greece): Perceptions of facial and emotional features by educable mentally retarded and non-retarded children

Ericksonian therapy
E. Hohn (West-Germany): Ericksonian approaches to treatment of mentally retarded persons: hypnotherapeutic, systemic and strategic ideas

Introductory Address to the Congress

This congress is a result of the mutual initiative and collaboration of the section Mental Retardation of the World Psychiatric Association (W.P.A.)and the Netherlands Organisation for Postacademic Education in the Social Sciences (PAOS). The section Mental Retardation of the W.P.A. is an organisation with the purpose of promoting mental health care for mentally retarded citizens and of incorporating experiences gained within this work on the one hand into general psychiatric knowledge, and on the other hand into the general mental retardation care. Organizing international scientific meetings is an important task of this section.

The PAOS is a very active organisation in the dissemination of knowledge in social and related sciences. Under the leadership of Mr. Engelen in the past few years PAOS has been very succesful in organizing international scientific meetings.

This is the second international scientific meeting in the Netherlands on this issue of psychiatric and behaviorally disturbed mentally retarded individuals, resulting from the cooperation between the section Mental Retardation and PAOS. The first meeting was two years ago. The subject was depression in the mentally retarded. A good response to the meeting from the workers in the field was a confirmation of the organizer's idea that within the field of care for the mentally retarded there is a need for better understanding of the phenomenon of frequent psychiatric and behavioral disorders among mentally retarded individuals.

It is becoming more and more clear that these disorders have to be detected, diagnosed and treated but that this can not be done sufficiently solely from the principles of classic psychiatry for the general population. Experienced professionals in the field of the psychiatric disorders in the mentally retarded are convinced that for good diagnostics and treatment in this population specific clinical and scientific understanding is needed. This understanding should not only derive from general psychiatry but also from discovering the specific existential and mental health needs of mentally retarded individuals. This means that in order to provide sufficient aid to these persons the professionals in this field have to have specific knowledge. At the moment it can not be denied that the specificity of the problems of mentally retarded individuals and the specificity of the knowledge required, demand the organisation of special care; that is, mental health care for the mentally retarded. In certain countries this special care is developing.

In most countries however such care simply does not exist. Moreover in many countries the workers in the mental retardation field are still ambiguous toward the concept of the coexistence of mental retardation and mental illness. I am thinking now not of the developing countries of the third world, but of various countries in Western Europe.

Meetings like this congress aim to focus the attention of professionals on behavioral and psychiatric disorders in the mentally retarded as well as to stimulate the professionals to search for new ways of serving these individuals. To meet the needs of these people new diagnostical approachs, new treatment methods and, above all, a new attitude in caregivers towards the existential and mental health issues of mental retardation are badly needed. This congress has to be seen as an attempt to make an overview of current developments in the treatment of behavioral and psychiatric disorders in different countries and within different professions. To this purpose we have invited a number of internationally known experts in this area. The diversity of methods and approaches which are going to be presented today and tomorrow during the plenary sessions, shows how actively new treatment possibilities are being looked for. Even the therapeutic methods which seemed unworkable in the treatment of the mentally retarded several years ago (such as psychoanalytic psychotherapies) will be discussed here.

Our call for papers for parallel sessions has resulted in a surprisingly high response. The congress committee has chosen 62 papers and workshops to be presented. The speakers come from 15 different countries.

I am convinced that today and tomorrow we all shall have an opportunity to share our experiences and our opinions, and to learn from each other.

Anton Došen

Došen, A., Van Gennep, A., Zwanikken, G.J. (Eds.) (1990). Treatment of Mental Illness and Behavioral Disorder in the Mentally Retarded. Proceedings of the International Congress, May 3rd & 4th, 1990, Amsterdam, the Netherlands. Leiden, the Netherlands: Logon Publications.

Chapter 1

Mental illness in the mentally retarded: diagnostic and treatment considerations

F.J. Menolascino

Introduction

A mental illness which occurs in conjunction with mental retardation poses both major diagnostic difficulties and intriguing treatment challenges. The differential diagnostic issues involved in separating the social-adaptive behavioral indices of a moderately retarded individual from his or her concurrent problems in interpersonal transactions can approach the complexity of the Gordian knot. Yet it is only the clear resolution of such issues that can enhance the probability of making astute selections among an increasing number of treatment options.

It may be prudent at the outset to recall how many of the recent advances made in the specialized area of mental illness in the mentally retarded came on the heels of an extended period of treatment nihilism. For example, the current cautious employment of psychopharmacological agents in this population followed a period during which the indiscriminate use of such agents was common (Lipton, 1970). The sedative role of psychotropic medications, by virtue of excessive dosages, was stressed as a thin rationalization for "keeping the patient quiet," which was presumed to be better than providing no treatment at all. Yet this "something" versus "nothing" approach fostered potentially harmful and restrictive practices. More bluntly, much of this early clinical psychopharmacology represented a *non*psychiatric approach, wherein the control of behavior was exclusively emphasized. Treatment guidelines based on the careful descriptive psychiatric study of an individualized clinical picture failed to be considered. Robert Sovner (1986) and others (Aman, 1985; Aman & Singh, 1986; Colodny & Kurlander, 1970; Stark, Menolascino & McGee, 1984) have, in a series of incisive papers, documented this period of dark clinical intervention during which the quelling of behavioral turmoil was viewed as the primary goal. Such was the ethos that pervaded the field of mental retardation before and during the 1950s and 60s.

The past two decades have taken a fresh appraisal of the psychiatric aspects of mental retardation (Menolascino, 1970), wherein the DSM-III (APA, 1980) and more recently the DSM-III-R (APA, 1987) diagnostic systems began to be applied to the behavioral syndromes noted in the mentally retarded. Modern treatment approaches are being increasingly embraced and clinical guidelines for the majority of modern psychiatric treatment interventions on behalf of the dually diagnosed are being actively promulgated (APA, 1989; Fletcher & Menolascino, 1989; McGee & Pearson, 1983; Stark & Menolascino, 1986).

Psychiatric assessment of persons with mental retardation

Objective behavioral assessment

The literature in both mental health and mental retardation research reveals a growing professional focus on *descriptive* diagnosis, on the objectively delineated phenomena that are clinically present as opposed to possible causative mechanisms or indirect dynamic formulations so typical of the recent past. For example, professional myths of the past regarding the "expected" behavioral symptoms of mentally retarded citizens led to stilted diagnostic approaches which tended to dismiss the efficacy of psychiatric treatment interventions and disallow hopeful prognoses. Many professionals were trained to believe (or had fixed personal views before ever starting advanced training) that, in contrast to normal persons, mentally retarded citizens displayed qualitative or quantitative distinctiveness in their expressions of the signs and symptoms of mental illness. A clear instance of this excessive concentration on extraneous factors was the commonly held assumption that individuals with Down's Syndrome were the "Prince Charmings" of the mentally retarded: overly friendly, extremely affable, given to mimicry, and essentially devoid of indices of mental illness. Unfortunately, this particular behavioral stereotype blinded generations of clinicians to the wide spectrum of abnormal behaviors which Down's Syndrome persons presented directly before their eyes, causing them to concentrate instead on the traditional interpretations of "anticipated" behaviors. However, as the psychiatric dimensions of Down's Syndrome began to be studied and reported in the literature, the "Prince Charming" facade fell away, revealing a wide array of psychiatric disorders (Lund & Munk-Jorgenson, 1988; Menolascino, 1966; Stark, Menolascino, Albarelli & Gray, 1988).

Table 1
Webster's primary psychopathology of mental retardation

1. Intellectual deficit
2. Slow rate of development
3. Immaturity of personality structure and simplicity of emotional life
4. Self-absorption
5. Repetitiousness, preference for the known rather than the novel
6. Inflexibility, preference for familiar routing and an insistence upon it
7. Passivity

Adapted from Webster, T.G. (1970). Unique aspects of emotional development in mentally retarded children. In. F.J. Menolascino (ed.), *Psychiatric Approaches to Mental Retardation.* New York: Basic Books.

Beyond the "diagnostic overshadowing" noted by Reiss, Levitan and Szyszko (1982) or the normal behavioral repertoire one often notes in moderately retarded citizens (see Table 1), progress is being made in the objective measurement and recording of atypical or abnormal behaviors via descriptive scales which are increasingly replacing the previously hypothesized presence of signs or symptoms of mental illness in the mentally retarded (Matson, 1988; Reiss, Levitan & Szyszko, 1982; Sonnander, 1986; Watson, Aman & Singh, 1988). Clinicians seem less comfortable observing and describing *multiple* symptomatic/syndromic phenomena and acting directly on same through multiple treatment interventions. Instead, they tend to follow the traditional training principle of seeking the major cause of a given symptom(s) configuration and then utilizing the rather myopic treatment procedures which flow from such a one-dimensional (and most often erroneous) approach. Admittedly, the challenge of diagnosing a mentally retarded-mentally ill person who may simultaneously display three to six major presenting disorders (see Table 2) tends to bewilder the clinician. It is becoming increasingly clear, however, that the evolving postures of descriptive diagnostic clarification as a prelude to specific treatment intervention will continue to help erase the aura of bewilderment that has clouded the vision of mental health professionals toward the dually diagnosed person in the past.

Table 2
Associated medical disabilities found in mentally retarded-mentally ill patients

1. Grand mal epilepsy
2. Cerebral palsy
3. Psychomotor epilepsy
4. Petit mal epilepsy
5. Acute/chronic otitis media and allied auditory problems
6. Congenital deafness
7. Visual disorders
8. Diabetes mellitus
9. Hypothyroidism

A particularly strong antidote to any ongoing over-reliance on behavioral stereotypes in the retarded is the multidisciplinary team approach with its more balanced strategies toward diagnosis and treatment interventions. Such an approach, which brings together a wide range of talents and skills in an effort to clarify these complex clinical challenges, entails an attendant professional posture wherein a premium is placed on the clear description of current behaviors. One can only treat what *is present*, whether in the mentally retarded-mentally ill or in the nonretarded-mentally ill. True, the psychoanalyst might scoff at such a simplistic view of human behavior, but he or she would have to concede that it is behavioral improvement that most conflicted or mentally retarded persons are requesting of our clinical intervention efforts, and that the psychoanalytical goal of re-education of the personality is now viewed as a rare luxury, both in its attainment and in terms of patient (or parental/caretaker) interest. In other words, most people want to obtain prompt relief for their headaches (read: disturbing feelings) and are not overly interested in knowing the symbolic basis for same.

Utilizing a wide variety of direct treatment approaches for objectively described behaviors has been a hallmark of developmentally oriented special education/vocational rehabilitation approaches in the field of mental retardation for the last three decades. It is now, and will increasingly be, more actively extended into the arena of clinical treatment-management of the mental illnesses which are so commonly noted in this population.

Primitive, atypical, and abnormal behavior in mentally retarded persons

Whether psychopharmacology is considered as a primary or secondary treatment intervention in the retarded, it is important to separate out that wide spectrum of behaviors emanating from the developmental, cognitive, and social-adaptive aspects of the symptom of mental retardation which distinctly colors the clinical presentation. Herein the behavioral accompaniments of primitive, atypical, and abnormal behaviors can help to clarify for the clinician just what does (and does not) warrant active treatment interventions. This diagnostic dimension is especially important when one notes that many instances of "self-injurious" or "non-compliant" behavior in the retarded are reflections of delayed development, uninspired parenting, and minimal educational opportunities rather than psychopathology (see Table 3).

Table 3
Essential aspects of primitive, atypical and abnormal behavior

PRIMITIVE	Untutored
	Benign autism
	Limited ability to interact with outside world
ATYPICAL	Self-stimulation in lieu of interpersonal interaction
	Idiosyncratic interpretation of interactions
	Incomplete personality development
	Developed but atypical defenses (e.g., head banging, skin picking)
ABNORMAL	Islands of ego intactness/regression
	Reconstruction of reality

Primitive Behavior

Primitive behavior is usually manifested by severely or profoundly retarded individuals who additionally display gross delays in their language development. The primitive behaviors most consistently displayed stem from the extremely limited behavioral repertoires so often noted in these patients, particularly within the context of excessive expectations from their families, their educational milieu, their group home staff, vocational training setting, etc. Such behaviors involve very rudimentary utilization of special sensory modalities, particularly touch, position, oral exploratory activity, and sudden verbalizations which have no apparent purpose in terms of interpersonal communication. In diagnostic interviews of individuals with primitive behaviors, one notes much mouthing and licking of objects, excessive tactile stimulation, weird – but not stereotyped – hand movements, skin picking, or body rocking. In severely retarded children, the very primitiveness of their overall behavior, in conjunction with interpersonal hesitancy and precious few avenues for communicating with the examiner, may initially suggest a psychotic disorder of childhood. If gently and indirectly approached in a unhurried atmosphere, however, such youngsters will slowly make sustained eye contact and interact with the examiner despite their minimal behavioral repertoire. Similarly, one might form the initial impression that the level and persistence of primitive behaviors are actually secondary to intrinsic (i.e., volitional) and/or extrinsic (i.e., psycho-social) deprivation factors. Yet upon thorough clinical investigation, a majority of these children clearly display concurrent multiple indices of developmental arrest of primary or congenital origin. Clarifying the diagnosis, realigning parental and professional expectations, and focusing upon specific developmental/educational transactional modalities are the keys to providing effective help to retarded individuals who display these primitive behaviors.

It is within this differential diagnostic framework of a primitive behavioral picture that the clinician must determine which dysfunctional behaviors (e.g., impulsiveness, hyperactivity, shortened attention span, etc.) should or should not be treated on a syndromic or – rarely – a symptomatic basis. The behavioral treatment interventions and possible psychopharmacologic agents to be utilized should then be selected. For example, a psychopharmacological agent may be employed for organic brain syndromes by matching the intervention with the etiologies which produced the symptoms(s) of mental retardation. Certain of the anti-convulsants may be indicated for post-traumatic injuries (i.e. head injuries in childhood) which have features of attention deficit disorders but no allied seizure phenomena. Similarly, in instances which reflect cranial malformations as an underlying etiology, pharmacological agents such as propanolol, should be considered because of their peripheral locus of action in selectively modulating primitive behavioral dysfunctions. Since these and similar psychopharmacological agents are used to selectively alter symptoms, it is imperative that they are always utilized within the context of a balanced educational/vocational and social-recreational management program.

Atypical Behavior

Atypical behaviors include poor emotional control (as evidenced by frequent emotional outbursts), a manipulative posture towards authority figures, sullenness, obstinacy, frequent (mild) legal transgressions, and generally poor interpersonal adaptation to prevocational or vocational training programs. For example, a retarded adolescent may be committed to an institution because of ongoing behavioral adjustment and legal difficulties (i.e., truancy,) within his or her home community, but it is important to note that such difficulties are not displayed or reported within the primary family structure. Instances of atypical behavior are usually only "atypical" for the community generic program or institutional settings in which these individuals find themselves since they are usually quite "typical" within the sub-culture of their primary family (i.e., dysocial phenomena). Viewed via the *Manual of Terminology and Classification in Mental Retardation* (Grossman, 1983), their etiologic diagnosis is usually in the realm of "cultural-familial mental retardation" or "idiopathic mental retardation." When individuals with this type of atypical behavior arrive at an institution, psychiatric consultation is most commonly requested because the patient refuses to cooperate with the training or social expectations of the institutional setting, or because continual abrasive comments and/or contacts from his or her family belittles the institution's ability to effectively help their family member. The family may actually deny the reality of any social-adaptive problems, or harass the institutional staff for focusing upon and attempting to modify problem behaviors. As Beitenman (1981) noted, however, the clarification of both familial expectations and the roles of clinicians and staff is necessary before these individuals can be managed appropriately for all concerned parties.

It would seem that formerly institutionalized mentally retarded individuals with atypical behavior are increasingly "flunking out" of community-based service programs and continue their persistently atypical behaviors within a social system other than the primary family. Clinical management of these complex cases is difficult unless close coordination exists between the administrative segments of community-based or institutional treatment teams (Cumming, 1990). During periods of persistent crises with these individuals, a dependable, benign, and developmentally oriented physical environment can be nicely provided by an institutional setting. Such an environment can help redirect motivational potential, effect realistic changes in the expectations these individuals have of themselves and others, and assist them in achieving more positive social-adaptive approaches to interpersonal transactions and the world of work (Bernstein, 1970).

The cautions previously noted as to when to treat or not to treat primitive behaviors also applies to the atypical behaviors presented by these mentally retarded citizens, who comprise 75% (+) of the youngsters (or adults) with Pervasive Developmental Disturbance. Typically, they have a very long-standing history of atypical general and behavioral developmental disturbance. These complex individuals can be quite challenging – especially as they grow older (and physically larger!) – as their behavioral repertories become increasingly difficult for parents, teachers, and vocational center helpers to manage. Often, ongoing psychoactive drug management becomes a series of attempts specifically designed to alter restlessness, aggressive propensities, and markedly self-centered or self-abusive behaviors and/or activities. To date, however, the available psychopharmacological treatment interventions for these complex individuals tend to be non-specific and tend to lose their effectiveness within several years' time (Donaldson, 1984; Menolascino & McCann, 1983). Nevertheless, current research and allied treatment approaches for more effective management of these types of atypical behaviors hold great promise in the near future for more specific and effective intervention.

Abnormal Behavior in Retarded Persons

A significant percentage of the clearly abnormal behavioral challenges encountered in institutionalized or community-based samples of retarded individuals tends to encompass psychotic behaviors. It is truly remarkable that one still sees psychotic patients who have been literally dumped into institutions for the mentally retarded because of the absence of specific treatment programs in their home communities. One typically notes a clinical history of great enthusiasm when treatment is initiated, but slowness of response is often disillusioning, and the patient is referred to another colleague as "nontreatable." A broad view of developmental potentials and psychotic characteristics must be wedded to specific treatment goals if this type of treatment failure is to be avoided.

In the clinical interview, retarded persons with psychotic disorders tend to present the following behavioral dimensions: 1) bizarreness of manner, gesture, and posture; 2) uncommunicative speech; 3) little or no discrimination between aminate and inanimate objects; 4) identification with most inanimate objects; 5) deviant affective expression; 6) few, if any, relationships with peers; 7) passive compliance to external demands or stimuli; and 8) marked negativism. Many institutions for the retarded have built up large backlogs of psychotic patients whose definitive treatment needs have never been appropriately addressed. Such patients are typically referred elsewhere during acute episodes, and returned in sub-acute remission states. Because institutional staff frequently view these individuals as "odd" or "dangerous", the psychotic process is often refueled by apprehensive personnel until the patient once again enters into an acute stage of mental illness.

Beyond these general considerations are the challenges inherent in attempting to confirm a psychotic disorder in a severely retarded, non-verbal individual. In approaching a final configuration of the indices of mental illness, it is important to remember the wide array of biological markers that have become available to us in recent years, such as the DST in instances of major depression and the lactate infusion assessment for panic disorders. In addition, the new neuroimaging techniques such as positron emission tomography (Jacobson, 1988; Montgomery, 1989) have provided modern psychiatry with one of its first biopsy techniques and hold great promise for objectively assessing the severely retarded, who so often cannot speak very well about their turmoil, if they are able to speak at all.

Through the use of DSM-III-R criteria, which arranges mental illness on Axis I and the concurrent presence of mental retardation on Axis II, the old diagnostic merry-go-round ("Which one came first?") can be more easily avoided. A diagnostic impression can be clearly stated and elaborated in terms of the specific time of developmental onset and the initial behavioral manifestations. For example, the syndrome of Pervasive Developmental Disturbance, whose symptoms tend to be amenable to psychopharmacological intervention, is now placed on Axis II, and only the acute, superimposed symptoms of concurrent mental illness (e.g., an Axis I Major Unipolar Depression) prompt the need for specific treatment intervention. Indeed, the presence of organic brain syndrome does not mean that the dually diagnosed are "nontreatable," since different treatment interventions are clarified by the Axis I/Axis II entities (e.g., the new DSM-III-R 307.30 Stereotypy/Habit Disorder entity). These considerations call for a closer examination of the bipolar disorders, the masked self-injurious behaviors noted in a wide variety of clinical syndromes, and the transitional adjustment disorders, which, in this writer's experience, have too infrequently been reported in the professional literature. Childhood depression can serve as an analogy here: Five years ago it was considered a "rare" phenomenon, but today it is commonly reported (although still rather rarely noted in the literature on mental illness in the mentally retarded).

Although it would be easy to straightforwardly state that the specific mental illnesses noted in the retarded *should* be those syndromes which fulfill DSM-III-R guidelines, it is important to remember that certain symptoms have literally been *elevated* to a status indicative of mental illness. For example, the descriptors "self-injurious behaviors" and "non-compliant behaviors" are often regarded as diagnostic entities in need of treatment. Yet both descriptors are noted: 1) in a high percentage of normal people (especially young people); 2) in schizophrenia; 3) in seizure equivalents; 4) in the affective disorders; 5) as a partial symptom of autism; and 6) as volitional behaviors (i.e., a variant of normal behavior or a slowly solidifying character disorder). Rather than engage in arbitrary diagnostic inclusion, it has been my repeated experience that close and prolonged observation always eventuates in a descriptive diagnostic impression. This posture, for which I strongly advocate, must include the utilization of "No Psychiatric Disorder" and the increased use of the relatively benign Adjustment Disorders with their parameters of 'crisis' and 'time.' Firm adherence to the medical model also helps to clarify those hazy behavioral pictures (i.e., clusters of what appear upon initial evaluation to be unrelated descriptive symptoms) so frequently seen in the retarded. These vague *initial* clinical pictures will consistently give way to clear DSM-III-R designations or other challenging entities, such as "organic anxiety" secondary to hyperthyroidism, B^{12} deficiency masking as atypical depression, or instances of amphetamine toxicity that for all the world look like schizophrenia in the retarded and the nonretarded alike. Again, close observation of symptom clusters, especially secondary to supportive, and initially nonspecific, care, will help to clarify diagnostic entities as a prelude to asking whether pharmacotherapy adjuncts are or are not needed.

An Allied Issue: The Most Complex Challenges

Three subgroups of the mentally retarded – the severely retarded-multiply handicapped, the mentally retarded-mentally ill, and the retarded person with criminal proclivities (i.e., the "mentally retarded offender") – also have major behavioral or personality difficulties as one of their core problems. Although the physical needs of the severely retarded-multiply handicapped tend to emanate directly from their extremely delayed and restricted abilities in dealing with the external world, their behaviors also have direct repercussions on their families, their caregivers, and society in general. These individuals tend to exhaust their parents, both physically and emotionally, and represent a huge dose of reality to overzealous treatment personnel who seem unable to wait for or tolerate the typically slow developmental timetables of these very handicapped complex retarded citizens.

Similar professional challenges surround the issue of providing treatment to the mentally retarded and chronically delinquent adolescent (or offending adult) who displays maladaptive, aggressive, or abnormal sexual proclivities. Indeed, the difficulties involved in providing effective care to this subpopulation are exceptional because the field of corrections (where the bulk of these individuals may belong, rather than in mental retardation service systems through inappropriate referral) has a much weaker base of professional involvement or ongoing parental support than do the developmental-educational mental health systems of care. Although this particular subgrouping is numerically not great, these individuals do tend to tie up excessive amounts of staff time, and their behavioral volatility is an ever present disruptive influence in mental retardation service systems. Although it has become a truism that the adolescent delinquent can and should be treated via the current models of care in adolescent psychiatry (Day, 1988), this truism awaits fuller implementation as increasing numbers of mental health personnel become actively involved. The mentally retarded adult who consistently has legal entanglements secondary to his or her poor impulse control does tend to respond to mental health treatment approaches. For these individuals, the future trend will be to involve them more directly in the correctional system of care while providing active mental health inputs and mental retardation services on an ongoing consultation basis.

General diagnostic concerns

As psychiatry more strongly embraces the biopsychosocial model, it has become increasingly clear that the complexity of the diagnostic entities noted above *must* be matched by equally complex and/or definitive treatment interventions. Just as the designation of "Early Infantile Autism" once occasioned erroneous diagnostic-etiological considerations and allied treatment approaches, current focus on such issues as the exploration of family histories associated with the affective disorders must now come to be more carefully understood: Is there significant genetic loading? Is psychosocially programmed passivity slowly erupting into manic (motoric) explosions? Is Organic Personality Syndrome (i.e., secondary to tumor, trauma, etc.) masking as a potentially treatable underlying cause? Similarly, the concept of diagnostic overshadowing (Reiss, Levitan & Szyszko, 1982), in which the symptoms of mental illness are overshadowed – in the clinician's mind – by the syndrome of mental retardation, applies to such blind spots. The clinical distortions so often noted in the mentally retarded-mentally ill (e.g., intellectual distortion, psychosocial masking, cognitive disintegration, and baseline exaggeration) and can indeed result in the "diagnostic vision problems" so clearly outlined by Sovner (1986; 1988).

Researchers have utilized the subtleties of behavioral psychopharmacology to examine the empirical treatment approaches which are increasingly being applied (and reported) in the literature of innovative care of the dually diagnosed. It is important to underscore the need for professionals to more flexibly utilize pharmacological agents, such as the anti-convulsants, as potentially helpful differential diagnostic instruments. The principle here is atypically traditional in that the closely monitored response to medication is viewed as being potentially both therapeutically helpful and clarifying in terms of concomitant diagnostic challenges. This approach becomes even more viable when working with the dually diagnosed. These complex retarded citizens truly require remediation over time, and not the "quick fix" of crisis-to-crisis pharmacological intervention.

As we continue to try to more fully understand the nature of mental illness in the mentally retarded, it has become clear that we need to re-examine the more frequently reported mental illnesses in the *nonretarded* (e.g., reactive psychosis, the adjustment disorders, crisis situations, etc.) and to question why they are so rarely reported in the mentally retarded population. The reality-based difficulties, for which the mentally retarded-mentally ill are always more "at risk," present us with a continuous professional challenge that we have as complete a grasp on the existential setting of these individuals as possible (Ghaziuddin, 1988). For example, deinstitutionalized retarded citizens tend to be ill-equipped to understand or adjust to the complexities of life in the community. Whether based on the passive conformity fostered in large public institutions or the limited capacities of these individuals for managing more demanding sets of psychosocial expectancies, the response has too often been the same: bewilderment, poor adjustment and, at times, major and prolonged emotional turmoil. This professional challenge has become acute as the number of public institutions for the retarded has decreased dramatically during the last decade. Similarly, more attention needs to be focused on the various chronological age groupings of the mentally handicapped regarding their distinctive diagnostic and possible treatment spectrums. The recent sharp increase in societal awareness of the care given our elderly citizens – whether retarded or not – demonstrates our evolving professional interface with truly unique psychopharmacological challenges and treatment opportunities (Menolascino & Potter, 1989a; Menolascino & Potter, 1989b).

Conclusion

Enhanced diagnostic understanding of the nature and types of mental illness in the mentally retarded has slowly begun to clarify those complex psychiatric disorders which we can or cannot effectively treat with the hope of obtaining optimum results. Current studies on evolving psychopharmacology for the mentally ill retarded citizen illustrate a new interest in the single case-study approach with its allied needs for increased research interaction, ongoing national pooling of results, and rapid dissemination of new treatment approaches (Agran, Moore & Martin, 1988).

Retarded persons with allied mental illnesses still tend to fall into the gap which has traditionally separated mental retardation from mental health services and research. In the past, the needs of the dually diagnosed have gone almost totally unmet as both systems floundered in their interest or ability to address these challenges directly. Those who have been closely identified with the fields have striven for years to clarify the distinction between mental retardation and mental illness. They have been frustrated by the general public's confusion regarding the two conditions, and concerned by the tendency of some professionals to apply mental health approaches inappropriately to mental retardation. Fortunately, erroneous interpretations are increasingly viewed as largely representative of historical professional postures. New contributions are underscoring the art of the possible in terms of how professionals can contribute to the developmental and general life enhancement of retarded citizens whose lives have been complicated by mental illness.

References

Aman, M.G. (1985). Drugs in mental retardation: treatment or tragedy? *Aust and NZ J Dev Dis,* 10, 215-226.

Aman, M.G. & Singh, N.N. (1986). A critical appraisal of recent drug research in mental retardation: the Coldwater studies. *J Ment Defic Res,* 30, 203-216.

American Psychiatric Association (1980). *Diagnostic and statistical manual of mental disorders – third edition.* Washington, D.C.: APA.

American Psychiatric Association (1987). *Diagnostic and statistical manual of mental disorders – third edition – revised.* Washington, D.C.: APA.

American Psychiatric Association (1989). *A task force report of the American Psychiatric Association.* Washington, D.C.: APPI.

Agran, M., Moore, S. & Martin, J.E. (1988). Research in mental retardation: under-reporting of medication information. *Res Dev Dis,* 9, 351-357.

Beitenman, E.T. (1981). The psychiatric consultant in a residential facility for the mentally retarded. In F Menolascino (Ed.), *Psychiatric Approaches to Mental Retardation.* New York: Basic Books.

Berstein, N. (1970). Diminished people: Problems and care of the mentally retarded. Boston: Little Brown.

Colodny, D. & Kurlander, L.F. (1970). Psychopharmacology as a treatment adjunct for the mentally retarded: problems and issues. In F.J. Menolascino (ed.), *Psychiatric approaches to mental retardation.* New York: Basic Books.

Cumming, J. (1990). The community as milieu: a memoir. *Comm Ment Health J,* 26, 1.

Day, K. (1988). A hospital-based treatment programme for male mentally handicappedoffenders. *Br J Psychiatry,* 153, 635-644.

Donaldson, J.W. (1984). Specific psychopharmacological approaches and rationale for mentally retarded-mentally ill children. In F.J. Menolascino & J. Stark (eds.), *Handbook of mental illness in the mentally retarded.* New York: Plenum Press.

Fletcher, R.J. & Menolascino, F.J. (1989). *Mental retardation and mental illness: assessment, treatment, and service for the dually diagnosed.* Lexington, MA: Lexington Books.

Ghaziuddin, M. (1988). Behavioural disorder in the mentally handicapped: the role of life events. *Br J Psychiatry,* 152, 683-686.

Grossman, H. (1983). *Manual of Terminology and Classification in Mental Reatdation.*Washington, DC: American Association on Mental Deficiency.

Jacobson, H.G. (1988). Positron emission tomography: a new approach to brain chemistry. *JAMA,* 260, 2704-2710.

Lipton, R.S. (1970). The use of psychopharmacological agents in residential facilities for the retarded. In F.J. Menolascino (ed.), *Psychiatric approaches to mental retardation*. New York: Basic Books, Inc.

Lund, J. (1988). Psychiatric aspects of Down's syndrome. *Acta Psychiatr Scand*, 78, 369-374.

Lund, J. & Munk-Jorgenson, P. (1988). Psychiatric aspects of Down's syndrome. *Acta Psychiatr Scand*, 78, 369-374.

Matson, J.L. (1988). The PIMRA test manual. Orland Park, IL: International Diagnosis Systems, Inc.

Menolascino, F.J. (1966). The facade of mental retardation: its challenge to child psychiatry. *Amer J Psychiatry*, 122, 1227-1235.

Menolascino, F.J. (1970). *Psychiatric approaches to mental retardation*. New York: Basic Books.

Menolascino, F.J. & McCann, B.M. (1983). *Mental health and mental retardation: bridging the gap*. Baltimore: University Park Press.

Menolascino, F.J. & Potter, J.F. (1989a). Delivery of services in rural settings to the elderly mentally retarded-mentally ill. *Int J Aging Human Dev*, 28, 261-275.

Menolascino, F.J. & Potter, J.F. (1989b). Mental illness in the elderly mentally retarded. *J Applied Gerontology*, 8, 192-202.

McGee, J.J. & Pearson, P.H. (1983). Personnel preparation to meet the mental health needs of the mentally retarded and their families: role of the university-affiliated programs. In F.J. Menolascino & B.M. McCann (eds.), *Mental illness and mental retardation: bridging the gap*. Baltimore, University Park Press.

Montgomery, G. (1989). The mind in motion. *Discover*, March, 1989.

Sonnander, K. (1986). Early identification and prognosis: parental developmental assessment of 18-month old children. *Ups J Med Sci Suppl*, 44, 70-75

Sovner, R. (1986). Limiting factors in the use of DSM-III criteria with mentally ill/mentally retarded persons. *Psychopharm Bull*, 22, 1055-1060.

Sovner, R. (1988). Behavioral psychopharmacology: a new psychiatric subspecialty. In J. Stark, F.J. Menolascino, M. Albarelli, V. Gray (eds.), *Mental retardation and mental health: classification, diagnosis, treatment, services*. New York: Springer-Verlag.

Stark, J., Menolascino, F.J. & McGee, J. (1984). Ethical issues in the use of psychoactive medications in the mentally retarded. In R. Breuning (ed.), *Psychoactive medications in Mental Retardation*. New York: Plenum Press.

Stark, J., Menolascino, F.J. (1986). Training of psychiatrists in mental retardation. *J Psychiatric Ed*, 10, 235-246.

Stark, J., Menolascino, F.J., Albarelli, M.H. & Gray, V.C. (1988). *Mental retardation and mental health: classification, diagnosis, treatment, services*. New York: Springer-Verlag.

Reiss, S., Levitan, G. & Szyszko, J. (1982). Emotional disturbance and mental retardation: diagnostic overshadowing. *Am J Ment Defic*, 86, 567-574.
Watson, J.E., Aman, M.G. & Singh, N.N. (1988). The psychopathology instrument for mentally retarded adults: psychometric characteristics, factor structure, and relationship to subject characteristics. *Res Dev Dis*, 9, 277-290.

Došen, A., Van Gennep, A., Zwanikken, G.J. (Eds.) (1990). Treatment of Mental Illness and Behavioral Disorder in the Mentally Retarded. Proceedings of the International Congress, May 3rd & 4th, 1990, Amsterdam, the Netherlands. Leiden, the Netherlands: Logon Publications.

Chapter 2

Developmental-Dynamic Relationship Therapy

A. Došen

Introduction

Both in the recent clinical practice and the professional literature the emphasis has been growing that individual psychotherapy is applicable to behaviorally and psychiatrically disturbed mentally retarded persons.

However, different authors have different opinions as to the applicability of this treatment at differing intelligence levels and in different kinds of disorder. Some authors are of the opinion that in the case of mentally retarded persons with an IQ lower than 50, a simple support, encouragement, and behavioral modification regimen would give better results than a real psychotherapy. There are also authors who assume that the IQ level is irrelevant as a criterion for the suitability of psychotherapy; rather, it is the motivation of the person to be helped and the ability to respond to a warm supportive relationship that should be the determining factor. In our experiences – gathered in the course of 15 years of clinical work with mentally retarded behaviorally and psychiatrically disturbed children – the emphasis has been that, when approaching the behavioral and psychiatric disorders of children from the developmental-dynamic startpoint, neither the IQ level nor the motivation or other abilities of the person should serve as determinant of the applicability of individual psychotherapy. The only important factor is the developmental needs of the child. Focusing on developmental needs, the therapist should adapt his method and strategy such as to permit the child to receive whatever help is needed for resolving his or her existential and psychosocial difficulties.

The theoretical basis of this treatment is the developmental-dynamic approach to mental illness among the mentally retarded (Došen 1989, 1990). The mainstay of the treatment is provided by the attachment theory of Bowlby (1971) notably his postulate that human beings have an existential need for bonding with other people. This bonding provides a psychological security base from which a child can explore and master his surroundings.

Using the classical terminology of Allen (1942) and Moustakas (1959), we called this treatment "Relationship therapy" (Došen 1984, 1990).

The theoretical base

Before I go on to describe the method of Relationship Therapy, an explanation of its theoretical base is in order. As stated earlier, the theoretical base of the therapy is the developmental-dynamic approach – one which we can touch upon here briefly.

Comparing different psychosocial developmental theories like those of Piaget's cognitive theory (Piaget 1955), Mahler's psychodynamic theory (Mahler e.a. 1975), Erikson's (Erikson 1963) and Bowlby's (Bowlby 1971) theories, one may assume that under normal circumstances cognitive, social and emotional aspects of the child's psychic life develop phasically and flow among parallel lines. Neurophysiological and neuropsychological findings suggest (Luria 1973), however, that the basic tone of psychic development is determined by the maturation rate of the different areas of cerebral cortex.
Summarizing and linking together all these psychological and physiological theories the following schema of socio-emotional development within the first 3 years of life may be conceptualized:

1. Adaptation phase
   a) integration of sensoric stimuli
   b) integration of the structure of place, time and persons.
2. Socialization phase
   a) bonding
   b) creation of a secure base
3. Individuation phase
   a) separation
   b) individuation
   c) development of a unique personality.

According to various investigators in this area, a normal and healthy socio-emotional development during the first three years of life is essential for the normal development of personality and for the mental health of the person.

Among mentally retarded children, however, due to genetic, organic, environmental and other reasons, socio-emotional development within the first 3 years may be exposed to various difficulties. For example, it is hypothesized by different investigators in this area that mentally retarded children might show maturational lag of different cortical areas.

A maturation disturbance may result in two sorts of problems. In case of a global disturbance, one may expect a delay of total psychological development. If this disturbance is partial a condition may occur such as to render the interaction of the child with the surroundings only partially integrated, thereby causing difficulties in the integration of new experiences in existing cognitive, social and emotional schemata. This may result in disturbance of the child's psychophysical homeostasis. Such encounters create difficulties in the achievement of particular cognitive, social or emotional skills leading to stagnation of these developmental aspects.

Similar problems may occur when the surroundings of the child are not stimulative enough for the achievement of different developmental skills. An adequate environmental stimulation is apparently also important for an appropriate maturation of the cerebral tissue.

According to Menolascino (1970) psychopathology in the mentally retarded can occur as a consequence of

a) disturbed socio-emotional development
b) aquired biological and psychological disturbances not related to development.

Following on this idea, we have sketched this model of onset for the psychopathology among mentally retarded children (Došen 1989).

Mental illness among mentally retarded children occurs

a) As a consequence of disturbed socio-emotional development, due to
   1. arrest of socio-emotional development
   2. deviation of socio-emotional development
b) As a consequence of acquired biological and socio-psychological disorders.

Our experience with many hundreds of clinically observed mentally retarded children and adults with behavioral and psychiatric disorders, is that in 70 to 80 % of the cases psychopathology is a consequence of a disorder in socio-emotional development and in 20 to 30 % a consequence of acquired psychiatric disorders (Došen 1990).

The clinical picture of the developmental psychopathology was mostly dependent on the phase of socio-emotional development in which the disturbance took place and on the cognitive level of the person. On the basis of this etiological assumption, we have developed a treatment method called Relationship therapy to which we now turn.

The method of relationship therapy

The basis of Relationship therapy is the developmental-dynamic diagnosis. This diagnosis may be seen as a holistic survey of biological, developmental, existential and psycho-social problems of a mentally retarded child. In using this approach the mentally retarded child is seen as a developing organism whose needs and sensitivities vary with his or her developmental levels, and whose developmental course is determined largely by biological substrate and interaction with the environment. The behavioral and psychic problems are viewed in terms of three dimensions: a) biological substrate b) interaction with surroundings and c) developmental course (Došen 1990).

Ad a) The therapist has to know which biological factors and central nervous system disorders have played a part in the general disorder of the child. This is necessary in order to get an insight as to how the child processes internal and external stimuli and the kind of stimulation he actually needs.

Ad b) Interaction with the surroundings may be of great importance for the behavioral pattern and psychic state of the child. The therapist has to be cognizant of the rules of the child's living system and about the place and role of each aspect i.e., member of the system. A systemic theoretical as well as psychodynamic mode of thinking, has to be utilized in this approach.

Ad c) Developmental course of the child is a dimension which receives very special attention by the relationship therapist. Not only cognitive development but also levels of social and emotional developmental aspects receive focal attention by the therapist since these may determine the strategy and the application of special treatment techniques.

For example, a 5 year old severely mentally retarded boy referred to the clinic because of severe problems in social contact and an autistic-like behavior. Concerning the biological dimension it is found that he is oversensitive to acoustic and visual stimuli. In a noisy and crowdy room he becomes frustrated and often distressed. Changes within his living space as well as entrance into an unfamiliar space may cause tantrums with autoaggressive outbursts. Concerning the interaction with the surroundings it deserves to be mentioned that his family is very burdened by the boy's handicap. The parents are unable to accept their child's handicap and are very active seeking aid for him. Every time they hear that the boy is mentally handicapped and that there is no hope of cure, they change the doctor. They are convinced that the boy is autistic and they want him to receive a special treatment for autistic children. Concerning the developmental course; examination of the psychological developmental course revealed an uneven profile, one in which the cognitive development was at the level of two years while the social and emotional levels of development were much more delayed, reaching a level not higher than 6 months.

The diagnosis is established as one involving arrest of socio-emotional development in the first developmental phase resulting in a contact disorder. Relationship therapy was indicated. The therapist starts off from the model of socio-emotional development. Firstly according to the rules of the first adaptation phase, environmental circumstances around the child must be so structured as to make possible for him to achieve a physical and psychic homeostasis with his surroundings. The surroundings have to be adapted to the biological substrate and physiological shortcomings of the child. Space, time and persons are structured according to the needs of the child. The stimuli are reduced so that he can process and integrate them into his cognitive and emotional schemas. The treatment aim is in the first place to adapt the surroundings to the abilities of the child and in the second place to stimulate the child to adapt to the surroundings. Once the child has adapted to his surroundings the therapist undertakes activities directed at providing the child with pleasurable bodily contact that is the moment of introducing of the treatment into the second developmental phase. Initially, the therapist is especially attentive to the abilities of the child for processing tactile stimuli and offers as much tactile stimulation as the child can integrate. These transactions permit the therapist to determine the child's capability, the degree of intensity needed, as well as duration and frequency of stimulation. This aims at achieving an emotional bonding with the child, attempting to help him to establish a certain emotional security and trust in the interaction.

Negative experiences by the boy – such as the failed initial attempts by his parents to involve him in the bonding process – cause difficulties for the therapist. A cautious, well-planned and patient approach to the child's needs finally gives a good result. The resistance to bodily contact disappears and the boy can find pleasure sitting on the therapist's lap and being caressed.

Once the bonding and trust are achieved, the therapist's aim shifts to activities designed to bring the child into the third developmental phase, the individuation process. The communication channel between the therapist and the boy changes from tactile contact to the communication via material objects and via acustic and verbal signals. The child is being stimulated to leave the lap of the therapist and to communicate at a distance. Since the cognitive level of the boy was not higher than two years, the therapeutic goal was to raise the emotional and social developmental levels to two years also. This goal was reached after 8 months of clinical treatment. From the treatment of children like this boy, we have learned that a contact disorder or autistic-like behavior in mentally retarded young children occurs in approximately 50 % of the cases as a consequence of an inappropriate stimulation of the child in his/her socio-emotional development. In the other 50% of the cases such disorder has another background like infantile autism, pervasive developmental disorders and others (Došen 1990).

The usefulnes of treatment according to the Relationship method is twofold. It may give good results in children subjected to inadequate stimulation and it can contribute to a better differential diagnosis of the psychopathology. In the example described we could say with a certain degree of confidence that the boy was not one who was autistic but one who was primarily severely mentally retarded with, additionally, inadequate stimulation in the socio-emotional spheres of development. Differentiation between contact disorder in mentally retarded children due to an inadequate stimulation and mentally retarded children with infantile autism is of much importance for both treatment and planning of the future of the child.

The characteristics of Relationship therapy are:

- The relationship is not only a tool but also a goal of the therapy.
- Once a firm affective bond has been established the child is motivated to cope with current conflicts and to learn new modes of behavior.
- The child is assisted in personal development until emotional and social levels are brought to par with cognitive ability.

Strategy and results

In relationship therapy three separate stages can be differentiated (Došen 1984).
First stage: Tolerance and acceptance.
Second stage: Meeting and growing together.
Third stage: (Re)education.

In the first stage attempts are made to accept the child and all his actions so that he may be enabled to find his own place and role in the environment. The symptoms of disturbed behavior are not combatted; rather; they are accepted as an aspect of the child's total existence. Accepting the child implies among other things that the surroundings have to be adapted to his abilities and inabilities, to his activities and inactivities. The initial task is to make the child feel at peace in his/her surroundings and to discover to what extent and in what way the child can be induced to communicate pleasantly.

During this stage there must occur basic therapeutical structuring of the environment in terms of space, time, persons and frequency and intensity of stimulation.

The second stage consists of the formation of a positive, affectionate relationship between the therapist and the child. The therapist tries to react positively to all aspects of the child's behavior. The child is stimulated to develop his own initiative in communication and to express his wishes and feelings, his anxieties and his pleasures.

On the basis of achieved bonding and increased trust the child is stimulated to solve his emotional and behavioral problems and to ameliorate his communication with his surroundings.

In the third stage, based on the positive and trusting relationship already built, the therapist tries to help the child rid himself of his established behavior and to teach him a new form of socially acceptable behavior. The child is engaged in an appropriate pedagogical structure within which he/she receives social reinforcement.

Social behavior and creative involvement with the material surroundings are stimulated. In this stage the therapist may also make use of other therapeutic techniques like classical play therapy, role play therapy, behavioral modification techniques and others.

The therapeutic goal of this stage is to get the child as much as possible into the individuation process and to make him free from physical and psychological dependence on the therapist. The therapists aim is to stimulate the development of the child as a social and unique personality and to strengthen his positive ego qualities. At the same time the therapist remains an emotional security base for the child in all situations of conflicts which the child cannot solve on his own. Gradually, this trusting relationship with the therapist spreads out to other persons in the surroundings, rendering the child's exploration and experiments with the outer world increasingly free.

Relationship therapy, as the foregoing suggests, follows strictly the developmental line of the child according to the model of socio-emotional development. In concrete terms, this means that when a child has contact disorder, one should not try to establish material or verbal communication before contact via the skin and proprioceptors is possible. Similarly, in dealing with a negative and destructive child the therapist should not try to induce structure within the group before there is a structure and a positive bond with the therapist. The same holds, indeed, for a depressive child, one should not try to engage the child in play and intensive interaction with other children before the child has built a trustful relationship with one adult (the therapist).

In our clinical practice this therapeutic method has given positive results in children with contact disorder, psychosis, negative-destructive behavior, depression, neurotic conditions and other types of developmental psychopathology (Došen 1990). An evaluation of the results reveals that 41% of the children were discharged free of symptoms (due to which they had been admitted), another 41% showed slight improvement and the remaining 18% showed no improvement (Došen 1983).

Modified relationship therapy was applied with good results to adult mentally retarded persons with developmental psychopathology. In an investigation of behaviorally and psychiatrically disturbed mentally retarded adults developmental psychopathology was noted in approximately 70% of the cases (Došen 1990).

Conclusion

In *the conclusion*, it can be stressed that relationship therapy is based on a developmental approach to psychopathology in mentally retarded persons. Neither organic handicap nor the IQ level sets a limit on the suitability of this therapy.

The indication has to result from the psychiatric developmentally-dynamic oriented diagnosis and the extant ability of the professionals to carry out such treatment.

The therapy focuses on compensation for the child's biological and physiological shortcomings, amelioration of the interaction with the surroundings and stimulation of socio-emotional development.

The model of socio-emotional development gives direction to and determines the goal and strategy of the efforts of therapeutic work.

The therapeutic method appears to be useful for the mentally retarded children and adults, especially because of their specific socio-emotional developmental problems due to which these persons are often burdened with developmental psychopathology.

References

Allen, F.H. (1942), Psychotherapy with children. New York: Norton.

Bowlby J. (1971), Attachment and loss. Vol I: Attechment, Hogart Press, London.

Došen A. (1983), Psychiatrische stoornissen bij zwakzinnige kinderen. Swets en Zeitlinger, Lisse.

Došen A. (1984), Experiences with individual relationship therapy within a therapeutic milieu for retarded children with severe emotional disorders. In J.M. Berg (Ed.), Perspective and progress in mental retardation, Volume II. Baltimore; Union Park Press.

Došen A. (1989), Diagnoses and treatment of mental illness in mentally retarded children – A development model. Child Psychiat. Hum. Devel. 20: 73-94.

Došen A. (1990), Psychische en gedragsstoornissen bij zwakzinnigen. Boom, Meppel, Amsterdam.

Erikson E. (1963), Childhood and society, Norton c.a. Toronto.

Luria A.R. (1973), The working brain. Penguin Press, London.

Mahler M., Pine F., Bergman A. (1975), The psychological birth of the human infant, Basic Book, New York.

Menolascino F.J. (1970), Infantile autism: descriptive and diagnostic relationship to mental retardation. In: Menolascino F.J. (ed): Psychiatric approach to mental retardation. Basic Books, New York.

Moustakas, C.E. (1959), Psychotherapy with children: The living relationship. New York: Harper & Row.

Piaget J. (1955), The child construction of reality. Routledge & Kegan, London.

Došen, A., Van Gennep, A., Zwanikken, G.J. (Eds.) (1990). Treatment of Mental Illness and Behavioral Disorder in the Mentally Retarded. Proceedings of the International Congress, May 3rd & 4th, 1990, Amsterdam, the Netherlands. Leiden, the Netherlands: Logon Publications.

Chapter 3

Toward a psychology of interdependence: a preliminary study of the effect of Gentle Teaching in 15 persons with severe behavioral disorders and their caregivers

J.J. McGee

Considerable attention has been given to behavioral interventions designed to decrease aberrant behavior in individuals with mental retardation. Recent reviews have evaluated procedures for the treatment of self-injury (Johnson & Baumeister, 1978; Favell, Azrin, Baumeister, Carr, Dorsey, Lovaas, Rincover, Risley, Romanczy, Russo, Schroeder & Solnick, 1982; Gorman-Smith & Matson, 1985; Rincover, 1986); aggression and disruption (Fehrenbach & Thelen, 1982; Lennox, Miltenberger, Spengler & Erfanian, 1988); and self-stimulation and stereotypes (Gorman-Smith & Matson, 1985; LaGrow & Repp, 1984; Schraeder, Shaull & Elmore, 1983). These strategies encompass a wide-range of aversive and non-aversive procedures. Yet, in an analysis of punishment procedures, Guess, Helmstetter, Turnbull and Knowlton (1987) urged further research in the area of non-aversive interventions so that severe and even life-threatening behaviors might be more effectively and non-intrusively modified.

Research related to intervention strategies that focus on the communicative dimension of behaviors has offered new insights into their nature and possible remediation. Their functional message value has been pointed out by Donnellan, Mirenda, Mesaros and Fassbender (1984) and Carr and Durand (1986). Self-injury has been studied as an escape function maintained by negative reinforcement (Carr, Newsom & Binkoff, 1976) or as reinforcing through its sensory consequences (Rincover & Devany, 1982). Self-stimulation and stereotypical behaviors have also been analyzed relative to their reinforcing qualities (Hung, 1978; Lovaas, Newsom & Hickman, 1987; Rincover & Devany, 1982), and their function as an escape from aversive conditions (Durand & Carr, 1987). Aggression and other disruptive behaviors have also been examined in a similar mode (Iwata, 1987). Although their communicative function has become more clearly established, research has also indicated that aberrant behavioral patterns are often multiply determined (Wahler, 1976; Carr, 1977) such as through a combination of organic factors and attention seeking (Carr & McDowell, 1980).

Beyond their communicative significance, little research has pointed toward the interactional nature of behavioral change and the role caregivers play in this change process. However, Bateson (1951) and Watzlawick, Beavin and Jackson (1967) pointed out that relationship are based on either control or reciprocity and concluded that those based on complementary conditions resulted in healthy emotional states. Sluzki and Beavin (1965) urged the study of the factors that constitute reciprocal relationships. In the care of persons with mental retardation, little research emphasis has been given to the analysis of dyadic relationships, even though such studies might broaden and deepen the current understanding of the communicative nature of aberrant behaviors both in relation to the persons with special needs and their caregivers. Sroufe and Waters (1976) indicated that bonded relationships were observable through mutual contact seeking and signalling behaviors such as hugs, smiles, vocalizations, holding eye contact, and reaching out. Ainsworth, Blehar, Waters and Wall (1978) pointed out that such observable behaviors comprise a behavioral system not to be equated with any specific bit of behavior, but as components of interactional processes. Main and Weston (1981) concluded that it is possible to form warm and authentic relationship in abused children given sufficient opportunity for interactions and that these relationships can mitigate insecurity and avoidance. Although these studies have centered on mother-infant relationships, they might offer potential benefit in the analysis of caregiving interactional patterns at any age. By identifying, defining, and evaluating the nature and role of dyadic interactions, it might be possible to isolate those interactions that facilitate the expression of pro-social reciprocal relationships in persons with severe behavioral problems and their caregivers (Patterson & Reid, 1970).

Past research has focused on behavioral interventions that utilize negative consequences. Recent studies and practices have resulted in an increased use of non-aversive procedures as well as communication strategies. Clinical evidence has suggested that the gentle teaching intervention can be a powerful treatment procedure for the treatment of aggressive and self-injurious behaviors (McGee, 1989; McGee, Menolascino, Hobbs & Menousek, 1987; Menolascino & McGee, 1983; Menolascino, McGee & Swanson, 1982). Walker (1989) has pointed out that gentle teaching has offered a large number of clinical observations, that it is amenable to more rigorous research, and that its focus can help in the search for new ways to promote growth and happiness in people with disabilities.

This intervention involves an interactional analysis of dyadic behaviors based on the assumption that specific behavioral change involves complex and mutual change. Its purpose is to not only decrease behavioral difficulties in individuals and increase pro-social interactions, but also to help caregivers decrease dominative interactions toward the individual and increase their non-contingent valuing. Gentle teaching (McGee, 1988; McGee et al., 1987) analyzes behavior from an interactional perspective and asks caregivers to identify and significantly decrease any dominative interactions and to adopt or substantially increase value-centered ones. It assumes that the purpose of caregiving is to help marginalized persons turn from feeling of apartness expressed through their severe behavioral problems to those of union expressed through human interdependence. It requires caregivers to initiate and elicit new interactional patterns based on unconditional and authentic valuing.

Gentle teaching revolves around five assumptions: (1) the meaning and power of value-centered interactions can be taught even to those reported to be unresponsive to positive reinforcement; (2) the continuous delivery of non-contingent value-centered interactions is critical to the deceleration of severe behavioral patterns; (3) the deceleration of the use of punishment, restraint, and other dominative interactions helps to remove the barriers that impede pro-social interactions as expressed in bonding, friendship, and human interdependence; (4) the concurrent acceleration of the caregiver's value-giving and warm assistance facilities and leads to reciprocal relationships as expressed in the person's ability to accept, seek out, and initiate human valuing; and (5) although aversive consequences might decrease maladaptive behaviors, the use of restraint, punishment, cold demands, and other mechanistic interactions goes against feelings of union and interdependence. Gentle teaching is a first step in the development of human interdependence. It centers on helping persons feel safe and secure by placing unconditional human valuing at the core of all caregiving interactions. Its purpose is to create a spirit of companionship in which both the caregiver and person with behavioral difficulties enter into a relationship that transforms each of them. The caregiver gives unconditional valuing, creates conditions to elicit it, provides warm assistance, and protects the person from harm. At the same time, the person with severe behavioral problems learns to reciprocate valuing, initiate it spontaneously, participate with the caregiver, and reach out to others. These assumptions form the basis of the gentle teaching intervention and create a process for the emergence of interdependence.

Methodology

This study investigates the clinical impact of gently teaching in four interactional dimensions: (1) the deceleration of severe and life-threatening behaviors; (2) the acceleration of client interactions indicative of pro-social behaviors with caregivers; (3) the deceleration of caregiver behaviors that involve the use of restraint, punishment and demands; and (4) the acceleration of their non-contingent value-giving.

The research utilized and AB design to evaluate the intervention's effects in the dyads. This was chosen due to the subjects' clinical histories of severe and sometimes life-threatening behaviors. Although not orthodox experimental research, such a procedure can lead to knowledge about treatment effects that approximate the information achieved in experimentation (Kazdin, 1981).

Subjects

The 15 persons who participated in this study were referred by their parents or guardians due to the severity and refractory nature of their behavioral problems (see Table 1). Each had a diagnosis of mental retardation based on standardized intelligence tests and various allied developmental and emotional disorders such as deafness, blindness, non-ambulation, cerebral palsy, epilepsy, autism, organic brain disorders, depression and schizophrenia. They presented complex behaviors often described as life-threatening or as dangerous to others. They bore stigmata such as scars, bruises, burns, scratched, tissue calcification and detached retinas. Their average age was 22.3 years with a range of 7 to 41 years old. All had previously been involved in a number of non-aversive and aversive behavioral interventions. Most has been subjected to mechanical restraint devises such as locked and masked helmets and restraint chairs in which they were immobilized by their arms, legs, and stomachs; others had been involved in physical restraint procedures during times of aggression or self-injury. Other recent interventions had included seclusion, time out, cost response, water mist sprayed in the face, overcorrection, verbal reprimands, and forced exercise. One child had been subjected to contingent-electric shock for 18 moths immediately prior to this study due to life-threatening self-injurious behavior. Also, 10 individuals had been receiving psychoactive medications (e.g., Chlorpromazine, Haloperidol, and Thioridazine); however, these medications regimens had not been utilized for 60 days prior to the initiation of this study. Based on case conferences, review of clinical records, and the inspection of programmatic charts, none of these interventions had been reported as successful.

Caregivers

Thirty caregivers participated in this study in their role as parents, primary caregivers, or participants in a gently teaching training program. They included parents, social workers, psychologists, teachers, and house parents. Their average number of years of formal education was 15.6 years with a range of 10 to 22 years. Their average number of years of experience was 9.3 years with a range of 2 to 25 years. Their average age was 36.6 with a range of 23 to 60 years. They reported prior training in behavior modification and had previously participated in aversive and non-aversive behavioral programs. Human right standards were safeguarded for all participants, both caregivers and persons with mental retardation.

Table 1
Subject Characteristics

Subject	Age	Level of MR	Primary Behavioral Patterns	Most Recent Prevalent Aversive Intervention
01	8	Moderate	SIB - Aggression	Forced Feeding and Time-Out
02	37	Severe	Aggression - SIB	Seclusion and Social Reinforcement
03	40	Profound	SIB - Aggression	Restraint Chair, Forced Relaxation
04	39	Profound	SIB - Aggression	Restraint Chair
05	19	Severe	Aggression - SIB	Forced Relaxation and Visual Screening
06	7	Severe	SIB - Active Withdrawal	Restraint Chair
07	17	Profound	SIB - Passive Withdrawal	Locked Masked Helmet and Primary Reinforcement
08	7	Mild	Aggression - Active Withdrawal	Water Mist Spray and Token Economy
09	17	Mild	Aggression - SIB	Restraint Chair
10	34	Profound	SIB - Aggression	Time-Out and Token Economy
11	10	Mild	Aggression - SIB	Arm Tubes and Physical Restraint
12	7	Profound	SIB - Active Withdrawal	Seclusion
13	40	Severe	Aggression - Active Withdrawal	Overcorrection and Forced Relaxation
14	41	Severe	Aggression - SIB	Verbal Reprimands and Token Economy
15	12	Moderate	SIB - Aggression	Contingent-Electric Shock and Overcorrection

Settings

Both conditions occurred in natural environments and were conducted in structured and non-structured sessions. The same type of setting was used for each person. Criteria for the selection of activities in the baseline conditions consisted of tasks that were described as routine parts of each person's individual program plan. In the intervention, activities were practical and varied such as placing silverware in a container, folding towels, washing and ironing, sorting household materials, and labelling envelopes. During both conditions, other individuals were present in the setting and no environmental modifications were made. The average staffing ratio in both conditions was one to one.

Table 2
Categories, Operational Definitions, and Examples: Caregiver Interactional Observation System (CIOS)

1. Value Giving (VG).	2. Reciprocity Eliciting (RE).	3. Assisting Warmly (AW).
Physical (P), verbal (V), or gestural (G) caregiver interactions that convey noncontingent social approval and are expressed at any time with or without reference to how the individual is interacting. They appear to express sincere friendship, warmth, acceptance, and the desire to share. Typical examples include: smiles, nods or approval, signing: "thumps up", warm eye contact, facial expressions appearing to express joy, pleasure or approval, playful interactions, giving "five", pats on the back, embraces, compliments such as "Good!" or "I like what you are doing!", reflective commentaries related to the person or the caregiver in the form of storytelling or personal sharing, such as describing interests, relationship, or concerns related to the caregiver or the person.	Verbal, gestural or physical interactions on the part of the caregiver that appear to be specifically aimed at creating opportunities for the person to reciprocate valuing toward the caregiver so that the relationship might become mutual. They are intended to teach the person to receive and accept valuing as well as to reciprocate it. The caregiver seeks to evoke these valuing responses through words, gestures, or physical interactions. These depend on the caregiver's elicitation, not on the person's response. Typical examples include: extending one's hand as a signal for a handshake or one's arms outward as a signal for an embrace, touching the person's face as an indication to smile, placing one's hand in the person's for a handshake, placing the person's arms over one's shoulders for a hug, asking the person to smile, and soliciting verbal comments.	Verbal, physical, or gestural caregiver interactions that enable the person to participate in tasks and activities with the caregiver, others, or alone. The primary purpose is to effectuate participation, not skill acquisition or task completion. The caregiver appears to express this helping relationship in a spirit of friendship and equality and diminishes any perception of an emotional of physical tug-of-war that might result in withdrawal, aggression, or self-injury. The expression of warmth is indicated in personalizing the assistance, helping the person start, being attuned to slight frustrations, working along side the person, and disregarding the "functional level" of the person. The type and degree of assistance can change from moment to moment since the central focus is on participation and its use as a vehicle for structured interactions with the caregiver. For example, if a caregiver says, "Let's start!" and the person screams and runs away, warm assistance would indicate that a less "forceful" prompt be used, such as accompanying individuals to wherever they might be doing the task with them. This variable is also accompanied by VG, RE, and when necessary, protective interactions. Although the type of warm assistance can change from moment to moment, other typical examples include prompting techniques such as: working side by side with the person, placing material in the person's hand, moving materials closer to signal an opportunity for initiation, passing materials to the person, inserting materials into the hand, working hand over hand, and verbally guiding the person through the task.

4. Protecting (PR).

Verbal, physical, or gestural caregiver interactions used to prevent harm or disruption without immobilizing the person and expressed in a warm, non-forceful manner.

They are responses directly related to potentially harmful behaviors. They are brief and can be accompanied by VG, RE and AW.

Typical examples are: holding one's forearm out to block an attempt at hitting, placing one's hand between the person's forehead and a wall when self-injury is the intent, "shadowing" a person's movements as ongoing attempts at self-injury occur, i.e., moving one's arm(s) or hand(s) in unison with the person's attempts at injury, scooting objects away to prevent them from being thrown, and conveying soothing messages, such as "Everything is fine. Nobody is going to hurt you."

5. Assisting Demandingly (AD).

Verbal, physical, or gestural caregiver interactions intended to help the person initiate., engage in, or complete a task or activity. They are similar to AW in that they occur during tasks and activities; however, they appear to be focused on compliance, task performance, or skill acquisition. AW expresses a friendly and equal relationship with the person and the willingness of the caregiver to focus on mutual participation, whereas AD indicates a cold, intolerant, or distanced relationship and the focus of the interaction is on the task, its correctness or orderliness, rather than on a flow of participation as in AW. The person's refusal to comply can result in the withholding of further instructions with no positive social interactions, or the escalation of the restrictiveness of the "assistance". Typical examples are: delivering verbal commands in a neutral or depersonalized tone, forceful physical movements, such as pulling a person's hand to accomplish a task, graduated guidance when it results in an emotional of physical tug-of-war, forced physical movement such as taking a person by the chin and ordering, "Look at me!", sternly pointing, firm or mechanistic instructions, such as telling the person, "Hands down!", and verbally or gesturally warning or threatening the person.

6. Restraint and Punishment (RP).

Restraint consists of any physical or verbal caregiver interactions or environmental arrangements that might partially or totally immobilize the person, whether done immediately of the display of a particular target behavior or as an on-going part of the person's life condition through restrictive devices or settings. Punishment consists of the presentation of aversive events or the removal of positive events after a response. Typical examples of restraint as an on-going life condition are the use of tubes on arms, mittens on hands, helmets, straitjeckets, locked wards, seclusion, and the use of chemicals; typical examples of its use as an immediate consequence can be any of the above, plus a range of traditional procedures, such as ordering someone, "Go to your room!". The use of punishment includes procedures such as: electric shock, white noise, slapping, pinching, placing noxious substances in the mouth, verbal reprimands, water squirted to the face, forced body movements, contingent exercise, contingent restraint, restitution, overcorrection, visual screening, and time out.

Table 3
Categories, Operational Definitions, and Examples: Person's Interactional Observation System (PIOS)

1. Value Reciprocation (VR).	2. Value Initiation (VI).	3. Participating Correctly (PC).
Physical, verbal, or gestural interactions on the part of the person that convey the return of valuing toward the caregiver as a response to the caregiver's elicitation. They are directly dependent on the caregiver's seeking them and include any degree of approximation, such as simply allowing the caregiver to place his or her hand in the individual's as a "handshake". They are intended to teach the person to not only receive and accept valuing, but also to reciprocate it. Typical examples are: warm gestures, smiles, vocalizations, hugs, handshakes, reaching out, gazing, cooing, and friendly verbal answers or comments.	Any spontaneous physical, verbal, or gestural valuing toward the caregiver. These interactions are not direct responses to RE. They are similar to those indicated in VR, but are independent of any direct value elicitation. If the person accepts the caregiver's gestural offer of a handshake but also warmly gazes at the caregiver, the handshake is measured as a VR and the gaze as a VI. Other examples include self-initiated interactions, such as smiling, reaching out, talking in a friendly manner, offering to help, and looking at the caregiver in a friendly manner.	Any correct responses to the approximation, initiation, performance, completion, or constructive manipulation of a prescribed task or activity with full, partial, or no caregiver assistance. Skill acquisition, task performance, and orderliness are secondarily important; the primary focus is on the value of social interactions with the caregiver since participation is a vehicle for VG, RE, VR and VI. It is the caregiver's responsibility to facilitate PC by providing whatever degree of warm assistance might be necessary regardless of the individual's "functional level". Typical examples of PC without help are: putting the pieces of a puzzle together, setting the table, playing a game, answering questions in a classroom setting. Typical examples of PC with help are: performing a task side by side with the caregiver in an assembly-line fashion, initiating a task by having the caregiver place the first piece of material in one's hand, any physical movement toward the task with the caregiver pointing to the next step, and approximating any level of participation in any step of the task with any degree of assistance.

4. Interdependence-Centering (IC).
Task-shared (IC-T) or person-centered (I-P) interactions beyond the primary caregiver that are based on sharing activities or directly valuing others beyond the dyad. These involve the integration of other caregivers or peers into the relationship. Typical examples of task-shared IC are: three children playing a game passing pictures to one another in turn or a group of adults working together in an assembly line. Task-shared IC involves observations of each step of the particular joint activity wherein comprises a shared experience. Typical examples of person-centered IC are: one child giving warm eye contact to another while playing a game or two adults, while working on a task, making friendly comments to one another. Both types of IC can occur concurrently.

5. Participating Incorrectly (PI).
Incorrect responses that a person makes while participating on a prescribed task or activity. These can occur with or without caregiver assistance. These errors are observed in any step of a task. Typical examples of PI without assistance are: a person is supposed to place silverware in a tray, but places it on the counter or a person is asked to sort cards by colours in pre-specified piles, but dumps them all together. Typical examples of PI with assistance are the same as the above, but with the caregiver providing prompts. In spite of caregiver effort, the person nevertheless makes errors.

6. Severe Interactional Problems (SIP).
Acts of aggression, self-injury, active withdrawal, or passive withdrawal. These also include attempts of same. Self-injury consists of behaviors that potentially or actually cause harm to self. Aggression consists of attempts at or actually inflicting harm or severe discomfort upon others. Active withdrawal consists of physical movement away from the caregiver. Passive withdrawal consists of self-stimulatory, stereotypic, or passively resistant behaviors. Typical examples of self-injurious behaviors are: head banging, face slapping, hitting walls, hand biting, pulling out fingernails, tearing flesh from body, choking self, eye gouging, ear gouging, rectal digging, kicking self, eye poking, and pica. Typical examples of aggression toward others are: biting, hitting, slapping, pulling hair, scratching, kicking, aggressive comments, throwing objects at others, poking others, spitting at people, and projectile vomiting. Typical examples of active withdrawal are: moving from one's chair, slaiding onto the floor, rolling under or climbing on tables, throwing materials on to the floor, running away, stomping feet, public masturbation, pounding fist on table, and yelling. Typical examples of passive withdrawal are: mouthing hands or objects, body rocking, finger flicking, arm waving, staring out of windows or at lights, moving head from side to side, echolalic speech, feigning sleep, folding one's arms, looking away, licking self, playing with spittle, rumination, and regurgitation.

Observational Instruments and Behavioral Definitions

Caregiver-person interactional patterns were assessed via two measurement instruments (see Tables 2 and 3). The Caregiver's Interactional Observation System (CIOS) and the Person's Interactional Observation System (PIOS) were designed to categorize, code, and recorded dyadic interactions. These were field tested and revised in two pilot projects supervised by the author involving 50 dyads over a 24 moth period in order to correct ambiguities and assure consistency. Tables 2 and 3 contain the interactional variables, operational definitions, and examples.

The six categories in CIOS and PIOS were subdivided into 18 and 16 subvariables respectively (see Table 4). The variables and subvariables were grouped into two broad caregiver categories: the value-centered dimension (VCD), VG + RE + AW + PR and the dominative dimension (DD), AD + RP. Similarly, the person's variables and subvariables were collapsed into the participatory dimension (PD), VR + VI + PC + IC and the maladaptive interactional dimension (MID), PI + SIP.

Both coding systems require the measurements of what the members of the dyad are doing and how they are doing it. Content analysis involves the identification of what it observed, e.g. VG-P or PR-P. Process analysis involves the determination of how a particular observed interaction is expressed, e.g. AW versus AD. Process analysis is based on the nature of the interaction along with inferences related to the observed affective state and intentionality. When a caregiver assists a person in a task, it is necessary to differentiate whether it is verbal, physical, or gestural and whether it is expressed warmly (AW) or demandingly (AD), or if a person is making a vocalization, the observer has to determine whether it is VR, VI, or perhaps SIP as in the case of passive withdrawal. Or, if the caregiver if engaged in VG on a continuous basis through words and touch and at the same time is involved in AW-V as well as in PR-P, the observer has to evaluate each interaction in terms of its occurrence and meaning. Likewise, the person could be engaged in multiple forms of other interactions, such as VR or VI while also being involved in PC of PI as well as in SIP.

Due to the complexity involved in the observation and recording of these interactional processes, this study established seven parameters to minimize discrepancies in scoring: (1) The variables could only be recorded if directly observed: (2) interactions were recorded separately for each member of the dyad in the same time intervals; (3) interactions lasting more than 10-seconds, such as a conversation or the use of a masked helmet, were counted as 1 occurrence per each 10-seconds; (4) discrete interactions such as a single pat on the back (e.g., the caregiver's hand touching the person's back in a momentary movement cycle, or a verbal reprimand, e.g., the caregiver saying, "Hands down!") were counted according to their number of occurrences; (5) the

Table 4
Interactional Variables and Subvariables

CAREGIVER: VALUE-CENTERED DIMENSION (VCD)	PERSON: PARTICIPATORY DIMENSION (PD)
VALUE GIVING (VG) – Physical (VG-P) – Verbal (VG-V) – Gestural (VG-G)	VALUE RECIPROCATION (VR) – Physical (VR-P) – Verbal (VR-V) – Gestural (VR-G)
RECIPROCITY ELICITING (RE) – Physical (RE-P) – Verbal (RE-V) – Gestural (RE-G)	VALUE INITIATION (VI) – Physical (VI-P) – Verbal (VI-V) – Gestural (VI-G)
ASSISTING WARMLY (AW) – Physical (AW-P) – Verbal (AW-V) – Gestural (AW-G)	PARTICIPATING CORRECTLY (PC) – With Help (PC-WH) – Without Help (PC-WoH)
PROTECTING (PR) – Physical (PR-P) – Verbal (PR-V) – Gestural (PR-G)	INTERDEPENDENCE-CENTERING (IC) – Task-Shared (IC-T) – Person-Centered (IC-P)
CAREGIVER: DOMINATIVE DIMENSION (DD)	PERSON: NON-PARTICIPATORY DIMENSION (NPD)
ASSISTING DEMANDINGLY (AD) – Physical (AD-P) – Verbal (AD-V) – Gestural (AD-G)	PARTICIPATING INCORRECTLY (PI) – With Help (PI-WH) – Without Help (PI-WoH)
RESTRAINT-PUNISHMENT (RP) – Physical (RP-P) – Verbal (RP-V) – Environmental (RP-E)	SEVERE INTERACTIONAL PROBLEMS (SIP) – Aggression (SIP-AGG) – Self-Injury (SIP-SIB) – Active WIthdrawal (SIP-ActW) – Passive Withdrawal (SIP-PasW)

frequency of multiple verbal interactions lasting less than 10 seconds was determined by their syntax (i.e., each sentence sequence was counted as one occurrence. For example, if the caregiver gave gruff commands, such as "Look at me! Pick it up! Put your hands here!", three AD-V interactions would be counted); (6) two or more simultaneous interactions were coded as separate events (e.g., as when a caregiver smiled (VG-G) and verbally praised a person (VG-V); (7) all interactions were categorized and counted regardless of their degree of intensity (e.g., tap on the face (SIB) and a severe head bang (SIB)).

Data Collection and Reliability

Dyads were continuously videotaped in their settings from 9.00-11.00 a.m. and 1.00-3.00 p.m. each weekday. A Sony mini-camera was placed non-obtrusively in a corner of the setting, typically 3 to 4 mm from the dyad. If the dyad's location changed, the camera was moved to the new location or was hand-held. Two-minute observation samples were randomly selected from these daily videotaped observations. These comprised the data recording intervals in both conditions.

A graduate student in psychology participated in the original field testing of CIOS and PIOS and then received observer training over an 80-hour period by coding and recording 15 varied analogous videotape vignettes. This author provided instruction and feedback to achieve a consistent level of accuracy. Reliability checks were conducted by observing and recording occurrences distributed evenly across approximately 15% of the observation intervals for each dyad. The percentage of agreement was calculated for each variable and subvariable by dividing the number of agreements by the number of agreements plus disagreements and multiplying by 100. Average overall reliability was 87% with a range of 76% to 100%. The average reliability for CIOS was 86.5% with a range of 80-100% and for PIOS was 87.5% with a range of 83-100%.

Design

An AB design was utilized in 14 cases. Case 16 involved follow-up observations and a reversal (ABA). The baseline condition involved caregivers carrying out routine behavioral intervention programs in natural settings. The intervention phase consisted of the implementation of gentle teaching. The following factors were introduced to strengthen internal validity (Kazdin, 1981): objective data based on video-tape observations, continuous assessment in both phases through random time samples, multiple and heterogenous cases, identification of target behaviors unresponsive to other interventions as verified in clinical histories and case conferences, the measurement of immediate and final effects, and statistical analyses. To verify the nature and severity of the behaviors and the type of procedures used, clinical histories were thoroughly reviewed. The types of procedures previously utilized varies in their intrusiveness and were classified using criteria established by Lennox et al. (1988):

Level I (58%) – environmental control, antecedent control, reinforcement, instructions, physical assistance; Level II (70%) – extinction, social disapproval, overcorrection, response cost, physical restraint, visual screening; Level III (62%) – time out, mechanical restraint, spray mist, and contingent electric shock. (Note that some subjects were exposed to several procedures and most subjects were also involved in positive programs.) The baseline averaged 3.0 observations and the intervention averaged 8.7.

Data Analysis

This study will report: (1) the graphic display of each dyad's frequency of change in each dimension; (2) the percentage of change in each interactional variable between both conditions; and (3) the statistical significance of the effect utilizing a t-test. Statistical differences between means with a probability equal to or less than .05 were accepted as significant, and analyzed were made using the SPSS-X computer package (Norusis, 1986).

Gentle Teaching Intervention

Prior to the intervention phase, each caregiver received a minimum of eight hours of hands-on didactic training in gentle teaching conducted by this author (McGee, 1988, 1989; McGee et al., 1987). The gentle teaching phase involved approximately two caregivers per person in alternating shifts. In addition to training in gentle teaching, caregivers were also specifically instructed: (1) to preclude the use of restraint and punishment, even though target behaviors occasionally appeared to momentarily escalate, e.g., when a person was freed from a restraint chair; (2) to use protective interactions (see Table 2, CIOS-Protecting) to prevent harm without immobilizing the person; (3) to avoid the use of edible reinforcers or tokens, and (4) to use age-appropriate and functional tasks while maintaining a similar level of difficulty as observed in the baseline, e.g., sorting silverware in a kitchen instead of sorting chips in a day room or folding towels in a laundry room instead of folding paper in a classroom.

In order to decelerate the targeted behavioral classes and to accelerate participatory interactions, the interventions simultaneously focused on the deceleration of dominative caregiver interactions and the substantive acceleration of value-centered ones. The central strategy was to resignify dyadic interactions by emphasizing unconditional value-giving and its frequent elicitation, while giving warm assistance and protection when necessary. The basis paradigm was for caregiver interaction to begin with, center on, and elicit valuing. While establishing new interactional meanings, the power of past interactional patterns was designified, i.e., attempts at aggression, self-injury, or withdrawal were given no meaning, except to prevent them or protect the particular individual or others. Regardless of the severity of maladaptive interactions, the caregiver cortinued the value-giving process. The central purpose of the paradigm was to resignify interactions, i.e., create bonded relationships, friendship, and a spirit of human interdependence as inferred in the caregiver's value-centred interactions and the person's participatory ones.

Several supportive techniques were employed throughout the intervention in order to carry out the central paradigm: (a) errorless teaching strategies (Cronin & Cuvo, 1979) to increase PC, facilitate AW and highlight VG; (b) task analysis (Gold, 1972) to facilitate PC and decrease PI and SIP; (c) precise and conservative prompting (Stokes & Baer, 1977) in order to increase PC and differentiate VG and RE from skill acquisition or task performance; (d) co-participation on tasks with the person (McGee, 1989) to decrease PI and create increased opportunities for VG, RE, VR, VI and IC; (e) the use of tasks as vehicles to focus interactions on VCD and PD (McGee, 1989; McGee et al., 1987); (f) the identification of precursors to target behaviors to decrease their intensity or duration and to signal the need for increased VG, AW or PR (McGee, 1988); (g) the reduction of verbal instructions or verbal and physical demands (Gold, 1972) in order to concurrently increase and highlight VG and RE; (h) choice-making (Shevin & Klein, 1984) to increase opportunities for VR and IC; (i) fading assistance (Becker, Englemann & Thomas, 1975) and integrating other caregivers and peers into the relationship to facilitate IC; and (j) the use of dialogue, i.e., personalized value-based verbal and on-verbal interactions throughout the process, (McGee, 1989) to facilitate VG, RE and VR as well as to increase the possibility of VI. The use of these supportive techniques involved a moment-to-moment decision-making process in which the caregiver determined which teaching condition might immediately help to decrease dominative interactions and increase value-centred ones while concurrently increasing the person's participation and decreasing the occurrence of target behaviors. Since the intervention package involved a dynamic, non-mechanistic approach, this author conducted practicum training prior to implementation of this study.

Effectiveness Criteria

Intervention effectiveness was evaluated according to the following interactional criteria: (1) near zero-level dominative interactions; (2) a ratio of at least 30:1 value-centered interactions to dominative ones; (3) a ratio of 8:1 participatory interactions to non-participatory ones; and (4) a deceleration of targeted behavioral classes by 75% in the total intervention process. To achieve these results caregivers were expected to identify, analyze, and diminish dominative interactions, such as reprimands; the use of physical, chemical, or mechanical restraint; the use of time out, overcorrection; and other similarly punitive actions found in aversive therapy. In addition, they had to significantly decrease any interactions that appeared to express mechanistic or authoritarian expressions, emotional tugs-of-war, any form of contingency or interactions that appeared to place compliance or skill acquisition over valuing the person.

Protective interactions were sometimes necessary due to the severity of the behaviors. These did not prevent attempts at aggression or self-injury, but diminished their impact (see Table 2, CIOS-Protection). These were done without immobilizing the person and while simultaneously expressing valuing in order to bring about participation. As caregivers centered themselves on this personal and social change process, they also assumed a commitment to help the marginalized person move from a state of maladaptive interactional difficulties toward that of participation by decreasing incorrect engagement in tasks and activities in other distancing interactions such as acts of aggression, self-injury, running from the caregiver, or self-stimulation. Concurrently, the individuals with behavioral difficulties had to learn to reciprocate valuing toward the caregiver as well as to participate in tasks and activities. This mutual transformation required sharp, ongoing caregiver values and praxis. Thus, the intervention process involved new definitions of caregiver valued and purposes, the dynamic use of a range of supportive techniques, and a complex process of interactional change.

Results

Visual Inspection

A visual inspection of the charts shows clear differences related to frequency changes between baseline and intervention (see Figures 1 and 2).

Figure 1 depicts the acceleration of the caregiver's value-centered interactions and the deceleration of their dominative ones. Figure 2 reveals each subject's acceleration of participatory interactions and the deceleration of non-participatory ones. The baselines indicate that the interactional levels were fairly constant in each case and dimension. Caregivers displayed almost no value-centered interactions and high frequencies of dominative ones; whereas, the subjects showed almost no participatory interactions and relatively high maladaptive ones. The intervention phase shows relatively rapid decreases in dominative and maladaptive interactions and similar increases in value-centered and participatory ones.

Although an AB design was utilized throughout the study, case 15 also included an 18-month follow-up as well as observations of a return to baseline conditions. This individual had been subjected to contingent electric shock and contingent restraint prior to the intervention-due to high frequency self-injurious behaviors. His life-threatening head-banging behavior was at a high level in the baseline, and, at the same time, his caregiver engaged in high levels of dominative interactions. In the first treatment phase, a caregiver trained in the intervention was able to decrease the self-injury to near-zero by the 11th session while simultaneously increasing value-giving. After 18 months, follow-up observations were made in the individual's classroom to determine the inter-

Figure 1
Caregiver Interactional Dimensions

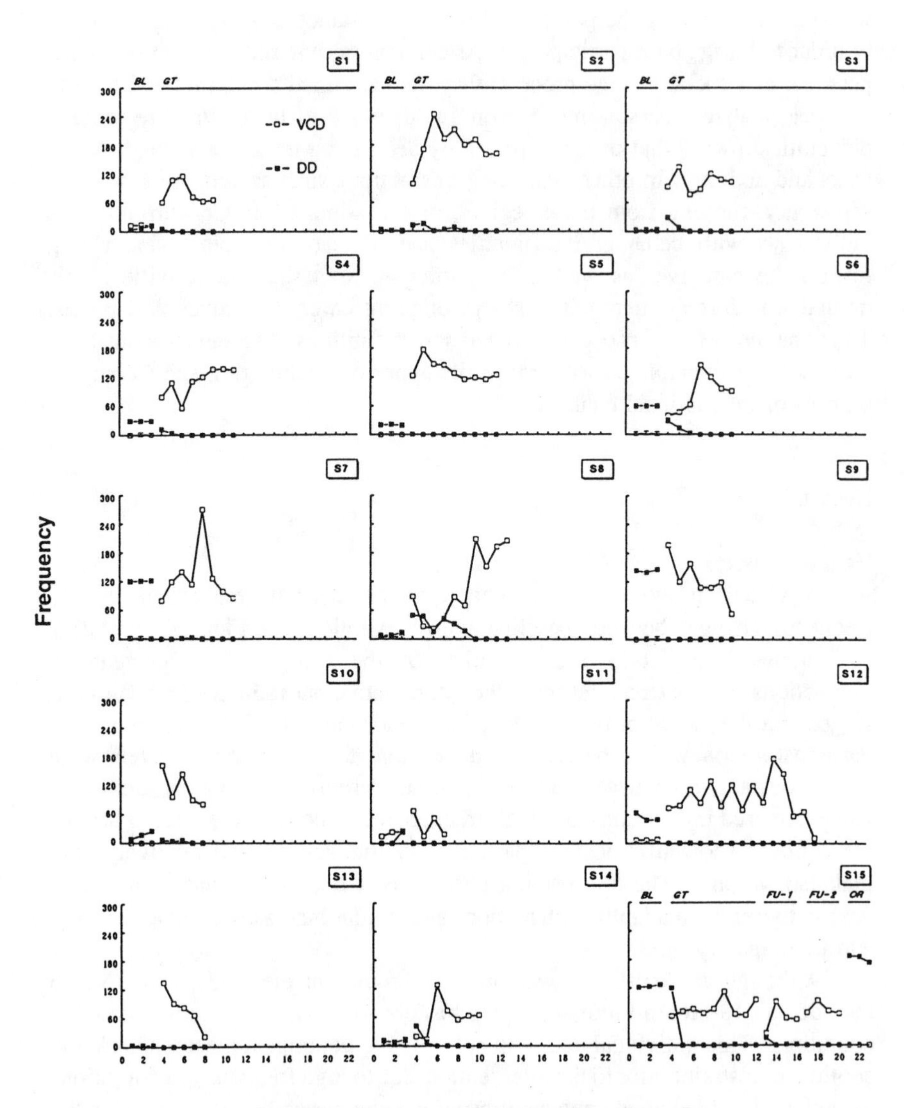

BL = Baseline
GT = Gentle Teaching Intervention
FU-1 = First Follow Up
FU-2 = Second Follow Up
OR = Observed Reversal
VCD = Value Centered Dimension
DD = Dominative Dimension

Figure 2
Person's Interactional Dimensions

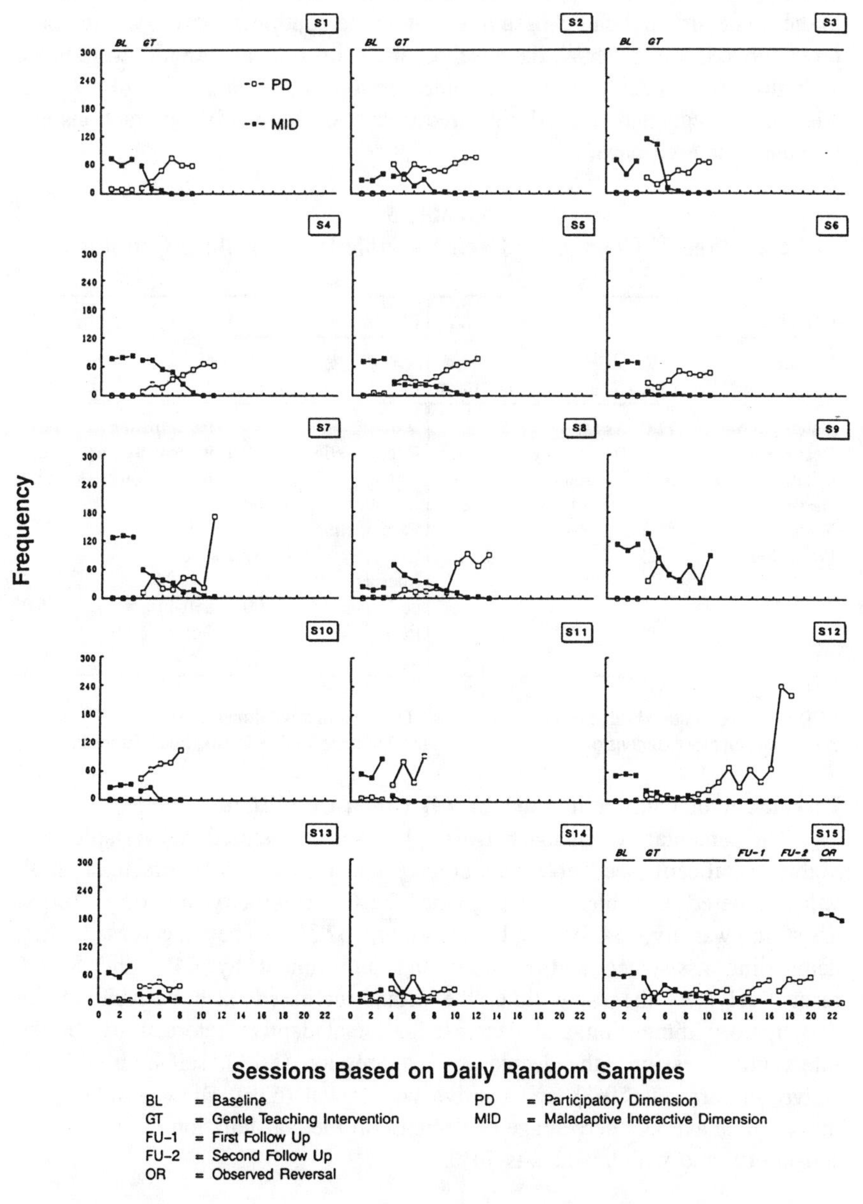

Figure 1 depicts the acceleration of the caregiver's value-centered interactions and the deceleration of their dominative ones. Figure 2 reveals each subject's

vention's effect. The individual's low level of self-injurious behavior had been maintained. It was also observed that the self-injury was no longer severe. However, in the child's institutional residence caregivers had not been trained in the procedure and had chosen to continue the contingent shock and restraint procedures. In this reversal, the observed incidents of head-banging were noted as higher in frequency than in the intervention phases and markedly severe. Also, the caregiver displayed high frequencies of dominative interactions and no value-centered ones.

Table 5
Percentage of Change for Each Variable Between Both Conditions

Caregiver				Person			
VCD	% Increase	DD	% Decrease	PD	% Increase	MIP	% Decrease
Value Giving	72.0	Assisting Demanding	14.0	Value Reciprocation	100.0	Participating Incorrectly	6.2
Reciprocity Elicition	100.0	Restraint-Punishment	89.4	Value Initiation	100.0	Aggression	86.0
Assisting Warmly	84.5			Participating Correctly	89.4		
Protecting	57.3			Interdependence Centering	100.0	Self-Injury	76.0
				Passive Withdrawal	63.0	Active Withdrawal	70.0

VCD = valued centered dimension
PD = participatory dimension
DD = dominative dimension
MID = maladaptive interactional dimension

Percentage of Change in Variables Between Conditions

The percentage of change between phases in all interactional variables was highly significant (see Table 5). Caregivers increased their interactions in all value-centered variables: value-giving, 72%; reciprocity eliciting, 100%; assisting warmly, 84.5% and protecting, 57.3%. They decreased their demanding assistance and restraint and punishment by 64% and 89.4% respectively. At the same time, the group increased each variable in the participatory dimension and decreased all maladaptive interactions. In the intervention sessions, the decreases in aggression (86%), self-injury (76%), active withdrawal (70%), and passive withdrawal (63%) showed substantial impact. The average percentage of decrease in the constellation of aggression, self-injury, and withdrawal was 74%.

Percentages were calculated based on change between baseline and intervention for total sessions.

Statistical Significance of the Effect

Differences in the four interactional dimensions were significant between both conditions (see Table 6). The baseline for the maladaptive interactional dimension behaviors was significantly higher (*M* = 61.8 ± 30.1) than the intervention (*M* = 5.6 ± 5.,0), p < .001. A the same time, the intervention revealed significantly higher participatory interactions (*M* = 56.4 ± 22.8) than the baseline (*M* = 1.9 ± 2.0) p < .001. Equally striking differences were seen in the caregiver's interactions. In the baseline, dominative interactions were high (*M* = 413 ± 49.0) and in the intervention these decreased significantly (*M* = 0.6 ± 1.2), p < .001; at the same time, baseline value-centered interactions (*M* = 3.0 ± 5.1) increased significantly (*M* = 108.1 ± 37.9), p < .001. These data indicate that the intervention had significant effects on dyadic performance.

Table 6
Group Interactional Means for Baseline (A) and Intervention (B)

	M		SD		*t*
Dimension	A	B	A	B	
Maladaptive	61.8	5.6	30.1	5.0	7.4**
Participatory	1.9	56.4	2.9	22.8	8.6**
Dominative	41.3	0.6	49.0	1.2	3.1*
Value-Centered	3.0	108.1	5.1	37.9	−9.9**

* p < .01
** p < .001
$n_A = 48$, $n_B = 124$

Discussion

The results of this preliminary study provide support that gently teaching facilitated substantial change in these caregivers and persons with severe behavioral difficulties. The inspection of the charts indicated important impact, and the statistical analyses showed significant differences. The percentage of change for each variable between conditions was important. The "participating incorrectly" variable had only 6.2% decrease due to the fact that there was little participation in the baseline and in the intervention the individuals received much help. Treatment effectiveness, both in regard to the group's acceleration of participatory interactions and deceleration of maladaptive ones, was evidenced in the interactional analyses. These findings are also consistent with our clinical experiences in recent years.

This author recognizes the weakness of the design utilized; however, Kazdin (1981) has noted that internal validity and the interpretation of treatment effects can be strengthened through an AB design utilized objective data, assessing performance on several occasions, and increasing the number of heterogeneity of cases. In spite of its current limitations, the present study met these criteria and the treatment effects of gentle teaching become the more likely interpretation. In essence, the results indicated that domination could give way to valuing and that non-participation could be replaced by participation. Further studied will concentrate on larger groups, more precise analyses of variables and subvariables, relationships between them, the qualitative dimensions of this change process, and long-term follow-up.

The baseline sessions presented a major issue relative to the frequency of aggression and self-injury in a group historically subjected to various forms of restraint and punishment. In order to design a study that reflected the actual conditions of the group, baseline data consistent with each person's actual intervention procedure were utilized. Due to the restrictiveness of the interventions in the baseline condition, most individuals were unable to display as high a frequency or as intense aggression or self-injury as they typically might have since their bodily movements were often limited through the use of tubes on their arms, masked helmets, locked rooms and wards, arms and legs tied to chairs, and immobilization in wheelchairs. However, based on their documented histories of extreme punishment and restraint-based procedures, observations of initial attempts at self-injury or aggression provided clear evidence of high frequency aggression and self-injury. Similarly, the baseline sessions might not have reflected the individual's ability to participate, due to the restraint used or the reluctance of caregivers to interact with them.

The 74% decrease in the constellation of the target behaviors required a finer qualitative analysis. Subjects who had engaged in severe forms of aggression and self-injury displayed very mild forms of passive withdrawal in the intervention process, such as looking at their hands or gazing at the surroundings. It appeared that such "withdrawal" was the beginning of a discovery of self and others. This phenomenon seems to have contributed to the lower decrease in the passive withdrawal subvariable. Clinical observation indicated that the remaining behavioral difficulties were non-harmful and non-disruptive. The "self-injury" observed during the last treatment sessions consisted of mild tapping of the cheeks or touching one's sore ears instead of head banging or gouging. Similarly, aggression involved observations that indicated mild gestures at hitting or bitting. Thus, even though there was a noted 76% decrement in self-injury and an 86% decrement in aggression, the balance of those interactions, as well as the withdrawal subvariables, were qualitatively different from those observed in the baseline and were not considered to be major clinical preoccupations.

A significant finding in this study was that, as caregivers rapidly accelerated their value and focused on eliciting it, each individual began to gradually reciprocate it. However, caregivers had to learn that valuing was nog just a matter of "delivering reward," but rather the expression of genuine caring and companionship even in the most behaviorally disruptive moments. Clinical observations indicated that caregivers were generally accustomed to giving reward contingent on appropriate behaviors. They reported great difficulty in unconditionally valuing the individuals, especially when in aggressive or self-injurious. They initially tended to give value only for deeds done. By concentrating on a relationship based on companionship, they reported that they ware able to express more natural and authentic value-centered interactions.

Another significant observation related to the need for caregivers to participate on tasks and activities with each person rather than "instructing" them to participate. This distinction helped them to recognize that they ware as initially disconnected in the relationship as the behaviorally involved person. This co-participation seemed to signal a common ground for the interactions rather than a mandatory deed to be done. It also helped caregivers to structure their interactions. Initial sessions also often centered on protective interactions consisting of blocking attempts at hits or shadowing attempts at self-injury. The initial tendency was for caregivers to grab the individual instead of protecting themselves and others. Also, during these moments caregivers had to learn to simultaneously resignify the interactions through warm assistance and on-going valuing. This process helped give a new meaning to the emerging relationship. The burden for initial change in the relationship fell on the caregiver's shoulders. The intervention process utilized many behavioral techniques and its findings were consistent with many past studies relative to these. Yet, it also asked caregivers to reflect on their values and their relationship with the individuals with these severe behavioral difficulties, to adopt values based on human interdependence, and translate these into value-centered interactions. The intervention required a mutually humanizing perspective relative to the human condition and expected caregivers to look at human needs and hopes based on not only what was seen, but also from what was felt.

Skinner (1969) defined a binary system of reward and punishment as the central principle in human behavior; the present study asked caregivers to give human valuing freely and unconditionally. Skinner's (1978) rejection of an inner-being has been repeated time and time again. Most recently, Baer, Wolf, and Risley (1987) admonished caregivers to shun mentalistic interpretations of human existence. This intervention was based on assumptions markedly different from behaviorism's--unconditional and high frequency valuing as opposed to contingent reward, its expression even in spite of the person's apparent rejection of it, the emergence of signs of bonded relationship as dominative interactions decreased and value-centered ones increased, and the development of a reciprocal relationship as opposed to only changing the other person's maladaptive behaviors of increasing their functional skills. This study's findings bolster these assumptions in that significant change was observed in every dimension.

This investigation's results are inconsistent with past research that has supported contingent electric shock and other forms of aversive intervention for persons with life threatening behaviors (Lovaas, Schaeffer & Simmons, 1965; Linsheid, 1988; Favell et al., 1982) as well as the control-by-contingency orientation often reported in the treatment of aggressive and disruptive behaviors (Lennox et al., 1988) through punitive practices such as time out, overcorrection, physical restraint, mechanical restraint, noxious taste, and water mist sprayed in the face in order to deal with aggression. The subjects in this study had been subjected to such procedures and yet their severe behaviors had continued. Our observed results indicated that change was possible without the use of restraint and punishment.

More specifically, these findings are inconsistent with a recent study that compared the use of gentle teaching to visual screening (Jordan, Singh & Repp, 1989), as well as an investigation that concluded that value-centered interactions failed to change self-injurious behavior in a single case study (Teodoro & Barrera, 1989). Variances in these results are derived from substantive deviations in procedures. The first study compared the intervention to visual screening and a task-training condition; however, the otherwise well designed study only used a minor aspect of the gentle teaching paradigm and, thus, cannot be considered as an investigation of the package. The second study was marked by a non-aversive behavioral procedure that did not meet minimal intervention criteria such as unconditional valuing, the use of dialogue, and an analysis of caregiver interactions. The observational instruments in the present study form a reference point for future research related to gentle teaching.

The individuals in this study had characteristics similar to persons treated in other studies via aversive procedures (Guess et al., 1987) and suffered from severe and even life-threatening behaviors, as indicated in their clinical histories and baseline conditions. Since prior aversive interventions appear to have had little impact on their target behaviors, the present results place into question the clinical need for aversive interventions. The attained decreases in target behaviors and the significant changes seen in other interactional patterns were reflected in each person regardless of age, sex, level of mental retardation, psychiatric diagnosis, or allied developmental disabilities.

These findings critically question behavioral psychology and many of its resultant practices which represent a psychology based on a oversimplification of the human condition (Bakan, 1966; O'Donnel, 1985). Gentle teaching encompassed a value system as well as an intervention approach. It urges caregivers to recognize and deal with the inner-being and interdependence of marginalized people. The initial purpose of gentle teaching is the convergence of the "I" and the "Thou" (Buber, 1955). It asks caregivers to form relationships based on unconditional valuing. It recognizes a dialectic within and between persons as they struggle to balance the fear of union with an innate hunger for interdependence (Unger, 1984). It involves an ongoing questioning of caregiver values and practices and movement toward feelings of solidarity with marginalized people. It acknowledges the vulnerability that exists in both caregivers and persons with special needs. Its ongoing and ultimate purpose is mutual liberation, impacting on the very roots of human spirituality (Boff & Boff, 1097). It mobilized actions based on values that strive for the hope of interdependence and the transformation of the self with the other (Yalom, 1980). It highlights dimensions such as companionship, commitment, freedom from dominative beliefs, joyfulness, reflection, and dialogue as crucial expressions of personal and interactional change processes. The ultimate test lies in the extent to which all persons find meaning in their lives. These findings indicate that these caregivers and persons with severe behavioral difficulties could mutually change through the gentle teaching paradigm; however, statistics alone cannot measure the total effects of human interactions. Hopefully, these findings will serve as a vehicle for further dialogue on the wholeness and interdependence of each person.

References

Ainsworth, M.D.S., & Blehar, M.C., Water, E. & Wall, S. (1978). Patterns of attachment: A psychological study of the strange situation. Hillsdale, NJ: Lawrence Erlbaum Associates.

Baer, D.M., Wolf, M.M., & Risley, T.R. (1987). Some still current dimensions of applied behavior analysis. *Journal of Applied Behavior Analysis, 20,* 313–327.

Bakan, D. (1966). Behaviorism and American urbanization. *Journal of the History of the Behavioral Sciences, 2,* 5–28.

Bateson, G. (1951). Information and codification: A philosophical approach. In J. Ruesch & G. Bateson (Eds.), *Communication: The social matrix of psychiatry.* New York: Norton & Company.

Becker, W.C., Engelmann, S., & Thomas, D.R. (1975). *Teaching: Cognitive learning and instruction.* Chicago: Science Research Associates.

Boff, L., & Boff, C. (1987). *Introduction to a theology of liberation.* Maryknoll, NY: Orbis Books.

Buber, M. (1955). *Between man and man.* Boston: Beacon Press.

Carr, E.G. (1977). The motivation of self-injurious behavior: A review of some hypotheses. *Psychological Bulletin, 84,* 800–816.

Carr, E.G., & Durand, V.M. (1986). The social-communicative basis of severe behavior problems in children. In S. Reiss & R. Bootuzi (Eds.), *Theoretical issues in behavior therapy*. New York: Academic Press.

Carr, E.G., & McDowell, J.J. (1980). Social control of self-injurious behavior of organic etiology. *Behavior Therapy, 11*, 402–409.

Carr, E.G., Newsom, C.D., & Binkoff, J.A. (1976). Stimulus control of self-destructive behavior in a psychotic child. *Journal of Abnormal Child Psychology, 4*, 139–153.

Chomsky, N. (1971, December). The case against B.F. Skinner. *New York review of books*.

Donnellan, A.M., Mirenda, P.L. Mesaros, R.A. & Fassbender, L.L. (1984). Analyzing the communicative functions of aberrant behavior. *Journal of the Association for the Severely Handicapped, 9*(3), 201–212.

Durand, V.M., & Carr, E.G. (1987). Social influences on "self-stimulatory" behavior: Analysis and treatment application. *Journal of Behavior Analysis, 20*(2), 119–132.

Favell, J.E., Azrin, N.H., Baumeister, A.A., Carr. E.G., Dorsey, M.F., Lovaas, O.I., Rincover, A., Risley, T.R., Romanczy, K.R.G., Russo, D.C., Schroeder, S.R., & Solnick, J.V. (1982). The treatment of self-injurious behavior. *Behavior Therapy, 13*, 529–554.

Fehrenbach, P.A., & Thelen, M.A. (1982). Behavioral approached to the treatment of aggressive disorders. *Behavior Modification, 6*(4), 465–497.

Gold, M.W. (1972). Stimulus factors in skill training of retarded adolescents on a complex assembly task: Acquisition, transfer and retention. *American Journal of Mental Deficiency, 76*, 517–526.

Gorman-Smith, D., & Matson, J.L. (1985). A review of treatment research for self-injurious and stereotyped responding. *Journal of Mental Deficiency Research, 29*, 295–308.

Guess, D., Helmstetter, E., Turnbull, H.R., & Knowlton, S. (1987). Use of aversive procedures with persons who are disabled: An historical review and critical analysis. *TASH Monograph Series, No. 2*. Seattle, WA: The Association for Persons with Severe Handicaps.

Hung, D.W. (1978). Using self-stimulation as reinforcement for autistic children. *Journal of Autism and Childhood Schizophrenia, 8*, 355–366.

Iwata, B.A. (1987). Negative reinforcement in applied behavior analysis: An emerging technology. *Journal of Applied Behavior Analysis, 20*(4), 361–378.

Johnson, W.L. & Baumeister, A.A. (1978). Self-injurious behavior: A review and analysis of methodological details of published studies. *Behavior Modification, 2*, 465–487.

Jordan, J., Singh, N.N., & Repp, A. (1989). An evaluation of gentle teaching and visual screening in the reduction of stereotype. *Journal of Applied Behavior Analysis, 22*(1), 9–22.

Kazdin, A.E. (1981). Drawing valid inreferences from case studies. *Journal of Consulting and Clinical Psychology, 49*(2), 183–192.

LaGrow, S.J., Repp, A.D. (1984). Stereotypic responding: A review of intervention research. *American Journal of Mental Deficiency, 88*, 595–609.

Lennox, D.B., Miltenberger, R.F., Spengler, P., & Erfanian, N. (1988). Decelerative treatment practices with persons who have mental retardation: A review of five years of literature. *American Journal of Mental Retardation, 92*(6), 492–501.

Linsheid, T.R. (May 1988). *Treatment of self-injurious behavior inhibiting system (SIBIS): A report on three cases.* Paper presented at the meeting of the Association for Behavior Analysis, Philadelphia, PA.

Lovaas, O.I., Newsom, C., & Hickman, C. (1987). Self-stimulatory behavior and perceptual reinforcement. *Journal of Applied Behavior Analysis, 20*, 45–68.

Lovaas, O.I., Schaeffer, B., & Simmons, J.Q. (1965). Building social behavior in autistic children by use of electric shock. *Journal of Experimental Research in Personality, 1*, 99–109.

Main, M., & Weston, D.R. (1981). The quality of the toddler's relationship to mother and to father: Related to conflict behavior and the readiness to establish new relationship. *Child Development, 52*, 932–940.

McGee, J. (1988). *Gentle teaching; Behavior change through respect and justice.* Toronto: G. Allan Roeher Institute.

McGee, J. (1989). *Being with others: Toward a psychology of interdependence.* Omaha, NE: Creighton University.

McGee, J., Menolascino, F.J., Hobbs, D.C., & Menousek, P.E. (1987). *Gentle teaching: A non-aversive approach to helping persons with mental retardation.* New York: Human Sciences Press.

Menolascino, F.J., & McGee, J.J. (1983). Persons with mental retardation and behavioral challenges: From disconnectedness to human engagement. *Journal of Psychiatric Treatment and Evaluation, 5*(2), 187–193.

Menolascino, F.J., McGee, J.J., & Swanson, D.A., (1982). The behavioral dimensions of the DeLange Syndrome. *Journal of Mental Deficiency Research, 26*, 259–261.

Norusis, M.J. (1986). *The SPSS Guide to data analysis for SPSS-X.* Chicago: SPSS, Inc.

O'Donell, J.M. (1985). *The origins of behaviorism.* New York: University Press.

Patterson, G.R., & Reid, J.B. (1970). Reciprocity and coercion: Two facets of social systems. In C. Neuringer & J.L. Michael (Eds), *Behavior modification in clinical psychology.* New York: Appleton-Century-Crofts.

Rincover, A. (1986). Behavioral research in self-injury and self-stimulation. *Psychiatric Clinics of North America, 9*(4), 755–765.

Rincover, A., & Devany, J. (1982). The application of sensory extinction procedures to self-injury. *Analysis and Intervention in Developmental Disabilities, 3*, 67–81.

Schraeder, C., Shaull, J., & Elmore, B. (1983). Behavioral treatment of self-stimulation in the developmentally disabled: A methodological review. *Behavior Modification, 7*(2), 267–294.

Shevin, M., & Klein, N.K. (1984). The importance of choice-making skills for students with severe disabilities. *Journal of the Association for Persons with Severe Handicaps, 9*(3), 159–166.

Skinner, B.F. (1969). *Contingencies of reinforcement: A theoretical analysis.* New York: Appleton-Century-Crofts.

Skinner, B.F. (1978). *Reflections on behaviorism and society.* Englewood, NJ: Prentice-Hall.

Sluzki, C.E., & Beavin, J. (1965). Symmetry and complementarity: An operational definition and typology of dyads. *Acta Psiquiatrica y Psicologica de America Latina, 11*(4), 321–330.

Sroufe, L.A., & Waters, E. (1976). The ontogenesis of smiling and laughter: A perspective on the organization of development in infancy. *Psychological Review, 83*(3), 173–189.

Stokes, T.F., & Baer, D.M. (1977). An implicit technology of generalization. *Journal of Applied Behavior Analysis, 10*, 349–367.

Teodoro, G., & Barrera, S.J. (1989). An experimental analysis of gentle teaching. *Clinical Bulletin of the Developmental Disabilities Program of the University of Western Ontario, 1*, 3.

Unger, R.M. (1984). *Passion: An essay on personality.* New York: Free Press.

Wahler, R.C. (1976). Deviant child behavior within the family: Developmental speculations and behavior change strategies. In H. Leitenberg (Ed.), *Handbook of behavior modification and behavior therapy* (pp. 516–543). Englewoods Cliffs, NJ: Prentice-Hall.

Walker, G.R. (1989). Gentle teaching: A behavior analytic perspective. *The Behavior Therapist, 12*(9), 225–226.

Watzlawick, P., Beavin, J.H., & Jackson, D.D. (1967). *Pragmatics of human communication.* New York: W.W. Norton & Co.

Yalom, I. (1980). *Existential psychotherapy.* New York: Basic Books.

Došen, A., Van Gennep, A., Zwanikken, G.J. (Eds.) (1990). Treatment of Mental Illness and Behavioral Disorder in the Mentally Retarded. Proceedings of the International Congress, May 3rd & 4th, 1990, Amsterdam, the Netherlands. Leiden, the Netherlands: Logon Publications.

Chapter 4

Individual Psychoanalytical Psychotherapy with Severely and Profoundly Handicapped Patients

V. Sinason

In 1610 Holland has its last execution for witchcraft – nearly 90 years ahead of the rest of Europe. The end of demonising emotional disturbance marked the beginning of a modern approach. It therefore feels particularly appropriate that we should be holding this conference in Holland and at the same time we revere the creativity of Van Gogh as well as feel concern for his disturbance! There is a further historical point. In 1977 Heaton-Ward noted that out of 5 International Congresses for the Scientific Study of Mental Deficiency 1300 papers were presented out of which only 40 were concerned with mental illness. At the 8th World Congress held in Dublin last year I made my own count. Out of approximately 500 papers, only ten were concerned with emotional disturbance or co-existing mental illness and only half of that ten were concerned with psychodynamic treatment (and most of that tiny international group are here!). So this conference is indeed a historic one.

It is also taking place at a historical moment in our field. The concept of normalisation (Nirje, Wolfensberger, 1972) has led to an increased awareness of the plight of many of our client-group and an increased motivation to improve their conditions. Not surprisingly, as all progress is double-edged, this has had its negative effects too. With growing pressure to move as many individuals as possible into the community, there has been an ambivalent attitude to mental illness and emotional disturbance. It can be hard for some community teams to accept that their clients are hallucinating or hearing voices if they have seen the long-stay psychiatric or subnormally hospitals as the "cause" of their clients' disturbance.

Some of the patients I see have challenging behaviour and it is important to emphasise that research on that subject by Oliver, Murphy and Corbett (1987) revealed that there was *no* evidence that the institutional environment caused this. Rather, the behaviour predated and often caused hospital admission. There are also handicapped individuals who were sexually and emotionally abused in their homes and who found the impersonality of large hospitals a relief. Some of these, when moved into the community, became ill because a home means being in a confined dangerous abusive space.

On the other hand, there are community or hospital workers trying to refer their clients for psychotherapy and being told that this is not a possible treatment. A. Reid (1982), whilst welcoming group therapy, commented "the scope for individual therapy is limited. Such patients do not have the intellectual resources to benefit from in-depth psychotherapy". However, psychoanalytical psychotherapists have to take some of the blame for the way such myths have spread. We too have clearly believed them! As a profession we have only been working continuously with this client group for ten years and there are still not more than four or five of us. Against that we need to bear in mind that in England there are only approximately 230 psychoanalysts and 200 psychoanalytical psychotherapists, a ludicrously small number if we consider the mental health needs of a country. It is not surprising then to find among other sobering facts the fact that the Oliver, Murphy, Corbett study revealed that of 596 self-injuring adults and children only 12 were receiving *any* psychological treatment, of which one (a patient of mine) was psychoanalytical.

Although the greater the severity of the handicap the greater the likelihood of coexisting mental illness, it is not the handicap in itself that causes the illness; rather, the burden of the handicap depletes the resources of the individual, making him more vulnerable to emotional disturbance. We can add to this the fact that the majority of our handicapped clients (Rutter et al 1970) come from the lowest social class and face the greatest economic difficulty and deprivation. Buchanan & Oliver (1977) have also pointed to abuse and neglect as a primary cause of retardation and I have frequently drawn attention to that situation as well. (Sinason, 1986) I consider trauma to be an important key in understanding mental illness in the handicapped.

In this paper I will show the first sessions of two patients. Both suffered from voices and hallucinations, and one was violent to herself and others. Firstly I will provide a synopsis of the findings that come from ten years of psychoanalytic psychotherapy with this group.

1. Formal psychoanalytic psychotherapy can be used by mildly, severely and profoundly multiply handicapped patients. Verbal language is not necessary. All patients, even the hyper-active, manage the same 50 minute hour for individual therapy and one and a half hours for group therapy.

2. We find it useful to differentiate between emotional intelligence and performance intelligence (Stokes 1987). A brilliant academic might be emotionally crippled and unable to be in touch with feelings and an intellectually crippled longstay hospital resident might be emotionally capable of facing painful truths about loss and handicap. Every patient in therapy has understood the nature and meaning of their handicap. There is no such concept as "ignorance is bliss". It hurts to be different.

3. The defensive ways in which someone exaggerates his handicap in order to have control of it can be more damaging than the handicap itself. For example, Don, aged 10, a boy with challenging behaviour, exaggerated his speech defect from cerebral palsy. It was so painful that his handicap was out of his control he found a way of creating his own one. Then when people laughed at his voice he was really laughing at them for being stupid ones who did not know his real voice.

4. There can be a more pathological kind of secondary handicap I have called "opportunist handicap" (Sinason, 1986). By that I mean that all the disturbed, envious and destructive aspects of the personality find a home.

5. Functioning can improve dramatically but not to normal. As Greenacre, P. (1953) has commented, no traumatic event is ever wholly processed and some vulnerability remains predisposing the individual to break down if the original trauma is later repeated. With out patients, there has been the trauma of the handicap and the traumatic response of the world to it and them. We are increasingly dealing with individuals who have been sexually abused, have untreated mental illness in addition to their handicap. In some cases treatment feels more like damage limitation than cure.

6. We have noted three main stages that have to be passed for therapeutic work to be of significant value. The first deals with secondary handicap, the defense exacerbations of the primary handicap that nevertheless deplete the communication level that is possible. Handicapped voice, body posture, language, literacy can change during this period. Don, for example, began therapy speaking like this – "I thgo tho htothpithall". It took six months for him to show he could say "hospital". The second stage is a period of crying/ depression. It seems to represent a proper mourning for the wasted years hidden behind secondary handicap, sorrow for the handicap itself and a terrible feeling of aloneness. This is a vulnerable period for terminating treatment, 22 year old Eve, for example, brought a photograph of herself on a beach, all twisted and contorted, lying next to her beautiful key-worker. She cried piteously at the sight. The third stage is an improvement again in internal and external functioning. We might leave the handicap behind and deal with the psychosis.

There is an overlap between mental illness and severe or profound mental handicap that needs treatment. After this therapy continues as with any other client group.

7. Where there is no organic primary damage trauma can in some cases be the prime causative agent itself. Even where there is clearcut primary organic handicap, trauma can be the cause of secondary handicap.

a) Mary

Mary is 25. She is severely mentally handicapped and lives in a small hostel. She has a mother who visits her weekly. Her father died a year ago. She was referred for violence to staff and herself. There was a question of moving her because they could not manage. The social worker asked if she could come with Mary's mother. Mary's mother was very angry with the Hostel and blaming them for Mary's behaviour.

So Mary came to the first meeting with her mother and her key worker and I invited them all to my room together. I introduced myself and asked if they preferred formal titles of first names. They preferred first names. (I always check as sometimes a 20 year old worker bringing a 50 year old man will say "I'm Miss Smith and this is John".)

Mary was fat, short, had dull short hair and wore the international false-self mental handicap uniform of short white socks, ugly blouse and a pleated skirt. She sat rocking and humming and biting her hand. I then asked Mary if she knew why she was here today. "No". I asked her worker to say why she was here and rather embarassedly the worker said how Mary hits herself or staff members. Mary sat still then, smiling quietly. "My Mary is really peaceful. She doesn't hurt anyone" said mother. "She has a really sunny nature. Look at that smile". Mary's smile broadened. I said perhaps Mary felt she had to be happy and sunny especially meeting me, a stranger. I asked when this violence began. "They say six months ago", said mother, "So don't say it was because of her father's death. She was fine for the first six months". "And she was not violent before then?" I asked the worker. "No".

Mary sat looking at me, narrowing her eyes and making her hum louder. I opened my mouth and before I started to speak Mary was silent. I said it sounded to me as if something very different happened to Mary six months ago. First there was a mary who never hurt herself or staff and then suddenly there was a Mary who did. Mary nodded and then suddenly slapped herself across her left ear.

It was a savage blow and left a red mark on the part of her face she touched. Mother rushed to hold her hand and looked at me accusingly. Mary was sitting quietly and peacefully. Her rocking has stopped. I said she looked very peaceful now she had hurt the Mary who had nodded to me. She looked at me very seriously and sadly. I said that when I spoke about a Mary who never hurt herself and she had listened to me so carefully there was someone else listening; another Mary who did not like that. She nodded and then started humming loudly. Suddenly she was very quiet and jerked her head to the right. I asked her if the other Mary was talking to her. "Yes". "What is she saying?" I asked. "Go 'way if I listen", whispered Mary. "She'll go away if you listen?" I checked. "Yes".

I said that made it very hard then. There was a pause. "Does this just mean she talks to herself?" asked mother, suddenly losing her sad expression. "Everybody talks to themselves. I do, don't I Mary". Mary nodded and then roared with laughter, rocking up and down. She knew her mother was being stupid and it filled her with despair as well as excitement! I said yes, people did at times but there was an important difference at occasionally talking to yourself in times of stress and actually having a voice in your head. "Hit staff! Hit staff!" shouted Mary suddenly, jumping up from her seat and just as quickly sitting quietly again as if nothing had happened. Her mother looked terrified. I asked if that was what the Mary in her head told her to do. "Yes" she said, sitting down again. Then she looked at her key worker, flinched as if she had been hit. Her head jerked backwards again and again and curled up terrified saying "Not me. Not me". I said she was so frightened we would all think she was the Mary who hurt people. She was so frightened she knew we would hurt her and right now she felt we had. She nodded. Slowly she sat up in her chair again.

Mother started sobbing quietly. "So she's mad too". I said she had received a big shock when she heard that Mary was violent and now she had seen it and perhaps we were now beginning to understand why. Mary jumped up again and shouted "Stupid Mary. Shut up. You'll give your dad his death". That was different from a voice – that was the painful words and reprimands she had received stuck inside her like a record, adding to her sense of guilt. There was a painful silence in the room and all smiles had gone. I said "poor Mary, you worry its because you were stupid your dad died." She sobbed and her mother held her hand.

We had four meetings all together in which it was possible to establish that the voice in her head started after her father's death. It was friendly at first and felt like a good companion filling the empty space. Then the voice started telling her she should be at home with her mother now Dad was not there. It was when her mother made clear this would not happen that the voice turned nasty and told her to hurt people.

After the first 4 meetings I saw by herself for a year. The voice slowly dwindled. She started getting angry with her mother, then with me and finally was able to talk of her loss of her father and her loss of herself as a normal person.

b) Edward aged 24

I first saw Edward when I was asked to observe him in a ward in an adult unit. Aged 24 he was mentally ill and mentally handicapped. His mother had died when he was 5 and he was brought up by his father. When his father died two years ago he was admitted to a short-stay unit and now to a long-stay hospital. As with many handicapped people, death produced a double loss, loss of family and loss of home.

He had autistic features and a prodigious memory for geographical detail and for train times and lines. His self-injurious behaviour, different "voices", public anal masturbation and depression were of concern. When I saw him he sat rocking on the side of his bed, talking to himself incessantly. Every so often he would bang his head as if the words or thoughts hurt. As I walked closer I could hear that what he was saying to himself was the name of all the stations on one train line. "He knows all of them – and British rail too and timetables and the prices of the tickets" said the Nurse. He started banging his head and moaning painfully. Suddenly it stopped. He turned to the nurse and asked in a completely normal tone "You have to live to breathe don't you?"

Rather taken aback the Nurse tried to alter that statement. "No, it's you have to breathe to live". "But you have to live to breathe" he repeated. I said yes, if you killed yourself or died you would not be able to breathe. He sat still for a moment.

When I saw him for the first time on his own we were given a small staff cubicle. "Valerie", he stated. I replied that was my name and he remembered it. "Valerie's come from London. From Tavistock Clinic, 120 Belsize Lane. Valerie came by car along the ... or she went by ... bus to ... and then got the train from ..." In fact he had completely accurately worked out my journey and my setting out time. I commented on this.

"Valerie" he said. I commented he was using my name to try and keep it and me in his head because once he had worked out my journey he did not know if there was any other way of being in contact with me. "Valerie", he tried the sound again. I said he knew my name and he was satisfied that if he said it I would be concentrating on him but then he did not know how to let it go.

"Mmmm". He started gouging his fist in his mouth. I asked if he was hungry. "Mmm, yes. See Valerie". Stuck it in his mouth again. I said he maybe felt hungry for me since he hadn't seen me for a week and would only see me two more times. He smiled and looked at me and relaxed. Then he spoke in a completely different voice. "Stupid Edward, stupid boy, shut up, get under". I said there was an Edward who thought Edward was stupid.

"Valerie". I said nothing. "Valerie. Is your clinic Finchley Road Frognal British Rail, Jubilee line Swiss Cottage Station, Metropolitan and Jubilee Line Finchley Rd station?" I said he could correctly place where I had come from because he did not feel able to place himself and me in a conversation right now.

He put a hand inside his trousers to touch his bottom and began a whispering litany. I said something had happened that had sent him away from me. Then I realised I was being a stupid coward and he was telling me something sexual but I could not bear it. As I thought this he stood up and jumped which frightened me a little. His harsh voice returned, "Stupid Edward, get under" and then he quickly returned to train lines. I said maybe he kept travelling on train lines because if he didn't he would have to think about more painful kinds of travelling in his bottom that made him jump. He shouted "No" and then went through an ear-piercing litany of train timetables.

On the second meeting he went through his litany of my name and my journey and when I was silent he started banging his head and moaning. I said how awful he felt when he moved from what he knew and what he could not bear to know. He looked at me intently for a moment and then started rocking and moaning again.

"Dad on top" he suddenly said. Then he began keening again even louder. "Dad under". I said his father was dead, was that what he meant by under? He nodded. I asked what he meant by "on top". I had a horrible feeling I already knew. "Bunk beds. Dad on top. Edward under". He started whispering and banging his head and punching the wall. I said maybe when he slept underneath he felt dead, as if he was buried under the ground. He started crying loudly. "Dad on top". I said maybe his dad did not just lie on top of the bed, maybe he lay on top of his body too. He nodded. "Stupid Edward, piece of shit. Piss off. Pyjamas off. Filthy piece of shit. Get under".

After this meeting he spent several days crying and was put on antidepressants. Staff then thought of other comments he had made which corroborated the idea of his father abusing him, although nothing could be done now that his father was dead.

On the third meeting Edward looked white and tired. He did not say anything when I saw him. I commented how tired he looked at the memory of being under his father and now his father was under the earth and it was hard to know what to do with his feelings. He sat looking intently at me, wanting me to speak. I said when his father had died he had lost his good father as well as his bad father and he had lost home.

He cried again and then stood up and assumed his harsh voice. "Get those pyjamas off, you piece of shit. Think you're going to mess up the sheets when I am on duty. I'll give you something to mess the sheets with you arsehole." He stood up, put his hands in his trousers and ran round the tiny room screaming and crying. I felt awful. I said it sounded to me that when his father died and he had been moved to a hospital, the one before this, or this one, a male staff member had done what his father did. He collapsed crying and whispering and returning to train maps.

Both of these extracts support Sheila Hollins' findings (1988) that the three secrets that need to be faced by the patient and the worker, and which require emotional intelligence, are handicap, sexuality and death.

A toddler I observed was hit by his mother for going near the radiator. "No. Hot" she shouted. A week later the toddler walking near the radiator stopped himself and turned away shouting "No. Hot" in the same tone as his mother, kicking a toy on the floor. Several months later he just did not walk near the radiator. It was possible to assume in a young child observation group that the child has processed his mother's anger and order, understood the reason for it, and dealt accordingly. We will not know if the physical shock is truly processed until the child grows up and has a child. Will he then unconsciously restrain his own toddler in the same way or will he able to use another method?

Where conditions are adequate enough and there is good-enough parenting society does not notice the way in which the mini traumas of everyday life are passed on wholesale to the next generation. Where the lucky-enough child absorbs other people's comments and internalises them and develops language the handicapped child faces greater developmental difficulty. If you cannot think and are severely handicapped then other people's words cannot get processed easily and if they are harsh or traumatic words even less so. The word then itself remains like a concrete object in the mind. Handicapped adults with a lifetime of institutionalisation have an encyclopedia of these concrete word-weapons hurting their minds.

With these individuals I have shown the mixture of voices and hallucinations that can occur. At times the hallucination is totally the authentic undiluted trauma, at others it moves into a more florid psychosis. Jaspers did not think there was a gradual transition between a true and a pseudo-hallucination but Fish does see transitions do occur. I wonder too how we can link this with the concept of disaster flashbacks. My abused patients who are not handicapped can also suddenly bring back the memory of abuse complete with smell, sound and visual image. Leff (1976) found that the perceptions of normal people undergoing sensory deprivation found it hard to distinguish between images and hallucinations and this overlapped with mental patients. If we consider the emotional deprivation and the problems in thinking handicapped people have had we can see how easy the transition is.

> Think of the times the ordinary individual is driven to speak aloud and then go to T.S. Eliot's words – "Words strain Crack and sometimes break under the burden"
> (T.S. Eliot (1954), Burnt Norton)

References

Buchanan, A & Oliver, J.E. (1977), Abuse and neglect as a cause of mental retardation. Brit. J. Psychiat. Nov. Vol.131, 458–67.

Corbett, J. (1975), Aversion for the treatment of self-injurious behaviour. Journal of Mental Deficiency Research, 19, 79.

Fish's Clinical Psychopathology (1974), Signs and Symptoms in Psychiatry, ed. Max Hamilton, Wright, Bristol.

Jaspers, K. (1962), General Psychopathology, Manchester University Press.

Heaton-Ward, A. (1977), Psychosis in Mental Handicap, Brit. J. Psychiatr. 130. 525–33.

Leff, J.P. (1968), "Perceptual phenomena and personality in sensory deprivation." Brit. J. Psychiatr. 114, 1499.

Oliver, C. Murphy, G.H., Corbett, J.A. (1987), Journal of mental deficiency Research 31, 147–62 Self-Injurious Behaviour in People with mental Handicap: a total population study.

Reid, A. (1982), The Psychiatry of Mental Handicap, London, Blackwell Scientific Publications.

Rutter, M. et al (1970), Education, Health and Behaviour, London. Longman.

Sinason, V. (1986), Secondary Mental Handicap and its relationship to trauma. Psychoanalytic Psychotherapy Vol. 2. No. 2. 131–54.

Sinason, V. (1988), Dolls and Bears; From Symbolic Equation to Symbol. The use of different play material for sexually abused children. British Journal of Psychotherapy Vol.4. No. 4.

Sinason, V. (1988), Smiling, swallowing, sickening and stupefying. The effect of abuse on the child. Psychoanalytic Psychotherapy, Vol.3. No. 2. p. 97–111.

Sinason, V. (1990), Psychotherapy for Abused Children. Chapter for UCH Handbook of Psychiatry. An Integrated Approach. Duckworth. Ed. Wolff, H. Bateman, A. and Sturgeon, D.A.

Sinason, V. (1989), the Psycholinguistics of Discrimination in *Crises of the Self*, further Essays on Psychoanalysis and Politics, ed. Barry Richards, Free Association Books.

Sinason (V), (1989), Psychotherapy for abused handicapped children. Chapter for Open University Book and Programme.

Sinason, V. (1989), Uncovering and responding to sexual abuse in handicapped patients in psychotherapeutic settings. In "Thinking the Unthinkable", *Papers on Sexual Abuse and People with Learning Difficulties*, ed. Hilary Brown and Ann Craft, Family Planning Association.

Sinason, V. (1989), Psychoanalytic Psychotherapy and its Application, *Social Work Practice, November 1989*.

Sinason, V. (1988), *Behaviourial Problems in Children*, BMA Home Encyclopedia.

Sinason, V. (1988), *Richard III, Echo and Hephaestus: Sexuality and mental/ Multiple Handicap*, Journal of Child Psychotherapy. Vol.14. No. 2.

McConachie, H. & Sinason, V. (1989), the Emotional Experience of Multiple Handicap: issues in Assessment. Child: care, health and development. 15. 75–78.

Sinason, V. (1991), "Stupid". A Book on Mental Handicap. Free Association.

Sinason, V. (1990), Chapter on Therapy with Handicapped patient in new Karnac book edited by Rolene Szur, Tavistock Clinic.

Sinason, V. (1991), Chapter in "Psychotherapy and Mental handicap", Sage Publications.

Sinason, V (1990), Passionate Lethal Attachments. British Journal of Psychotherapy.

Sinason, V. (1991 forthcoming), Therapy with Abused handicapped patients. Chapter for new book on sexuality and handicap edited by Ann Craft.

Stokes, Jon (1987), Insights from Psychotherapy, RSM paper Feb. 25th.

Wolfensberger, W. (1972), Normalization in Human Services, National Institute of Mental Retardation: Toronto.

Došen, A., Van Gennep, A., Zwanikken, G.J. (Eds.) (1990). Treatment of Mental Illness and Behavioral Disorder in the Mentally Retarded. Proceedings of the International Congress, May 3rd & 4th, 1990, Amsterdam, the Netherlands. Leiden, the Netherlands: Logon Publications.

Chapter 5

Group Analytic Therapy with People with Mental Handicap

S. Hollins

Introduction

This paper aims to show the place of group analytic therapy within the range of treatment options available for people with learning disabilities. Clinical material is used to illustrate theoretical and technical issues and to raise research questions and problems of research methodology.

The popular image of group therapy is of a number of highly intelligent neurotic adults sitting round baring their souls. But in reality the medium of therapy is not exclusively verbal and therapists works to increase the group's awareness of non verbal communication. With people with mental handicap therapy may be complicated by conceptual and communication difficulties, and another medium may need to be used as an added channel for communication, for example art, music or drama. This can lead to idiosyncratic ways of working perhaps deriving useful ideas from play therapists.

The clinical material is presented primarily to look at the process of therapy rather than the content, and refers to work with adults who themselves have learning disabilities. Before I move on to describe some of this work, I must remind you of the relevance of group work with parents who have handicapped children to help them with their grief and their adjustment. Some work has been done with siblings in groups and there is an increasing interest in using family therapy with families who have a disabled member.

Review of Literature

For the 25 years since 1965 very few relevant papers written in English could be traced. Several papers described work with groups of adolescents or adults living in institutional care (e.g. Cogan et al (1966), Miezio (1967), Slivkin & Bernstein (1968), Pantlin (1985)) but few references to outpatient group work (Hollins & Evered (1990). Some papers described work with groups of parents (Smith et al (1976)). A number of papers discussed the pros and cons of a psychotherapeutic approach (e.g. Stavrakaki and Klein 1986, Matson 1984, Coffman et al 1980, Woody et al 1966) and the use of play, music or drama therapy or techniques such as role play (Weinstock 1977). It is clear there has been very little confidence in the past in the use of group analytic approaches with people who have a mental handicap. The authors of published case reports are modest in their claims, although enthusiastic and optimistic about the value of their work. Stavrakaki and Klein (1986) warn against the risk of dilution of the skills of the psychiatrist through overlap with more informal patient meetings, educational or experimental groups. They argue that the aim of group psychotherapy in this field should focus clearly upon the need to comprehend and alter disordered personality functioning, and to improve communication and social interaction. Given that social style and temperament contribute more to adjustment as an adult than intellectual levels, such aims are valuable.

Getting started and setting the boundaries

Working in relatively uncharted waters can elicit different reactions from unwarranted and even reckless self confidence to a more timid dipping of a toe in the water just to see.... I have been therapist to a number of outpatient or community groups since 1982 varying in duration from 6 months to 3 years and I have supervised groups run by trainees. My co-therapist has usually been a senior registrar in psychiatry with their maximum commitment to a group being 12 months. Decisions made in advance about the group, e.g. the duration of therapy, have invariably been influenced by counter transference feelings. Thus if supervision is available – and I believe it is always helpful – the supervisor should be involved from the early stages of planning. Commonly expressed feelings of prospective therapists include a fear of being bored, a fear of encouraging dependence and guilt about termination and not offering enough.

The same time and space boundaries should be observed as with any group and I have found it helpful to choose a setting where there is a waiting room or where the group room is available before the appointed hour so that the members can gather. Some of the people have major difficulty with time, and others need to allow a large margin of error, so it is not uncommon for someone to arrive an hour or more early.

The group are asked to telephone their apologies in advance if they are unable to come. I have found it helpful to give the group written reminders of the date of the next meeting at the last session before a break.

Assessment

Realistic requests for therapy will arise from a wish to come to terms with the internal and external experiences of the individual who has a disability. To understand this further demands knowledge of the features which are often seen in the psychological adjustments of families who have a member with a disability. Bicknell (1983) describes the reaction to the bad news of disability as akin to a bereavement. The stages of grief described include shock, panic, denial, anger including guilt and blame, depression and finally acceptance and adjustment. We can only surmise about the experience for the individual of being a disappointment to parents. Each person will have feelings and attitudes about their own limitation and its effect upon the family. (Selwa (1971).

For any patient the main aim of group analytic therapy is to improve relationships and to enable the individual to accept their own limitations. Psychotherapy may have more clearly defined goals related, for example, to maturation, or to accepting the loss of a parent.

The therapeutic alliance and confidentiality

There is a technical problem which must be considered before the group can start. Beginning work with people who have developmental intellectual handicaps such that they require special services to lead an ordinary life, raises the problem of the therapist's relationship with the caregivers. When we think of the traditional psychoanalytic model of therapist and patient or patients, we think very much of intimate relationships which are bound by the confidentiality of the treatment setting.

Of course the institutionalized life led by many people with mental handicap is far from ordinary, and to offer treatment to people living in long stay hospital wards provokes considerable curiosity. It is very rare in such a setting that anything is totally private, and explanations about the reasons for the desired privacy are readily misunderstood. If therapy is such an important part of the treatment programme, why are the carers being excluded from it? The more the maintenance of privacy is insisted upon, the more suspicious and uncooperative the carers may become. In addition the therapist(s) may be party to information about the client between sessions with pressure exerted on them to take day to day issues up in the therapy. Similar problems can be expected in work with adults who still live with their family of origin. For the parents of an adult "child" who functions in many ways like a four or five year old, there is little they do not already know about him, and they will expect to know the details of anything new which happens. The Child Psychiatry model of someone working with the person who has a mental handicap, and someone else working with the parents, with an occasional meeting together, may be appropriate. The confidentiality of both therapeutic alliances must be respected, and the effect of the involvement of the care givers on the therapeutic process borne in mind.

To illustrate this I will describe a young woman who attended an outpatient group in a District General Hospital.

J was 19 and had lived in residential care since her early teens when her mother died. Her father visited her about once a year and she had developed a rich fantasy life to compensate for her painful feelings of abandonment. She used a manic defence as a thin disguise for her depression. J was one of only 2 members who had to be escorted to the group, and the escort was unreliable, obviously having no idea of the nature of the treatment and the need for confidentiality. Although time boundaries were adhered to strictly it was not unusual for a new escort to walk in before the end and to stand and wait for the group to finish. Needless to say the escort would be asked to wait outside until 'time', but these few occasions showed the change which took place in J after the intrusion, as she reverted to the 'giggly little girl' known in the hostel, her depression once again hidden.

Transference and counter transference

In psychodynamic work therapeutic use is made of the transference and counter transference feelings in the relationship between therapist and client or clients. The main requirement therefore of psychotherapy candidates is that they are capable of making an emotional relationship. One misconception about people with mental handicap is that their limited intellect will preclude them from a treatment mode which seeks to increase affective understanding. But all that is required to engage in therapy is emotional contact between 'patient' and therapist, and the belief that the 'patient' has even a limited ability to make object relationships.

It is appropriate for the therapist(s) to be able to share the reality of the handicap; to be able to feel the hopelessness and the sense of disappointment and even panic which the handicapped individual with some insight may have about himself. The main work of therapy will be done through interpreting the transference and counter transference in the relationship between therapist(s) and patient or group members.

In a report of one of my groups (Hollins 1991) I wrote:

The therapists sometimes experienced profound feelings of boredom leading to difficulty staying awake. In supervision it became clear that these heavy feelings were in the counter transference – it was not boredom: we were being challenged. We were in touch with some of the pain for our clients of being damaged, and some of our own pain and intolerance of their disability. These feelings were usefully shared with the group. The problem of the idealisation of the therapist(s) and of an individual's caretakers can be addressed, the group members can give up their expectation of being 'cured' and the therapists can drop the burden of being expected to 'cure' the members' handicaps (Menaloscino et al (1986).

The Three Secrets

The secrets of sexuality, death and dependence or disability are usually exposed and explored in psychoanalytic psychotherapy. Experiences of major loss appear to be more common in this client group, but mourning is often discouraged by carers. In one group a young woman chatted happily and endlessly about hairdo's and royalty, until another woman showed her own operation scar and talked about her mothers' terminal illness. The first woman dropped her manic defence and blurted 'I haven't got a mother'. A common feeling of the experience of being different as 'hurting inside' is usually shared in later sessions, and therapists may have difficulty in confronting the groups initial denial. Sexuality provokes a range of responses from curiosity to disgust, and transference interpretations are sometimes relevant.

Termination of therapy

As each group moves through different phases of initial rejection to partial acceptance and hopefully to sharing, the reality of the short life of the group is held in mind. A theme which one man in my 3 year group returned to time and again was that of the insincerity of 'normal' people who welcomed him one day and rejected him the next. Towards the end of the group he became very quiet, and eventually owned up to the sad insight he had gained that his idealised image of other people was false. His disappointment was real but he accepted it, and felt better able to face life on his own without the group's help.

My own feeling is that a year is too short – the therapists are just beginning to face the group's depression by then. The trainee therapist will have had a useful experience but this could be deepened if he/she is enabled to leave the group in the care of a new therapist. The letting go which is required of such a therapist mirrors the letting go of the parent of an adult handicapped child. The feelings aroused in the group by events such as this will provide a major focus for work.

In the final session of a group which I was supervising, the members shared their bewilderment – they still could not understand why the group was ending. Their fantasies about the therapists, which had been vividly spelt out in earlier groups, persisted with the assumption that they must be going on to better things.

Research

Attitude and personality assessments are very difficult with this client group. It is also possible that some concepts used in psychotherapy are unmeasurable. Repertory grids have been used to study personality and behavioural difficulties in individuals with mental handicap (Spindler-Barton et al 1976) and to compare individuals in resettlement groups (Hulbert & Atkinson 1987). I used repertory grid analysis as an assessment and evaluation tool before and after a 1 year closed outpatient group. While realising that each individual creates a unique set of constructs, it seemed likely people with very similar life experiences might show some similar changes in their grids over time. The grid is rated by putting a set of elements – in this case important people in the life of each patient, against a set of bipolar constructs. In my study the constructs were fixed by the researchers and included upsetting, caring, happy, handicapped, exciting etcetera. The results are complex to interpret but an example may be illustrative. (Evans et al 1990).

Mike saw himself as the most handicapped element and his biggest self/ideal – self discrepancy was here, where he wanted to be only the 7th most handicapped. This seemed a reasonable ambition and he did achieve it. He wanted to be the most happy which he did not achieve, having seen himself as the 6th most happy at the beginning. His other self ratings had changed very little except that he saw himself as more respecting of other people.

Whilst this is an interesting research tool, it cannot replace the therapists' clinical observation. There was ample rich evidence of a reduction in distressing symptoms and of emotional maturation with many of the research group. For example Mike developed an intimate relationship with a young woman, and despite having severe epilepsy, negotiated with his mother for his own front door key so that he could let himself in to the house in the late evening after visiting his girlfriend.

Conclusions

Group analytic therapy is effective but is not an easy option for the therapists. They must be prepared to tolerate the fact that there is no cure for their patients handicaps. Group approaches to treatment are an economical way of working and require little more than an accessible and comfortable room with enough chairs for the members, a guarantee of no outside interruptions, a commitment to training and supervision for the therapists. To me its all common sense, but without training and supervision, these insights are uncommon.

The necessary expertise can be brought into settings where people live and work in order to meet their emotional needs in a preventive way rather than by expensive hospital admission at a point of crisis and breakdown. Group therapy and family therapy as I have practised them have fallen within my role as a developmental psychiatrist. This includes an understanding of the emotional and social development of the disabled person in the context of his family or carers, his teachers and peers. We know that psychological distress, low self esteem and depression are much more common in young people with mental handicap, and those with physical disability (with or without learning disability). (Offer et al, 1984, Rutter et al, 1974). We know that problem behaviour which challenges the resources of carers is much increased in people with mental handicap. Group analytis therapy is not an either/or treatment, and can be offered in conjunction with other treatment approaches.

With regard to research it is probably too early to attempt any large scale studies. Some detailed case histories would add to the literature and there is scope for collecting and documenting our experience of using some different measures.

References

Bichard S. (1990) Psychological Assessment of Change. Paper given at The Royal Society of Medicine Forum – Meeting on Evaluating Psychotherapy. 9th March 1990.

Bicknell J. (1983) Inaugural Lecture: The Psychopathology of Handicap. British Journal of Medical Psychology, 56, 167-178.

Coffman Thomas L., and Harris Malcolm C.J. (1980) Transition shock and Adjustments of Mentally Retarded Persons. Mental Retardation, Vol. 18, No.1. 3-7.

Cogan F, Monson L, Bruggeman W. (1966) Concurrent Group and Individual Treatment of the Mentally Retarded. Soc. Psychiat. Journal 12, 5, 404-409.

Evans C.D.H., Hollins S., Evered C. (Submitted 1990). A Repertory Grid Study of Change in a Psychotherapy Group for Young Adults with Mental Handicap based on a paper presented to the Forum on Mental Retardation, Royal Society Medicine, London, March 1990.

Hollins S., Evered C. (1990) Group Process and Content: The Challenge of Mental Handicap. Group Analysis 23(1).

Hollins S. (in press) Group Analytic Therapy. Chapter X in 'Psychotherapy and Mental Handicap' ed. Waitman A & Conboy-Hill S. Sage, London.

Hulbert C., Atkinson D. (1987) 'On the Way Out, and After'. British Medical Journal Subn., Vol. 33, 2, No. 65, pp 109-116.

Matson Johnny L. (1984) Psychotherapy with persons who are mentally retarded. Mental Retardation, Vol. 22, No.4, 170-175.

Menolascino F.J., Gilson S.F., Levitas A.S. (1986) Issues in the treatment of Mentally Retarded Patients in the Community Mental Health System. Community Mental Health Journal, 22(4).

Miezio Stanley. (1967) Group Therapy with Mentally Retarded Adolescents in Institutional Settings. In. Journal Group Psychotherapy, Vol. 17, Part 3, 321-7.

Offer D., Ostrov E., Howard K.I. (1984) 'Body image, self perception and chronic illness in adolescents' in Blum, R.W. (Ed) Chronic Illness and Disabilities in Childhood & Adolescent. Orlando, FL: Grune & Stratton.

Pantlin A.W. (1985) Group-Analytic Psychotherapy with Mentally Handicapped Patients. Group Analysis XV111/1. 44-53.

Rutter, M., Ttzard J., Yule P, Graham P, Whitmore K. (1974) Isle of Wight studies, Psychological Medicine 6, 313-332.

Selwa B.I. (1971) Preliminary considerations in psychotherapy with retarded children. I school Psychol. 9 : 1, 12-15.

Slivkin Stanley E., and Bernstein Norman R. (1968) Goal-Directed Group Psychotherapy for Retarded Adolescents. American Journal of Psychotherapy, Vol. 22, Part 1, 35-45.

Smith E., McKinnon R., Kessler J.W. (1976) Psychotherapy with Mentally Retarded Children. Psychoal. Study Child. Vol. 31. 493-514.

Spinder-Barton E., Walton T & Rowe D. (1976) Using grid Techniques with the handicapped. In Slater P (Ed) The Measurement of Interpersonal Space by Grid Techniques. Publisher Wiley.

Stavrakaki O & Klien J. (1986), Psychotherapies with the mentally retarded. Psychiatric clinics of North American, Vol. 9, No.4, December 1986.

Weinstock A. (1977) Group Treatment of Characteriologically Damaged Developmentally Disabled Adolescents in a Residential Treatment Center.
Woody R.H., Billy J.J. (1966 Counselling Psychotherapy for the Mentally Retarded: A survey of opinions and practices. Mental Retardation, December, 20-23.

Došen, A., Van Gennep, A., Zwanikken, G.J. (Eds.) (1990). Treatment of Mental Illness and Behavioral Disorder in the Mentally Retarded. Proceedings of the International Congress, May 3rd & 4th, 1990, Amsterdam, the Netherlands. Leiden, the Netherlands: Logon Publications.

Chapter 6

Psychotropic drug therapy prescribing principles for mentally retarded persons

R. Sovner

The use of psychotropic drugs to treat emotional and behavioral problems in persons with mental retardation requires a conceptual framework which can integrate treatment within broader habilitative and behavioral contexts (33). Treatment must be directed towards legitimate drug-responsive disorders, administered in such a way that determinations of efficacy can be made, and monitored to insure the client's safety and compatibility with habilitative programming.

Drug therapy, in addition, is not necessarily in competition with other forms of treatment. The decision whether or not to implement a psychotropic drug regimen should be based upon what is known about the efficacy of specific drugs in the treatment of psychiatric disorders. It cannot be based soley upon premises which have been borrowed from other disciplines such as behavioral psychology (36) nor myths about drug effects (35).

As will be discussed in subsequent sections, the use of drug therapy should also require that there be an agreement on the part of clinicians and caregivers that mental illnesses do exist and that the client has such a disorder. To justify treatment for "behavioral control" is counter to the logic which underlies psychopharmacology.

In this article, six psychotropic drug prescribing principles for the treatment of mentally retarded persons will be presented (see Table 1). These principles take into account theoretical as well as practical considerations. They do not mandate the choice of a specific drug so much as they describe a rational basis for decision-making about drug therapy.

Table 1
Six psychotropic drug prescribing principles

1. Carry out a functional assessment of the patient's behavior.
2. Establish a psychiatric diagnosis.
3. Develop a behavioral methodology for assessment and treatment-response measurement.
4. Select a disorder-concordant psychotropic agent.
5. Screen for behavioral side-effect.
6. A drug discontinuation strategy should be part of the prescribing protocol.

1. Carry out a functional assessment of the patient's behavior

Maladaptive behavior is best viewed as a "final common pathway" reflecting an individual's adaptation to environmental demands and physical discomfort as well as to disturbances in neurochemistry and neurophysiology. Consequently, there can be no drug therapy for behavior, *per se*. Except for clearcutictal phenomena (e.g., self-injury associated with temporal lobe seizures [7]), behavior cannot be understood entirely in biochemical and physiological terms.

Clinical and pre-clinical studies, for example, have implicated a reduction in CNS serotonergic neuronal activity with irritable/impulsive aggressive and suicidal behavior, but only under certain conditions (5). Pathological behavior will only be manifest if there is an environmental change which increases the individual's irritabilty or a change in internal milieu such as dysphoria associated with a major depression. This strongly suggests that *the individual's perception of the change in his or her psychological steady-state is a mediating step between biology and behavior.*

Thus, a pre-treatment psychiatric assessment must include a functional analysis of the problematic behavior (including a physical examination) to identify the various factors which promote and reinforce it. Only after the client's affective state, physical status, and the psychosocial milieu are evaluated, can the significance of any behavior can be appreciated. From a psychiatric perspective, the assessment goal is to "see past" non-specific maladaptive behavior and ascertain whether an underlying mental disorder is present.

2. Establish a psychiatric diagnosis

Psychopharmacology is a medical specialty and its practice must be grounded within medicine. In particular, drug selection based upon the patient's diagnosis is a fundamental treatment principle which also applies to psychiatry (12). When used in a mental retardation context, it implies that certain maladaptive behaviors and emotional complaints may cluster together to form distinct disorders (syndromes) with defineable clinical features, natural history, and specific treatments (9). Several factors, however, complicate the diagnostic process when working with mentally retarded persons.

Pathoplastic Effects of Mental Retardation

Limited communication skills and a diminished ability to think abstractly ("intellectual distortion"), stress-induced information processing deficits, ("cognitive disintegration"), and a stress-induced increase in the severity of longstanding maladaptive behavior ("baseline exaggeration") make it difficult to elicit evidence of psychiatric disorders (32) as described in the *Diagnostic and Statistical Manual of Mental Disorders, Third Edition-Revised* disorders (6). These factors often produce a "pseudo-psychotic" clinical picture which can be mistaken for schizophrenia (25).

Presence of Co-morbid Disorders

Co-morbidity can be a confounding problem. A bipolar illness, for example, may be superimposed upon an autistic disorder so that mania may present as increase in the severity of longstanding autistic stereotypic behavior (14, 15, 45). This can produce a clinical picture in which more than one psychopathological state is driving the patient's maladaptive behavior.

State vs Trait Disorders

A useful construct in thinking about psychiatric disorders in mentally retarded persons is to differentiate between state and trait syndromes. State syndromes represent classic psychiatric disorders such as schizophrenia and major depression; their signs and symptoms are qualitative departures from normal function (e.g., hallucinations) and meet the criteria for true illnesses (29). On the other hand, trait syndromes can be considered to represent exaggerations of normal function and temperment caused by CNS dysfunction. A rage attack, for example, is an exaggeration of the normal response to frustration, but is pathological because it is precipitated by minor provocation. (It is not uncommon to find individuals in clinical practice who have both state and trait drug-responsive problems, e.g., the coexistence of an affective disorder and chronic anxiety.)

In the mentally retarded, trait syndromes are the consequence of perinatal and childhood onset organic brain syndromes, analagous to the types of behavioral problems observed in brain injured persons. They are relatively common amongst residents of developmental centers (especially those with severe and profound handicaps) and are manifest by hyperactivity, self-injury, aggression, impulsivity, and disturbed sleep (26). The behavioral responses to these fundamental disturbances tend to be very treatment-resistant (26, 27).

3. Develop a behavioral methodology for assessment and treatment-response measurement

The clinician cannot rely on his or her own impressions based upon a mental status examination. In most cases, patients are unable to accurately report their symptoms or the response to treatment. In addition, several other factors complicate the assessment process. First, chronic maladaptive behavior may vary in severity and frequency over time so that it may take several months of assessment before the true baseline rate of the problem can be appreciated (10, 13). Second, in cases in which there are two causes for maladaptive behavior, e.g., autism and bipolar disorder, the expression of the psychiatric disorder may only be recognized by demonstrating an increase in the severity and/or frequency of the targeted behavior, not the onset of a new behavior during periods of illness (42). Third, frequency and severity may vary in different environments (e.g., the workshop vs the residence). This will only be appreciated if information is collected in both settings.

Therefore, the processes of establishing a valid diagnosis and measuring treatment response must rely on objective behavioral data collected by caregivers providing residential and habilitation services. These data enable clinicians to compare response rates to pre-treatment levels of behavior, provide consistent reporting, and provide consistent data across settings.

4. Select an disorder-concordant psychotropic agent

It is important to recognize that it is a superimposed mental illness treated and not the patient's mental retardation.
Therefore, if it can be demonstrated that the individual is suffering from a specific disorder, evidence of drug specificity for that disorder should suffice.

When a classic psychiatric disorder is present, the choice of medication is relatively straightforward. On the other hand, when the presence of maladaptive behavior reflects an underlying organic brain syndrome (i.e., a "trait syndrome") in the absence of a disorder such as bipolar illness, drug selection is more difficult for several reasons. Drug therapy does not "turn off" the disorder (i.e., achieve a complete symptom remission) as may occur in the treatment of affective disorders. Instead, a reduction in the rate or severity of maldaptive behavior, is the primary treatment goal. In other words, it will take a stronger stimuli to produce a maladaptive response. This is particulary true for problems such as irritability and overarousal. Irritable individuals, for example, may engage in tantrums (in which aggression may be a presenting complaint) when excessive demands are placed upon them because these demands increase their discomfort. Consequently, treatment is directed at the irritability, not the aggression.

The following treatment recommendations are based upon the author's clinical experience in the treatment of behavioral problems in mentally retarded persons. They are summarized in Table 2.

Overactivity

In general, the overactivity observed in persons with moderate or greater handicaps does not represent classic attention deficit disorder or respond to psychostimulant therapy. In some cases, the overactivty is a reflection of chronic mania and may respond to anticonvulsant therapy with carbamazepine (27, 34) or valproic acid (36, 39). Lithium ion has been reported to be effective in overactive and aggressive patients (40, 46). Valproic acid derivatives are effective in some cases in which the overactivity is related to a chronic organic mood disorder which has been present since childhood (36). Reid *et al* (27) found that carbamazepine, in the absence of manic-like behavior, is not particularly effective in overactivity.

Overarousal

Overarousal in autistic adults may respond to beta blocker therapy either with centrally acting lipophilic agents (e.g., propranolol) or peripherally acting hydrophilic agents (.e.g, nadolol) (22). Recently, buspirone has been reported to be effective in some cases of anxiety or arousal in autistic and handicapped adults (23) and autistic children (24). Naltrexone, an oral opiate antagonist, shows some promise in autistic children (4), even in the absence of self-injury.

Irritability

Irritability may present as self-injury or aggression. It is a common finding in individuals who have sustained CNS damage whether from closed head injury or dementia (17, 18) and may prove responsive to drugs such as carbamazpine (19, 20) and serotonergic antidepressants (8, 31). Animal and clinical evidence suggesting that a CNS hyposerotonergic state is associated with hype-exciteability, hypersensitivity, and hyperirritability, and may be due to a loss of serotonergic inhibition of noradenergic and dopamergic activity (5).

Table 2
Proposed drug selection guidelines for organic brain syndromes in mentally retarded persons

Function*	Alterations in Psycho-biological Behavior Presentation	Possible Psycho-pharmacological Intervention	Comments
anxiety	self-injury, aggression	benzodiazepines, buspirone	Perseverative speech and agitation may be response-predictors.
excitement	aggression, self-injury	carbamazepine, lithium, valproic acid	May be a reflection of an organic mood syndrome especially when associated with a sleep disturbance and overactivity.
irritability	tantrums with self-injury, aggression	carbamazepine, low-dose neuroleptics, serotonergic antidepressants, lithium	A sleep disturbance is often present and represents difficult in regulating sleep wake cycles rather than an affective disorder.
overactivity	aggression	lithium, carbamazepine?, valproic acid?	Chaotic sleep pattern often predicts treatment response.
overarousal	aggression, self-injury	buspirone, beta blockers, clonidine	Usually a problem in autistic individuals and those with Fragile X syndrome.
rage	aggression, self-injury, swearing	beta blockers	Often occurs in absence of other psychopathology.
self-stimulatory behavior	overactivity, self-injury	opiate antagonists, neuroleptics, buspirone?	This is a common problem in autism.

* This table assumes that the indicated behaviors are present in the absence of a classic psychiatric illness such as bipolar disorder. In such cases, treatment is directed at the underlying condition.

Clinically, the affected person is irritable and impulsive and may manifest aggression, tantrums, and/or SIB. Pharmacologically irritability might be addressed by increasing serotonin activity (with serotonergic antidepressants) or inhibiting catecholaminergic activity. This may explain why low dose treatment with neuroleptic agents (which block dopaminergic receptors) are useful in the treatment of agitation associated with dementia and also some types of self-injury (10). Drugs such as lithium and carbamazepine have multiple effects on serotonergic and catecholaminergic mechanisms which may mediate their therapeutic effects. "Organic irritability" may have been the drug-responsive target problem in reports of therapeutic effects of carbamazepine in mentally retarded persons (2, 11, 21, 33, 34).

Rage Attacks

Organic personality disorder, explosive type, can occur in mentally retarded persons (22). As in non-handicapped populations, this problem responds to lipophilic beta blocker therapy with agents such as propranolol (16).

Self-Injury

Opiate antagonists have shown some (but inconsistent) success in a few controlled case reports, especially when the behavior reflects self-stimulation (2, 3, 30). Some self-injurious individuals, however, are suffering from an affective disorder and the behavior remits or decreases in severity when appropriate treatment is prescribed (9). SIB may also be a reflection of irritability. In these cases, the irritability not the self-injury is the primary drug responsive feature. Gualtieri and Schroeder (10) have demonstrated that low dose neuroleptic therapy can be effective in some cases of SIB.

5. Screen for behavioral side-effects

Drug side-effects without objective measures are particularly difficult to manage because mentally retarded persons cannot express their subjective distress. Antidepressant-induced amphetamine reactions and antipsychotic-induced akathisia, for example, may present as an increase in the severity of the maladaptive behavior being treated (41). Table 3. lists common behavioral drug side-effects.

6. A drug discontinuation strategy should be part of the prescribing protocol

Long term psychotropic drug therapy is indicated only when it can be established that the person will relapse when drug therapy is discontinued. In some cases, the patient's clinical history argues against drug withdrawal based upon previous drug free trials. In other cases, the nature of the problem, e.g., a chronic rapid cycling bipolar illness, suggests that relapse will occur.

Table 3
Some behavioral drug side-effects*

Behavioral Reaction	Clinical Signs	Drug or Drug Class
akathisia	anxiety overactivity	neuroleptics
akinesia	withdrawal depression	neuroleptics
amphetamine-like reaction	jitteriness irritability	tricyclic and MAO inhibitor antidepressants, fluoxetine and buproprion
disinhibition	increase in behavior severity	benzodiazepines
excitement	overarousal overactivity irritability	sedative/hypnotics
nightmares	middle of the night awakening	tricyclic antidepressnts

* Adapted from Sovner and Hurley (41).

A drug free trial should be considered when: 1) a patient has a psychiatric disorder which is known to be episodic with long periods of remission (e.g., major depression); 2) a behavioral side-effect is suspected and cannot be treated with an adjunctive medication; and 3) the patient has received longterm neuroleptic drug therapy and is at risk for tardive dyskinesia.

Conclusion

Psychotropic drug therapy, in the eyes of many caregivers who work with developmentally disabled persons, has been tainted by past abuses of neuroleptic drug therapy (43). Treatment has come to be viewed as an intervention of last resort, to be used only when other types of "active treatment" have been unsuccessful. On the other hand, the fact that the mentally retarded suffer from the full range of mental disorders and the availability of innovative drug regimens point to a broader and first-line role for pharmacotherapy for handicapped persons with significant behavioral and emotional problems.

References

1. Barrett, R.P., Feinstein, C., Hole, W.T. Effects of naloxone and naltrexone on self-injury: A double-blind, placebo-controlled analysis. *Am J Ment Retard* 1989; 93: 644–651.
2. Barrett, R.P., Payton, J.B., Burkhart, J.E. Treatment of self-injury and disruptive behavior with carbamazepine (Tegretol) and behavior therapy. *J Multihandicap Person* 1988; 1: 79–92.
3. Bernstein, G.A., Hughes, J.R., Mitchell, J.E., Thompson, T. Effects of narcotic antagonists on self-injurious behavior – a single case study. *J Am Acad Child Adolesc Psychiatry* 1987; 26: 886–889.
4. Campbell, M., Overall, J.E., Small, A.M., Sokol, M.S., Spencer, E.K., Adams, P., Folt, R.L., Monti, K.M., Perry, R., Nobler, M., Roberts, E. Naltrexone in autistic children: An acute open dose range tolerance trial. *J Am Acad Child Adolesc Psychiatry* 1989; 28: 200–206.
5. Coccaro, E.F. Central serotonin and impulsive aggression. *Br J Psychiatry* 1989; 155 (suppl 8): 52–62.
6. *Diagnostic and Statistical Manual of Mental Disorders, Third Edition Revised.* Washington DC: American Psychiatric Association, 1986.
7. Gedye, A. Extreme self-injury attributed to frontal lobe seizures. *Am J Psychiatry* 1989; 94: 20–26.
8. Gleason, R.P., Schneider, L.S. Carbamazepine treatment of agitation in Alzheimer's outpatients refractory to neuroleptics. *J Clin Psychiatry* 1990; 51: 115–118.
9. Gualtieri, C.T. The differential diaognosis of self-injurious behavior in mentally retarded people. *Psychopharmacol Bull* 1989; 25: 358–363.
10. Gualtieri, C.T., Schroeder, S.R. Pharmacotherapy for self-injurious behavior: Preliminary tests of the D1 hypothesis. *Psychopharmacol Bull* 1989; 25: 364–371.
11. Gupta, B.K., Fish, D.N., Yerevanian, B.I. Carbamazpeine for intermittent explosive disorder in a Prader-Willi syndrome patient. *J Clin Psychiatry* 1987; 48: 423.
12. Guze, S.B. Nature of psychiatric illness: Why psychiatry is a branch of medicine. *Compr Psychiatry* 1978; 19: 295–307.
13. Hardy, P.M., Waters, J.M., Cohen, M.S. A biomedical basis for self-injury. In Griffin, J.C., Start, M.T., Williams, D.E., Altmeyer, B.K., Griffin, H.K. (ed.), *Advances in the Treatment of Self-injurious Behavior* Austin, Texas: James C. Griffin, 1984; 153–164.
14. Kerebeshian, J., Burd, L., Fisher, W. Lithium carbonate in the treatment of two patients with infantile autism and atypical bipolar symptomatology. *J Clin Psychopharmacol* 1987; 7: 401–405.
15. Komoto, J., Usui, S., Hirata, J. Infantile autism and affective disorder. *J Autism Devel Disorders* 1984; 14: 81–84.

16. Lader, M. B-adrenoceptor antagonists in neuropsychiatry: An update. *J Clinical Psychiatry* 1988; 49: 213–223.
17. McCallister, T.W., Carbamazepine in mixed frontal lobe and psychiatric disorders. *J Clin Psychiatry* 1985; 46: 393–394.
18. McQuiston, H.L., Adler, L.A., Leong, S. Carbamazepine in frontal lobe syndrome: Two more cases (letter) *J Clin Psychiatry* 1987; 48: 456.
19. Marin, D.B., Greenwald, B.S. Carbamazepine for aggressive agitation in demented patients during nursing care. *Am J Psychiatry* 1989; 146: 400.
20. Patterson, J.F. Carbamazepine for assaultive patients with organic brain disease. *Psychosomatics* 1987; 28: 579–581.
21. Carbamazepine and behavior therapy for aggressive behavior. *Behav Mod* 1983; 7: 255–265.
22. Ratey, J.J., Mikkelsen, E.J., Smith, G.B., Upadhyaya, A., Zuckerman, H.S., Martell, D., Sorgi, P., Polakoff, S., Bemporad, J. B-blockers in the severely and profoundly mentally retarded. *J Clin Psychopharmacol* 1987; 6: 103–107.
23. Ratey, J.J., Sovner, R., Mikkelsen, E., Chmielinski, H.E. Buspirone therapy for maladaptive behavior and anxiety in developmentally disabled persons. *J Clin Psychiatry* 1989; 50: 382–384.
24. Realmuto, G.M., Aughust, G.J., Garfinkel, B.D. Clinical effect of buspirone in autistic children. *J Clin Psychopharmacol* 1989; 9: 122–124.
25. Reid, A.H. Schizophrenia in mental retardation: Clinical features. *Res Devel Disabil* 1989; 10: 241–249.
26. Reid, A.H., Ballinger, B.R., Heather, B.B. Behavioural syndromes identified by cluster analysis in a sample of 100 severely and profoundly retarded adults. *Psychol Med* 1978; 8: 399–412.
27. Reid, A.H., Naylor, G.H., Kay, D.S.G. A double-blind, placebo controlled, trial of carbamazepine in overactive, severely mentally handicapped patients. *Psychol Med* 1981; 11: 109–113.
28. Reiss, S., Levitan, G.W., Szysko, J. Emotional disturbance and mental retardation: Diagnostic overshadowing. *Am J Ment Defic* 1982; 86: 567–574.
29. Robins, E., Guze, S.B. Establishment of diagnostic validity in psychiatric illness: Its application to schizophrenia. *Am J Psychiatry* 1970; 126: 983–987.
30. Sandman, C.A., Datta, P.C., Barron, J., Hoehler, F.K., Swanson, J.M. Naloxone attenuates self-abusive behavior in developmentally disabled clients. *Appl Res Ment Retard* 1983; 4: 5–11.
31. Simpson, D.M., Foster, D. Improvement in organically disturbed behavior with trazodone treatment. *J Clin Psychiatry* 1986; 47: 191–193.
32. Sovner, R. Limiting factors in the use of *DSM-III* criteria with mentally ill/mentally retarded persons. *Psychopharm Bull* 1986; 22: 1055–1059.

33. Sovner, R. Behavioral psychopharmacology: a new psychiatric subspecialty. In Stark, J., Menolascino, F.J., Albarielli, M., Gray, V. (eds.), *Mental Retardation and Mental Health: Classification, Diagnosis, Treatment, Services*. New York: Springer Verlag, 1988; 229–242.
34. Sovner, R. Anticonvulsant drug therapy of neuropsychiatric disorders in mentally retarded persons. In McElroy, S.E., Pope, H.G. Jr (eds.), *Use of Anticonvulsants in Psychiatry. Recent Advances*. Clifton NJ: Oxford Healthcare, 1988; 169–181.
35. Sovner, R. Introduction to Gadow, K., Poling, A.G., *Pharmacotherapy and Mental Retardation* Boston: College-Hill Press, 1988; vi-xii.
36. Sovner, R. The use of valproate in the treatment of mentally retarded persons with typical and atypical bipolar disorders. *J Clin Psychiatry* 1989; 50(3 suppl): 40–43.
37. Sovner, R. Developments in the use of psychotropic drugs. *Curr Opin Psychiatry* 1989; 2: 636–640.
38. Sovner, R. Bipolar disorders in persons with developmental disorders: An overview. In Došen, A., Menolascino, F.J. (eds). *Depression in Mentally Retarded Children and Adults*. Leiden: Logon Publications, 1990; 175–198.
39. Sovner, R. Divlaproex-responsive rapid cycling biplar disorder in a patient Down's syndrome. *J Ment Defic Res*, in press.
40. Sovner, R., Hurley, A.D. The management of chronic behavior disorders in mentally retarded adults with lithium carbonate. *J Nerv Ment Dis* 1981; 169: 191–195.
42. Sovner, R., Hurley, A.D. Psychotropic drug side-effects presenting as behavior disorders. *Psychiatr Aspects Ment Retard* 1982; 1: 45–48.
43. Sovner, R., Pary, R. Affective disorders in developmentally disabled persons. In Matson, J.L., Barrett, R.P. (eds.), *Psychopathology in the Mentally Retarded, 2nd Edition*. New York: Psychological Corporation, in press.
44. Sprague, R. Litigation, legislation, and regulations. In Breuning, S.E., Polinmg, A.D. (eds.), *Drugs and Mental Retardation*. Springfield IL: Charles C Thomas, 1982; 377–414.
45. Steingard, R., Biederman, J. Lithium responsive manic-like symptoms in two individuals with autism and mental retardation. *J Am Acad Child Adol Psychiatry* 1987; 26: 932–935.
46. Tyrer, S.P., Walsh, A., Edwards, D.E., Berney, T.P., Stephen, D.A. Factors associated with a good response to lithium in aggressive mentally handicapped subjects. *Prog Neuro-Psychopharmacol & Biol Psychiatry* 1984; 8: 751–755.

Došen, A., Van Gennep, A., Zwanikken, G.J. (Eds.) (1990). Treatment of Mental Illness and Behavioral Disorder in the Mentally Retarded. Proceedings of the International Congress, May 3rd & 4th, 1990, Amsterdam, the Netherlands. Leiden, the Netherlands: Logon Publications.

Chapter 7

Treatment of antisocial behaviour

K. Day

The focus of this paper is the mentally handicapped offender, but the treatment strategies described are equally appropriate for mildly and borderline handicapped people who display antisocial behaviour but have not come before the courts.

Epidemiology and clinical features

Offending is uncommon in mentally handicapped people. In a large scale survey of 22,000 mentally handicapped people in Denmark (Svendsen and Werner, 1977) found only 190 offenders, a prevalence of less than 1%. This low prevalence is reflected in the low percentage of mentally handicapped people found in remanded or convicted males (Table 1).

The typical mentally handicapped offender is a young male functioning in the mild to borderline intellectual range from a poorish urban environment with a history of psychosocial deprivation, to have displayed other behavioural problems, who is likely to have spent substantial periods in residential care, to show evidence of personality disorder and to have a family history of criminality (Day, 1988; Lund, 1990). Female offenders are rare; they are invariably grossly disturbed and extremely difficult to help, although their offending behaviour tends to be trivial.

Mentally handicapped offenders thus have many features in common with non-handicapped offenders but differ significantly from mentally ill offenders, whose offending is secondary to psychiatric disorder, (Robertson, 1981; West and Farrington, 1973, 1977). As in the general population, theft and burglary are the commonest offenses, but sex offenses and arson are over-represented and serious personal violence is under-represented in mentally handicapped populations (Kugel et al, 1968; Shapiro, 1969; Tutt, 1971; Walker and McCabe,

1973; Svendsen and Werner, 1977; Robertson, 1981; Craft, 1984; Day, 1988; Lund, 1990). Recidivism and involvement in a wide range of offenses is common (Kugel et al, 1968; Day, 1988).

Assessment

A comprehensive assessment of the individual and his offence forms the basis for the management plan (Day, 1990; Campbell, 1990): the essential elements are listed in Table 2. Current offence should be thoroughly explored and statements from the victim(s) and witnesses, together with any photographs, always carefully scrutinised. Detailed information about previous offenses/ convictions, including dates, nature and disposal should always be obtained. In taking the history, particular regard should be paid to factors pertinent to the offending behaviour including evidence of brain damage, subcultural factors and family psychopathology. Information should be collected from as many sources as possible including relatives, careworkers, the probation service and previous medical and social records, always, of course, with the patient's agreement.

Table 1
Prevalence of mentally handicapped offenders in remanded and convicted males

Author	Location	Population studied	Percentage mentally handicapped
East et all (1942)	Wormwood Scrubs Prison, U.K.	4,000 Convicted youths	3.5%
Messinger & Apfelberg (1961)	Psychiatric Clinics Court of General Sessions New York County	57,000 Felons	2.5%
Gibbens (1963)	England - Sample	200 Borstal boys	3%
Bluglass (1966)	Perth Prison U.K.	3,000 Convicted male prisoners	2.6%
Guze (1976)	Missouri Probation Board U.S.A.	223 Paroles & flat timers	1%
Faulk (1976)	Winchester Prison U.K.	72 Convicted male prisoners	5.5%
Taylor & Gunn (1984)	Brixton Prison U.K.	1241 Remanded males	1.9%

Table 2
Assessment of the mentally handicapped offender

HISTORY
- Current Offence
- Previous Offence(s)
- Neuropsychiatric Disorder
- Personality Disorder
- Family & Social Background
- Family Psychopathology

EXAMINATION
- Physical
- Mental State
- Special Areas
    - Fitness to Plead
    - Competence as Witness
    - Attitude to Offence
    - Concepts of Right & Wrong
    - Dangerousness

INVESTIGATIONS
- Psychometry
- Electroencephalography
- Genotype

A full physical examination should be carried out, noting any minor as well as physical defects. In addition to level of mental handicap and the presence or absence of superadded psychiatric illness, mental state examination should cover attitude to offending, concern for the victim, concepts of right and wrong, fitness to plead and competence as a witness. An assessment of dangerousness and the likelihood of further offending should always be made. A full psychological assessment - including IQ, educational attainments, personality and an exploration of specific points related to the offence - sexual knowledge, attitude to offence, for example, is invaluable. EEG studies should be carried out if brain damage of epilepsy is suspected and chromosome studies to exclude a genosomal abnormality.

Management

Offending in the mentally handicapped person is usually the consequence of under-socialisation, poor internal controls and faulty social learning; educational under-achievement, lack of social and occupational skills and a poor self image are frequently additional factors. The aims of treatment, therefore, are to assist maturation, facilitate the development of adequate levels of self control, instil a sense of personal worth and responsibility, establish acceptable social mores and improve social, occupational and educational skills.

The majority of mentally handicapped offenders can be managed in the community supported by the mental handicap services and, where appropriate, the probation service. Hospitalisation is indicated when the offence committed is a serious one, when the patient is considered to be dangerous, or where the general needs of the individual for training, control and care cannot be met in a community setting.

The Treatment Package

A properly formulated treatment programme with explicitly stated goals is essential. All personnel involved in care should work together to an agreed strategy and meet regularly to monitor progress and review plans. The principal elements of the treatment programme, whether it is implemented in the community or hospital, are listed in Table 3. Counselling should be kept simple using concrete examples arising out of everyday incidents. Group work around the themes of relationship problems, behaviour, attitudes to staff and the need for rules and regulations, is particularly useful in institutional settings. Role play and psycho-drama are potentially valuable but under-used techniques. Social and occupational training and further education should focus on those areas (work habit, personal care, basic literacy and numeracy, constructive use of leisure, development of hobbies) which will enable the individual to better integrate and cope in society. Specific behavioural programmes and drug therapy, to control aggression or libido, may be required in some cases (see later).

Institutional Management Programmes

A number of institutional programmes based on token economy regimes have been developed for mentally handicapped offenders (Burchard et al, 1967; Denkowski and Denkowski, 1984; Denkowski et al, 1984; Sandford et al, 1987; Day, 1988). They aim to link personal behaviour with its consequences through the systematic issuing of tokens or points, which can be exchanged for a range of back-up reinforcers from cigarettes or sweets to attendance at social events contingent upon appropriate behaviour, and can be applied globally or to specific aspects of behaviour. Proper application requires a controlled environment, a high staff/patient ratio, well trained and experienced personnel and intensive support from a multi-professional team. They are only suitable for use in specialised units for mentally handicapped offenders as part of an overall programme which includes the treatment package described above. Most specialised units operate a phased treatment programme (Denkowski et al, 1984; Denkowski and Denkowski, 1984; Sandford et al, 1987;Day, 1988) with admission to a closed unit and progression, once set goals have been satisfactorily achieved, to an open unit and eventually a halfway hostel or house as a final preparation for discharge. Good results have been reported (Sandfort et al, 1987; Day, 198). A detailed description of one scheme is given later in this paper.

Table 3
Treatment package - key elements

Socialisation Programmes
Practical Skills Training
Further Education
Counselling/Supportive Psychotherapy
Drug Therapy
Specific Behavioural Programmes

Sex Offenders

Most sex offenses committed by mentally handicapped people are of a minor nature (mainly indecent exposure and minor indecent assault) and are the consequence of a normal sex drive coupled with limited opportunities for normal sexual outlets and compounded by poor self control, sexual naivety and limited social skills (Day - to be published). They are symptomatic of a general lack of maturation rather than true sexual aberration and treatment programmes should reflect the wider need for social skills training and personality development, and not focus too narrowly on sexual difficulties. Sex education with the emphasis on personal relationship and regular contact with a peer group of the opposite sex are nevertheless important components (Thompson and Back, 1987). Progress should be judged on a global basis including improvements in general behaviour, level of self control, personal responsibility and social awareness as well as sexual behaviour.

Sex suppressant drugs can be a useful adjunct to treatment, helping to facilitate social training and avoiding the need for institutional care in some cases. Cyproterone Acetate, in doses of up to 300 mg. daily, is the drug of choice, being both effective and relatively free from side effects. Dosage should be titrated according to the required result. It is not always necessary to completely eliminate sexual drive, the aim in most cases being to reduce this to a level which the patient can control. Monitoring depends on self report supplemented by observations of relatives and care staff. Compliance is not usually a problem, but where it is, a depot preparation is available. Specific consent to the use of this drug must always be obtained prior to commencing treatment; the vast majority of mentally handicapped offenders are capable of giving this.

Most mentally handicapped sex offenders can be managed quite safely and satisfactorily in the community. Hospitalisation is only indicated for serious or persistent offenders, the level of security required depending upon the perceived dangerousness of the patient. Serious offenders constitute a small group who invariably come from highly disturbed family backgrounds, show evidence of marked personality disorder and exhibit a variety of social problems and other offending.

Aggressive Behaviour

Although crimes of personal violence are uncommon, a low flashpoint is not infrequently encountered in all groups of mentally handicapped offenders. In these cases medication can play a useful role in stabilising mood, reducing irritability and aggression, and facilitating co-operation with treatment. Neuroleptics like Moditen Enanthate and Clopenthixol, (particularly in their depot forms) the anticonvulsant, Carbamazepine, and Lithium have all been shown to be effective (Yar-Khan, 1981; Mlele and Wileu, 1986). Finding the best drug is usually a matter of trial and error. Lithium and Carbamazepine, if effective, are to be preferred because of their freedom from serious long term side effects (Sovner, 1990). As with all drug therapy, a systematic approach is essential and monotherapy the goal (Snaith et al, 1979) although combinations of the above drugs can be effective, when by themselves they are not. Training in anger management is a potentially fruitful but currently under-used technique in the mentally handicapped. The patient is taught to recognise a hierarchy of physical feelings which accompany anger and how to terminate these at an early stage by engaging in alternative behaviour. Advantages are that it encourages a sense of personal responsibility for behaviour and there are none of the problems of generalisation encountered with other behavioural techniques (Gardner et al, 1983; Fleming and Tosh, 1984; Woods and Lowe, 1986).

Arson

The offence of arson is particularly associated with mental handicap (Walker and McCabe, 1973; Lewis and Yarnell, 1951). The act is usually unpredictable and difficult to understand or explain. Some patients talk of the feeling of power induced whilst in others it appears to be attention seeking or a manipulative response to conflict. The management of the mentally handicapped fire setter poses special difficulties because of the risk of repetition and potentially serious consequences to life and property. It is usually an indication for close supervision in a hospital setting, sometimes under conditions of special security. Treatment should focus on general principles - there are no specific measures. Close supervision and a complete ban on personal matches and lighters, together with regular searches, is usually advisable in the early stages. Conflict with authority constitutes a high risk situation for further fire setting (Tennent et al, 1971). Duration of inpatient care will depend upon overall progress and an assessment of the risk of repetition. The latter is often difficult to gauge and, as in all dangerous offenders, the first consideration must be the risk to the general population and it is always best to err on the side of caution.

Rehabilitation of Aftercare

Return to the community after a period of hospital care should be a carefully phased process beginning with a lessening of restrictions in hospital and progressing through weekend and then longer leaves to eventual discharge. Discharge should be arranged initially on a trial basis: this facilitates co-operation with the aftercare programme and enables a quick return to hospital should be situation break down. Careful preparation of the family and/or receiving facility is essential and the family and community personnel should be involved in planning rehabilitation at an early stage. Intensive support is required during the immediate post-discharge period when the risk of breakdown and further offending is high (Day, 1988). This is best provided jointly by hospital personnel and community workers, the former being gradually phased out.

A comprehensive package of aftercare including domiciliary support, occupational placement, residential placement where required, and leisure activities is essential if social breakdown and a drift back into offending is to be avoided (Walker and McCabe, 1973; Hunter, 1979; Craft, 1984; Day, 1988). It is essential that staff in community day and residential placements have a full knowledge of the individual and his problems and needs. Experience indicates that mentally handicapped offenders can rarely be satisfactorily managed in regular occupational and residential services for mentally handicapped people which are not geared to catering for their continuing need for structure and supervision (Day, 1988). Specialised provision is required in the early stages of rehabilitation for the majority, and on a longer term basis in some cases, but is currently rarely available.

Prognosis

Studies show that between 40 and 60% of hospitalised mentally handicapped offenders are reconvicted during the follow-up period and that nearly a third are rehospitalised or imprisoned (Walker and McCabe, 1973; Gibbens and Robertson, 1983; Craft, 1969, 1984; Day, 1988). The majority reoffend during the first year but in one 15 year follow-up study (Gibbens and Robertson, 1983) nearly 20% of patients did not reoffend until four years or more after discharge. Very few commit serious offenses (Gibbens and Robertson, 1983; Craft, 1984) and reconviction rates paint an unduly pessimistic picture. Global assessments indicate a rather better outcome. Using a range of social adjustment measures Day (1988), for example, found that whilst 55% of his offender group were reconvicted following discharge (40% more than once) nearly 70% were rated as well adjusted or reasonably well adjusted at last contact.

Factors which may affect prognosis have been identified in a number of studies. A positive correlation has been demonstrated between good outcome and a duration of two years or more of inpatient care (Day, 1988), stable residential placement, regular daytime occupation and regular supervision and support (Craft, 1984; Day, 1988) - emphasising the crucial importance of the quality of aftercare. Poor outcome has been shown to be associated with a history of previous convictions (Payne et al, 1974; Gibbens and Robertson, 1983) and a poor response to inpatient treatment (Day, 1988). There is some evidence that offenders against the person have a better prognosis than property offenders (Payne et al, 1974; Day, 1988). This may reflect real differences between the two groups - offenses against the person being essentially problems of poor self control and immaturity with the potential to respond to socialisation programmes, whilst property offenses are more a function of overall lifestyle and subcultural influences to which the offenders so frequently returns after discharge. Long term studies, however, have reported a low but persistent tendency towards reconviction in sex offenders (Soothill and Gibbens, 1987; Day, to be published).

Service provision in the UK

The special management needs of mentally handicapped offenders have long been recognised in practice, service provision and legislation throughout the western world. Recently, however, the more extreme elements of the normalisation lobby have challenged the justification for special treatment, arguing that the mentally handicapped should be treated within the penal system like any other offender. This is a fundamental misunderstanding of the principle of normalisation for as Jackson (1983) point out "recognition of an individual's human worth does not logically require that society has to accord a retarded citizen identical treatment to that accorded to a non-retarded citizen".

In the United Kingdom mentally handicapped offenders have always been cared for within the mental handicap services under mental health legislation (Day, 1990; Bluglass, 1990; Whatmore, 1990). When supervision and treatment in the community is required this can be achieved by making a Guardianship Order under the Mental Health Act 1983 or a psychiatric probation order. If the general needs for care and management are already being adequately met, fines and other simple punishments are sometimes appropriate and have a positive role in making the offender feel accountable for his actions. Offenders who would normally have received a custodial sentence are admitted to hospital on a hospital order under the Mental Health Act 1983. Special restrictions on discharge can be applied. The Mental Health Act Commission (Mental Welfare Commission in Scotland) look after the welfare of detained patients and the continuing need for detention is regularly reviewed by Mental Health Review Tribunals.

The care of the offender in the community is shared by the mental handicap services, social services and the probation service, their respective roles being determined by the needs of the individual. Many offenders continue to live at home with psychiatric oversight, supported by social workers, community nurses or probation officers and attend community facilities. Others may be placed in local authority or probation residential and/or day services at the direction of the court. The majority of those requiring inpatient treatment are cared for in mental handicap hospitals within which special units have been developed (Shapiro, 1969; Craft, 1984; Day, 1988). For those convicted of more serious crimes who require a higher level of security, four Special Hospitals (three in England and Wales and one in Scotland) jointly run by the DHSS and the Home Office, are provided on a national basis (Hamilton, 1985, 1990). In the early 1970s the Government accepted the recommendation of a special committee on the mentally abnormal offender that a number of Medium Secure Units should be established throughout the country on a regional basis for these offenders who required more security than could be provided in local mental hospitals but less than that provided by the Special Hospitals (HMSO, 1974; Glancy, 1974). At the same time, criteria for admission to Special Hospitals was tightened. The development of Medium Secure Units have been generally slow (Snowden, 199) and the provision of units for mentally handicapped people has lagged well behind those for the mentally ill (Isweran and Bardsley, 1987; Smith, 1988).

The Department of Health has recently reviewed services for mentally handicapped offenders in the light of changing patterns of acre, and particularly the planned phasing out of mental handicap hospitals (DoH, 1989). The study team carrying out the review concluded that a comprehensive range of specialised facilities in required from community services for the majority to high security provision for the most dangerous offenders together with specialised rehabilitation and aftercare services for hospitalised offenders and some long term facilities for those requiring continuing care with minimal security. The principal components of this service, together with estimates of bed requirements are listed in Table 4. The local hospital unit is the cornerstone of the service: an example is described below.

Table 4
Model for services for mentally handicapped offenders in UK

Special Hospitals (5 places/million popn.)
Regional Medium Secure Units (10 places/million popn.)
Local Units (20 places/500,000 popn.)
Rehabilitation Facilities
Aftercare Services
Community Services

The Northgate Unit

Northgate Hospital is a medium sized mental handicap hospital situated in the North East of England near Newcastle upon Tyne. The unit for male offenders was developed as part of a 100-bedded specialised psychiatric unit for mentally handicapped people established within the grounds of the hospital in the early 70's (Day, 1983). Initially it comprised an 8-bedded self-contained flat in one of the treatment villas with a few rehabilitation beds in a separate villa (Day, 1988) but it has subsequently expanded, in response to demand, and currently provides a total of 38 beds as follows: a semi-secure locked villa offering a moderate level of security and sub-divided into three self-contained flats, two of 6 beds and one of 8 beds; a 10-bedded open villa for rehabilitation and two 3-bedroomed houses in the hospital grounds for pre-discharge preparation. Future plans for the unit include the reprovision of the semi-secure villa, scheduled for 1992, provision of workshop and other day activities with perimeter security and the establishment of a Medium Secure Unit and a community based halfway hostel. The unit was deliberately established as a single sex facility because of previous unsatisfactory experiences with a mixed unit. Patients have ample opportunities for meeting an equivalent female peer group within the hospital and this level of segregation and controlled exposure has been found to be advantageous and to reduce pressure on both sexes.

The unit is under the direction of two Consultant Psychiatrists in Mental Handicap and the clinical team comprises one full time Senior Registrar, one Registrar, two psychiatric Social Workers, a Clinical Psychologist and input from Occupational Therapy, Further Education and Industrial and Recreational Therapy. The nursing establishment is 18 comprising 1 manager, 1 charge nurse, 6 registered nurses and 10 nursing assistants. There are always 3 staff on duty at night and at least 4 on duty during the day. Learners also do placements on the units. All senior staff have a qualification in mental handicap nursing and have received training in the care of disturbed and violent patients, including periods of secondment to Special Hospitals and Forensic Units.

The unit serves the hospital's catchment population of 600,000 but patients are increasingly admitted from further afield because of absent or inadequate facilities. Between 1974 and June, 1990 72 patients were treated in the unit. The majority were admitted directly through the courts on a hospital order under the Mental Health Act 1983; 12 were transfers from Special Hospitals for the next stage in their rehabilitation and 5 were admitted as a condition of probation. Index offenses are listed in Table 7 and are similar to those reported in other units (Walker and McCabe, 1973; Isweran and Bardsley, 1987; Smith, 1988; Kearns and O'Connor, 1988). Sexually motivated physical assaults are categorised under sex offenses.

Prior to admission the functioning of the unit is fully discussed with the offender of his relatives and their agreement to participation in the treatment programme obtained. Patients are admitted to one of two self-contained admission flats in the locked villa. For the first 2-3 months following admission they are strictly supervised and thereafter, according to progress, are given progressively more freedom moving from ground parole to escorted and then unescorted community parole. Relatives are encouraged to visit and home leave is introduced as soon as practicable. A detailed review is carried out month after admission with progress reviews at 2-3 monthly intervals and a further detailed review three months prior to discharge, at multi-disciplinary case conferences attended by all the unit staff, staff from the training departments, community personnel responsible for aftercare and relatives. No time limit is set for length of stay, the policy being that individuals are only discharged when they are considered to be ready.

Table 5
Index offence of 74 consecutive admissions of males to the Northgate Unit 1974-1990

SEX			33 (46%)
Manslaughter	1	Indecent Assault	14
Grievous Bodily Harm	2	Indecent Exposure	2
Assault	1	Buggery	2
Rape	3	Gross Indecency	3
Rape & Robbery	1	Indecent Assault on Male Person Under the Age 16 years	1
Attempted Rape	1	Trespass	1
		Theft	1
ASSAULT			16 (22%)
Murder	1	Assault Occasioning Actual Bodily Harm	2
Manslaughter	1	Burglary & Wounding	11
Grievous Bodily Harm	3	Common Assault	2
Malicious Wounding	2	Carrying Offensive Weapon	1
Wounding with Intent	1	Breach of Peace	1
ARSON			6 (8%)
Arson with intent to endanger life			1
Arson being reckless to whether life endangered			1
Arson			4
PROPERTY			17 (24%)
Burglary & Theft	2		
Burglary	4		
Theft	9		
Criminal Damage	1		
Taking Away & Driving a Vehicle	1		
TOTAL			72 (100%)

Table 6
Northgate training opportunities

FURTHER EDUCATION	WORK TRAINING	SOCIAL TRAINING	COUNSELLING & GROUP WORK	LEISURE ACTIVITIES
Numeracy	Woodwork	Personal Hygiene	Relationships	In House
Literacy	Gardening	Clothes Care	Sex	Meals Out
Current Affairs	Printing	Money Matters	Behaviour	Keep Fit
Craftwork		Shopping	Other Problems	Sports
Art		Cooking		Outdoor Activities
Outings		Basic Domestic		Fund Raising
		Skills		Evening Classes

Table 7
Northgate incentive scheme

GRADE	SOCIAL PRIVILEGES	EARNINGS
5	No restrictions Full home leave	Up to £14 determined solely by performance & behaviour at work
4	7 Social activities with 8.00 p.m. restriction Overnight home leave	
3	2 Social activities with 8.00 p.m. restriction	£4 Pockey money
2	1 Social activity with 8.00 p.m. restriction	£3 Pockey money
1	No social activities No social outings	£2 Pockey money

* A social activity is any event taking place outside the normal working day, educational trips excepted.

The unit treatment programme aims to tackle the principal underlying factors in offending in the mentally handicapped by providing a comprehensive package of personal and social skills training coupled with a socialisation programme within a structured and supportive living and work environment. Each day is carefully structured, the basic weekly programme comprising 3-4 days occupational activity, 1-2 sessions social training and 1-2 sessions further education. Leisure training takes place in the evenings, at weekends and during holiday periods. The range of activities available is listed in Table 6. The programme is carried out partly within the unit and partly in the occupational, recreational and further education departments which serve the whole hospital. A separate woodwork shop exclusively for offender patients is provided for those who require a high level of supervision. Patients also attend courses at the local Further Education College on a part-time basis. Individual counselling on a range of matters is provided by members of the unit clinical team and there are also weekly group sessions attended on a voluntary basis. Sex counselling sessions, both individual and group, are held separately. Drugs which reduce aggressivity and control libido are used frequently.

An incentive scheme, deliberately kept simple for ease of understanding and application and designed to link behaviour with its consequences, underpins the weekly programme. It consists of a weekly grading system with five grades, each carrying a range of privileges (Table 7). Patients enter on grade 3 and rise or fall one grade at a time. Grades 1 to 3 carry a fixed amount of pocket money, but on grades 3 and 4 pocket money is determined entirely to work performance. Gradings are decided at weekly meetings attended by all staff and each patient is called in turn to discuss his previous week's behaviour and new grade. New gradings are immediately effective and payment on the new scale is made on the following day. Christmas and annual holidays are independent of the scheme and granted at the discretion of the medical and nursing staff. Typical response patterns are shown in Figure 1. Patterns A in which grade 5 is rapidly achieved and sustained is uncommon and usually indicates that the patient is experiencing little difficulty in coping with the system and is probably deriving little benefit from it. Pattern B, which is by far the commonest pattern, is an indication that the scheme is working well, eventual conversion to Pattern A, which may take months or years, being an indication of real improvement.

A daily points system is also operated for the small number of patients unable to cope with the weekly scheme and who require more immediate rewards. Points are awarded daily on a sliding scale of 0-3 for a range of activities in the areas of domestic and personal skills, relationship and work output. The maximum number of points is awarded if the activity is carried out without prompting, fewer if prompting is required, and none if the activity is not carried out. The total points obtained at the end of each 24-hour period entitled the individual to both monetary and social rewards within specified bands. Initially in some cases, rewards may be given on a sessional basis, two to three times a day. A bonus payment and weekend leave can also be earned by achieving a specified weekly points total. Each scheme is individually tailored, begins with easily attainable targets and is adjusted upwards according to progress. Patients move on to the weekly incentive scheme if and when it is judged that they are able to cope with this.

Figure 1
Incentive scheme – typical response patterns

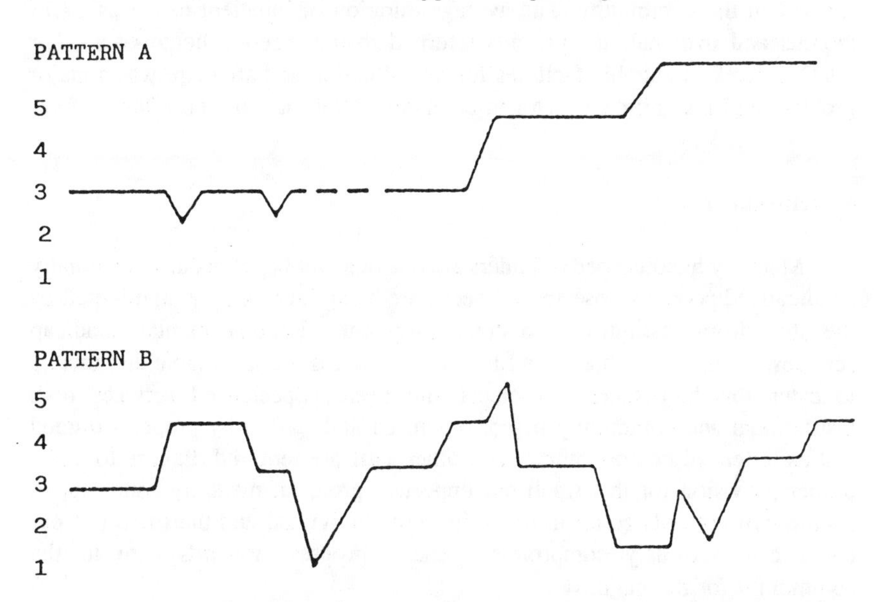

Following a satisfactory period in the admission unit (one to several years) patients are transferred to a less structured environment where they have more freedom and personal responsibility to either the third flat in the locked villa or the open unit in the hospital grounds. After a satisfactory period in this setting (usually one year) and when there is a firm prospect of a community placement, patients move into one of the houses for further preparation for life in the community (normally six months). Here, in addition to the normal weekly programme which continues, they are responsible for the care of the house, planning, purchasing and cooking evening and weekend meals, laundry, ironing and personal care. Supervision and training is provided by the house staff, initially on a fairly intensive basis and is progressively withdrawn according to progress. Failure at any stage leads to a return to the previous stage. Patients are discharged home or into statutory or private/voluntary community facilities. All receive psychiatric follow-up, often for several years, and initial support from the unit social workers and/or community nurses.

So far, results have been encouraging. In a study of 20 patients, all serious or persistent offenders, admitted to the unit and followed up after discharge for an average of 3.3 years, 85% were found to have made a good of fair response to the treatment programme and 65% were judged well-adjusted or reasonably well-adjusted at last follow-up contact. A good outcome was associated with more than two years inpatient care, good response to the treatment programme and stable residential placement, regular occupation and regular supervision and support in the community. The average duration of inpatient care was 17.75 months and over half the patients returned to the parental home or another relative. Lack of suitable facilities for rehabilitation and aftercare was a major problem and a significant factor in breakdown and readmission (Day, 1988).

Conclusion

Mentally handicapped offenders are one of a number of groups of mentally handicapped people whose special needs are being increasingly highlighted by the shift from institutional to community care. Regular mental handicap services, forensic psychiatry and the penal services are unsuitable and unable to cater for their special problems and needs. Specialised services both institutional and community based, organised and staffed by properly trained and experienced doctors, nurses and other staff are required. Failure to make proper provision for this small but important group of mentally handicapped people will not only result in hardship to the individual and their families but could also seriously compromise general progress towards care in the community for the majority.

References

Bluglass, R. (1966). A psychiatric study of Scottish convicted prisoners. M.D. Thesis. University of St. Andrews, Scotland.

Bluglass, R. (1990). The Mental Health Art 1983. In: Bluglass R. and Bowden P. (Eds.). Principles and Practice of Forensic Psychiatry. Churchill Livingstone, Edinburgh.

Burchard, J.D. (1967). Systematic socialisation: a programmed environment for the rehabilitation of antisocial retardates. Psychosocial record. *17*, 461-476.

Campbell, L. (1990). Impairments, disabilities and handicaps: assessment for court. In: Principles and Practice of Forensic Psychiatry. Eds. R. Bluglass and P. Bowden. 419-424. Churchill Livingstone, Edinburgh.

CMND 5698 (1974). Interim report of the committee on mentally abnormal offenders (The Butler Report). HMSO, London.

Craft, M. (1969). Ten studies into psychopathic personality. Wright, Bristol.

Craft, M. (1984). Should one treat or goal psychopaths? In: Mentally Abnormal Offenders. Eds. M. and A. Craft. 384-396. Balliere Tindall.

Day, K. (1983). A hospital based psychiatric unit for mentally handicapped adults. Mental Handicap. *11* 137-140.

Day, K. (1988). A hospital based treatment programme for male mentally handicapped offenders. British Journal of Psychiatry. *153* 635-644.

Day, K. (To be published). A study of male mentally handicapped sex offenders.

Denkowski, G.C. and Denkowski, K.M. (1984). Community based residential treatment model for mentally retarded adolescent offenders. In: Perspectives and Progress in Mental Retardation. Volume 1. Ed. J.M. Berg. Baltimore University Park Press.

Denkowski, G.C., Denkowski, K.M. and Mabli, J. (1984). A residential treatment model for MR adolescent offenders. Hospital and Community Psychiatry. *35* 279-281.

DoH (1989). Needs and responses: services for adults with mental handicap who are mentally ill, who have behaviour problems or who offend. Department of Health Leaflets Unit, London.

East, W.N., Stocks, P. and Young, H.T.P. (1942). The adolescent criminal: a medico-psychological study of 4,000 male adolescents. Churchill, London.

Faulk, M. (1976). A psychiatric study of men serving a sentence in Winchester Prison. Medicine, Science and the Law. *16* 244-251.

Fleming, I. and Tosh, M. (1984). Self-control procedures: a useful means of helping people who are mentally handicapped to overcome problems of temper and aggression. Mental Handicap. *12* 110-111.

Gardner, W.I., Cole, C.L., Berr, D.L. and Nowinski, J.M. (1983) Reduction of disruptive behaviours in mentally retarded adults: a self-management approach. Behaviour Modification. *7* 76-96.

Gibbens, T.C.N. (1963). Psychiatric studies of borstal boys. Maudsley Monographs No. 11. Oxford University Press, Oxford.

Gibbens, T.C.N. and Robertson, G. (1983). A survey of the criminal careers of hospital order patients I and II. British Journal of Psychiatry. *143* 363-369, 370-375.

Glancy, J. (1974). Revised report of the working party on security in NHS psychiatric hospitals. DHSS, London.

Guze, S.B. (1976). Criminality and Psychiatric Disorders. Oxford.

Hamilton, J. (1985). The Special Hospitals. In: Gostin L. (Ed.) Secure Provision, Tavistock, London.

Hamilton, J. (1990). Special Hospitals and the State Hospital. In: Principles and Practice of Forensic Psychiatry. Eds. R. Bluglass and P. Bowden. 1363-1374. Churchill Livingstone, Edinburgh.

Hunter, H. (1979). Forensic psychiatry and mental handicap. In: James F.E. and Snaith R.P. (Eds.) Psychiatric Illness and Mental Handicap. Gaskell Press, London.

Isweran, M.S. and Bardsley, E.M. (1987). Secure facilities for mentally impaired patients. Bulletin, Royal College of Psychiatrists *11* 52-54.

Jackson, R. (1983). Mental retardation and criminal justice: some issues and problems. Mental Subnormality. *29* 7-12.

Kearns, A. and O'Connor, A. (1988). The mentally handicapped offender: A 10 year study of two hospitals. British Journal of Psychiatry. *152* 848-851.

Kugel, R.B., Trembath, J. and Sagar, S. (1968). Some characteristics of patients legally committed to a state institution for the mentally retarded. Mental Retardation. *6* 2-8.

Lewis, N.D.C. and Yarnell, M. (1951). Pathological fire setting. Nervous and Mental Disease Monographs. No. 82. Coolidge Foundation, New York.

Lund, J. (1990). Mentally retarded criminal offenders in Denmark. British Journal of Psychiatry. *156* 726-731.

Messinger, E. and Apfelberg, B. (1961). A quarter century of court psychiatry. Crime and Delinquency. *1* 343-362.

Mlele, T.J.J. and Wylie, Y.V. (1986). Clofenpenthixol Decanoate in the management of aggressive mentally handicapped patients. British Journal of Psychiatry. *149* 373-376.

Payne, C., McCabe, S. and Walker, N. (1974). Predicting offender patients reconvictions. British Journal of Psychiatry. *125* 60-64.

Robertson, G. (1981). The extent and pattern of crime amongst mentally handicapped offenders. Journal of the British Institute of Mental Handicap. *9* 100-103.

Sandford, D.A., Elzing, R.H. and Grainger, W. (1987). Evaluation of a residential behaviour programme for behaviourally disturbed mentally retarded young adults. American Journal of Mental Deficiency. *91* 431-434.

Shapiro, A. (1969). Delinquent and disturbed behaviour within the field of mental deficiency. In: The Abnormal Offender. Eds. A.V.S. de Reuck and R. Porter. 76-90. J.A. Churchill Ltd., London.

Smith, J. (1988). An open forensic unit for the borderline mentally impaired offenders. Bulletin, Royal College of Psychiatrists. *12* 13-15.

Snaith, R.P., James, F.E. and Winokur, B. (1979). The drug treatment of mental illness and epilepsy in the mentally handicapped patient. In: Psychiatric Illness and Mental Handicap. Eds. F.E. James and R.P. Snaith. Gaskell Press, London.

Soothill, K.L. and Gibbens, T.C.N. (1978). Recidivism of sexual offenders: a re-appraisal. British Journal of Criminology. *18* 267-276.

Sovner, R. (1990). The use of psychotropic drug therapy. In: Proceedings of International Congress on Treatment of Mental Illness and Behaviour Disorder in the Mentally Retarded.

Svendsen, B.B. and Werner, J. (1977). Offenders within ordinary services for the mentally retarded in Denmark. In: Research to Practice in Mental Retardation: Volume I. Care and Intervention. Edited by Mittler P.

Taylor and Gunn (1984). Violence and Psychosis I. Risk of violence among psychotic men. British Medical Journal. *288* 1945-1949.

Tennent, G., McQuaid, A., Loughnane, T. and Hands, A.J. (1971). Female arsonists. British Journal of Psychiatry. *119* 497-502.

Thompson, M. and Back, T. (1987). Counselling sessions for sexual offenders prove successful. Social Work Today. June 15th. 9-10.

Tutt, N.S. (1971). The Subnormal Offender. British Journal of Subnormality. *17* 42-47.

Walker, N. and McCabe, S. (1973). Crime and insanity in England: Volume 2: New Solutions and Problems. Edinburgh University Press, Edinburgh.

West, D.J. and Farrington, D.P. (1973). Who becomes delinquent? Heinemann, London.

West, D.J. and Farrington, D.P. (1977). The delinquent way of life. Heinemann, London.

Whatmore, P. (1990). The Mental Health (Scotland) Act 1984. In: Bluglass R. and Bowden P. (Eds.). Principles and Practice of Forensic Psychiatry. Churchill Livingstone, Edinburgh.

Woods, P.A. and Lowe, C.F. (1986). Verbal self regulation of inappropriate social behaviour with mentally handicapped adults. In: Science and Service in Mental Retardation. Ed. J.M. Berg. 353-362. Methuen, London.

Yar-Khan (1981). The psychiatrically violent patient. British Medical Journal. *282* 1400-1401.

Došen, A., Van Gennep, A., Zwanikken, G.J. (Eds.) (1990). Treatment of Mental Illness and Behavioral Disorder in the Mentally Retarded. Proceedings of the International Congress, May 3rd & 4th, 1990, Amsterdam, the Netherlands. Leiden, the Netherlands: Logon Publications.

Chapter 8

Mental Health Services for Mentally Ill/Mentally Retarded Persons: A Community Mental Health Center Model

R.J. Fletcher

Individuals who have the coexistence of mental illness and mental retardation present unique challenges to community based mental health and mental retardation service systems. This is an underserved population (Reiss et al 1982) which has a complexity of needs requiring a multiplicity of service provisions.

Recent research literature reveals that between twenty-five to thirty-five percent of the mentally retarded have associated psychiatric symptoms that would warrant a psychiatric diagnosis (Menolascino and Stark, 1984; Jacobson, 1982, Reid, 1972).

Mentally retarded persons are nearly twice as likely to develop mental illness and with the same range of psychopathology as the population at large (Menolascino, 1989).

Despite the evidence of a high prevalence of mental illness among persons who have mental retardation, mental health services in the United States are at best inadequate and more often non-existent.

The lack of mental health services for persons who have mental retardation has been documented in the literature for decades in the United States. Studies as early as 1962 have demonstrated that mentally retarded persons who receive outpatient mental health services are provided relatively brief services (Chandler et al 1962) or limited to only evaluation and diagnosis without further treatment (Burton 1971). A report from the 1978 President's Commissions on Mental Health stated, "Mental Health delivery system for mentally retarded persons are described as unresponsive, woefully inadequate, and often non-existent" (PCMH, 1978). Nearly ten years later the President's Committee on Mental Retardation (PCMR) sponsored the "National Strategy Conference on Mental Retardation and Mental Health" (PCMR 1985) and published the proceedings of the conference (Stark, Menolascino, Albarelli, Gray, 1988) in where the theme of the near absence of mental health services for mentally retarded persons was clearly and repeatedly noted.

Community Mental Health Centers (CMHC's) in the United States as reflected by the CMHC legislation of 1963, was intended for accessible community-based mental health services for all citizens including persons who have mental retardation (Kennedy, 1963).

However, within a decade the initial promises of the CMHC for the mental health service needs for mentally retarded persons were noted to be seriously wanting (Swanson and Menolascino, 1983). To marshall attention to this issue, the National Association for the Dually Diagnosed (mental illness/mental retardation) has developed a policy statement and conducted a national petition drive calling for CMHC's to stop the discriminatory practice of excluding persons who have mental retardation and mental illness (NADD, 1989).

The purpose of this presentation is to describe a model designed to provide mental health services to persons who have a mental retardation and mental illness within the context of a community support system. The setting of this model takes place at Ulster County Mental Health Services (UCMHS), a Community Mental Health Center (CMHS) located in a semi-rural area in New York State. Within the framework of the model the following three related aspects will be addressed:

1. Need Assessment and Planning
   - consumer demand
2. Model of Outpatient Mental Health Services
   - Client Population: Characteristics and Psychiatric Disorders
   - Facility Based vs. Service Based Models
   - Treatment Approaches
3. Inter-Organizational Coordination and Integration

Assessment and Planning

Ulster Country Mental Health Services began responding to the mental health needs of persons with mental retardation in 1979 with the development of a successful dual diagnosis day treatment program (Fletcher, 1984 a.). As we entered the mid 1980's there was a growing recognition however that significant service gaps for the mentally ill/mentally retarded persons have become increasingly more critical, (Landsberg, et al 1987). The continuation of social policy of deinstitutionalization created a consumer demand for an array of community based service provisions for mentally retarded persons who displayed psychiatric symptoms.

Ulster County Mental Health Services conducted a comprehensive needs assessment survey in 1985 to identify the number of dual diagnosis persons and their service needs. The survey revealed that in Ulster County:

1. *Survey Results:*
   a. There were 200 adult mentally ill-mentally retarded persons (this represented approximately twenty-five percent of the total number of the mentally retarded in community settings).
   b. Of this population:
      - 50% lived in residential settings inappropriate to their needs.
      - 65% received no mental health clinic treatment.
      - 30% needed day programming not presently available for their needs.
      - Obtaining needed psychiatric inpatient care was extremely difficult.
      - 40% were not receiving adequate case management services.
      - staff of mental health and mental retardation agencies needed training to work with this population.

2. *Plan:*

With this data, the community agencies were able to develop a comprehensive plan, covering multiple year time frame, to address the needs of this population. The plan envisioned the following actions:

- Increase outpatient mental health services to this population.
- Develop more community residences for dually diagnosed.
- Enlarge the day treatment capacity to serve more clients.
- Secure needed inpatient psychiatric care.
- Obtain more case management resources.
- Develop staff training programs.
- Establishment of mechanism for coordination of services.

A model of outpatient mental health services

Based upon the survey data which provided a specific direction, Ulster County Mental Health Services (UCMHS) has been actively working with the other service providers and State regulatory agencies toward the development of a comprehensive system. Although an array of service provisions have been initiated in Ulster County in response to the multiple needs of individuals who have mental retardation and mental illness, I will focus primarily on the provisions of the outpatient mental health services for this population.

In response to an identified need UCMHS developed a mental health service delivery model designed to address the clinical needs of mentally ill-mentally retarded persons. The service provides comprehensive community based mental health services including: assessment and diagnosis, individual and group therapy, case management services, and medication treatment. Additionally, we provide consultation services to community agencies.

The model was developed as part of the Adult Services of UCMHS. Although the staff are specialized, the service model is integrated into the existing structure of the organization. The staffing pattern for the MH/MR Unit consists of one unit leader, two psychiatric social workers, one case manager, and ons psychiatrist. Additionally, psychological testing services are available to the MH/MR Unit.

The staff are considered mental retardation specialists and are specifically designated to provide mental health services to dual diagnosed persons and their families. The staff have experience and training in both mental health and mental retardation. The cross-fertilization of knowledge between these two fields make the staff uniquely qualified to work with this population. They have an understanding of the various treatment models and theoretical underpinnings that are employed in both the mental health and the mental retardation fields. This is important, as the various treatment technologies – even the language used, have different meanings and interpretations.

Characteristics and types of psychiatric disorders

In order to understand the client population we treat, this section is intended to present some salient characteristics and frequency of types of psychiatric disorders found in the persons served in the model.

Characteristics

In community-based sample of 80 retarded subjects, by age

PSYCHIATRIC DIAGNOSIS	18-22	23-37	28-32	33-37	38+
1. PSYCHOTIC DISORDERS N = 16 (20%)					
a. Schizophrenic Disorders	1	1	1	1	5
b. Atypical Psychosis					1
c. Schizoaffective Disorder			1	1	2
2. ORGANIC BRAIN SYNDROMS N = 13 (16%)					
a. Organic Personality Syndrome	1	1		1	4
b. Organic Mood Disorder		1	2		3
3. ADJUSTMENT DISORDER N = 9 (11%)		1	2	2	4
4. PERSONALITY DISORDER N = 14 (18%)					
a. Mixed					1
b. Borderline			1		
c. Dependent	1				1
d. Antisocial			1		1
e. Paranoid		1			
f. Avoidant Disorder				1	1
g. NOS	1			2	2
5. AFFECTIVE DISORDER N = 18 (23%)					
a. Bipolar Disorder					3
b. Major Depression	1	1	3	1	4
c. Dysthymic Disorder				1	4
6. ANXIETY DISORDER N = 5 (6%)					
a. Generalized Anxiety				1	1
b. Post-Traumatic Stress Disorder					3
7. DISORDERS OF IMPULSE CONTROL N = 2 (3)					
a. Intermittent Explosive Disorder	1				1
8. PERVASIVE DEVELOPMENTAL DISORDER N = 3 (4%)	1	1		1	

There are, as of April 1990, 80 mentally ill/mentally retarded persons being served in the treatment model. Of these there are 51 males (64%) and 20 females (36%). The average age is 37 years and the average IQ is 65.

With regard to living environments of the sample population, 39 (49%) live in community residences. These are supervised and regulated group homes. Of the 39 people, 12 live in mental health licensed group homes, while 27 live in group homes operated by the mental retardation system. Another 10 persons (13%) reside in supportive apartment placements. These are apartment programs that have some but limited staff supervision. Of these 10 people, 1 is in a mental health program and the other 9 are under the auspices of a mental retardation program. Ten (13%) of the sample live with their natural families. Twenty-one of the individuals (26%) live independently.

Diagnostic Findings

Diagnoses in this group were formulated, based on the DSM III-R criteria (DSM III-R, 1987). A diagnosis was given only after careful diagnostic assessment (i.e. interview, mental health status examination, review of developmental history).

The types of mental illness in mentally retarded persons based on this sample are seen in the Table. There are eight diagnostic categories that are associated with the study group: 1) Psychotic Disorders, 2) Organic Brain Syndrome, 3) Adjustment Disorder, 4) Personality Disorder, 5) Affective Disorder, 6) Anxiety Disorder, 7) Disorders of Impulse Control, and 8) Pervasive Developmental Disorder.

The largest group fell into the diagnostic category of Affective Disorder, represented by 18 out of the 80 (23%). It is interesting to note that major depression is diagnosed in 10 of the 80 people in the sample. The second largest group is found in the Psychotic Disorder category. Of the study group 16 (2%) were identified in this category within which 11 were identified as having Schizophrenic Disorder. Personality Disorders represented 14 (18%) of the sample. The specific types of personality disorders are fairly evenly distributed. Organic Brain Syndrome was found in 13 of the 80 (16%) in the study group. The remaining diagnostic findings are: 9 (11%) in Adjustment Disorder; 5 (6%) in Anxiety Disorder, 3 (4%) in Pervasive Developmental Disorders, and 2 (3%) in Disorders of Impulse control.

Delivery of mental health services

Location of Service

In designing mental health services for persons who have mental retardation and mental illness, it is important to consider how and where the services will be rendered. The MH/MR Team of UCMHS provides treatment services in both the context of the traditional facility based model and in the service centered model.

In the facility based model, clients come to the clinic to avail themselves for services. This has the advantage of representing a normalized experience for the consumer, as non-retarded persons usually go to the clinic for mental health services. In our experience, we find that some clients prefer to come to the clinic rather than receiving services at their work or home environment. These clients want a clear separation of mental health services from other services they receive.

In the client service model, the clinician travels to the environment where the client lives, works, or attends a day program. The service based model has the advantage of integrating mental health treatment with ongoing rehabilitative services (Chanteau, 1988). This model of service delivery is useful in working with the other service providers which facilitates coordination and integration. On-site services provides opportunity for staff to engage in cross training in mental retardation and mental health technologies. When providing mental health services it is important within the environment of another agency, that a quiet space is available "on-site" where the client can feel safe, supported, and where the principle of confidentiality will be maintained.

In our service half of the clients are seen on-site in their natural environments and the other half receive mental health services at the clinic. The decision as which model is selected, is based on a decision made between the client and the clinician.

Service Provisions

In our model of mental health a variety of services are offered. These typically include: mental health assessment, individual and/or group therapy, medication treatment, and case management services.

Mental Health Assessment

Before treatment services begin, it is essential that a comprehensive mental health assessment be completed. The assessment provides the historical and clinical data upon which a diagnosis is formulated. Additionally, it provides clinical guidance for selection of treatment modality and initial goal planning.

The mental health assessment is done in two parts – one by the psychiatric social worker and the other by the psychiatrist. After reviewing historical records on clients referred to our service, the social worker conducts a mental health assessment.

In conducting the mental health assessment the clinician focuses on the presenting problem, history of the problem, frequency, intensity, and precipitance related to the problem. Personal and family history as well as psychosocial assessment are essential parts of the assessment process. Based on this, an initial diagnostic impression is formulated. Then, the client is referred to the psychiatrist who conducts another assessment to confirm the diagnosis, asses the possible need for medication, and provides input on treatment recommendations.

Formulating a psychiatric diagnosis is a clinical challenge even for an experienced clinician. Nevertheless, it can be done with confidence for most people who have moderate to mild mental retardation. However, with those who have severe or profound mental retardation, a psychiatric diagnosis becomes a more difficult and sometimes impossible task. The vast majority of our clients fall into the mild range of mental retardation.

Guidelines to Assessment

Psychiatric Assessment: (Does *not* have to be done by a psychiatrist).

This is the review and assessment of psychiatric status of client at the present time. It leads to and give validity to the diagnostic impression that follows. Areas to include would be:

a. Factors contributing to determination of Axis I and II diagnostic impressions.
   - psychiatric symptoms present including emotional, behavioral, substance abuse, onset, severity, and duration of symptoms.
   - behavioral aspects of symptomatology (appetite, sleep changes, disturbance of anxiety).
   - mental status –
     1. Appearance
     2. Motor and Behavior Activity
     3. Relationship to Examiner – Attitude/Rapport
     4. Mood/Affect
     5. Perception (intactness of sensation, information processing)
     6. Intelligence and Judgement
     7. Attention and Concentration

Sources of Assessment

The mental health assessment is usually completed from input from other reports, family members, and care providers, direct observation and clinical interview. Unlike the non-retarded counterparts, persons who have mental retardation, who exhibit severe emotional problems usually have difficulty in providing a full self report of symptoms, problems and history. Therefore, the clinician needs to rely on multiple sources of information. The following is a list of sources used:

1. Review reports
   - medical
   - neurological
   - psychosocial
   - psychological
   - psychiatric
   - school
2. Interview family
   - parents
   - siblings
3. Interview care providers
   - group home
   - work environment
4. Direct observation
   - group home
   - work setting
   - mutual home environment
5. Clinical interview
   - mental status
   - level of relatedness
   - self report

Treatment services

Psychotherapy
Group Therapy
Psychiatric Treatment
Case Management

Psychotherapy with Mentally Retarded Persons

Psychotherapy with the persons who have mild mental retardation is essentially the same as with the general population. However, the techniques are modified and adapted relevant to communication patterns and interpretation of the process (Szymanski, 1980).

Our experience is that psychotherapy can be an effective treatment modality with moderate-mild mentally retarded persons who have mental health problems. We have witnessed measurable improvement in interactional skills and coping abilities in many of the clients we treat. This is consistent with the numerous studies conducted in the 1950's and 1960's which revealed that psychotherapy with mentally retarded persons can be effective in improving coping abilities and ameliorate psychopathological symptoms (Sterndicht, 1966, Lott, 1970).

Many dually diagnosed persons need to learn how to appropriately express their feelings rather than to inappropriately act them out. Many of these clients have not had the experience to verbally express feelings in an environment in where they have felt secure and with a person they trust.

Establishing a therapeutic relationship is based on trust and is fundamental to any therapeutic process. The clinician is the instrument of therapy particularly during the initial stages at which time a working alliance creates the framework for future growth and development. Once this key process is developed, then the client can work more specific goals and objectives toward altering some undesirable behavior, thoughts or feelings.

Case Illustration

Bob is a 32 year old man who has mild mental retardation and significant mental health problems who lives in an apartment with his wife. His main problem is managing to cope adaptively with stress. A stressful experience leads to anger and with him, the anger can lead to volatile and assaultive behavior. This mid-directed behavior too often has resulted in psychiatric hospitalizations and even incarceration. Once we established a therapeutic relationship, the focus of our treatment sessions began with him identifying potentially stressful circumstances and to explore appropriate alternatives that would enable him to cope more effectively with everyday circumstances that produce stress. The treatment goal is for him to verbally express his feelings rather than to strike out at others.

In therapy, the clinician needs to view the client in the context of a total person who has inherent dignity and uniqueness (Monfils and Menolascino, 1984).

With many of our clients, we use relationship therapy as a technique to enable clients to examine how emotions operate and influence their interactional behaviours.

Common Goals

1. Understand and accept handicap
2. Improve frustration tolerance and impulse control
3. Develop appropriate social skills
4. Increase independent decision making skills
5. Understand limits and boundaries
6. Appropriate expression of feelings and thoughts
7. Increase self-esteem
8. Develop appropriate interpersonal relationships.

Regardless of the specific goal, on overarching goal is to enhance one's ability to relate adaptively to peers, staff, family, and the community at large by gaining increased emotional self control. Psychotherapy should result in the client's improvement in self-esteem and increased ability to cope with stressful situations.

Group Therapy

Group treatment approaches, in our model, had demonstrated an important function in helping to meet the mental health needs of mentally retarded/ mentally ill clients. Although group therapy is commonly used for non-retarded persons, mental health practitioners have been reluctant to use it with persons who have mental retardation because of the mistaken belief that subnormal intelligence precludes its use. Recent literature has illustrated its effectiveness with the mentally retarded population in areas such as appropriate expression of feelings (Matson and Senatore, 1981) assertiveness training (Brogman, 1984), and social skills training (Monfils, 1985).

This modality of treatment with mildly retarded mentally ill persons is modified but the same principals of group therapy apply with this population as with any other group.

Participating in a group with peers can foster a sense of security, trust and belonging (Fletcher, 1984 b).

Benefits of Group Therapy

A. Peer Support
- decrease feelings of inadequacy, isolation & defeat
- foster meaningful relationships
- develop sense of belonging & cohesion
- share experiences

B. Problem Solving
- learn and develop effective coping strategies
- change maladaptive behavior to adaptive behavior
- experience the relationship between cause and effect (insight)
- develop interpersonal relationship skills

C. Efficient Use of Resources
- 6–8 persons per group
- 1 or 2 therapists per group
- applied to variety of settings

The same kinds of goals previously mentioned apply to mentally ill-mentally retarded persons who participate in group therapy. The therapist needs to take an active role in facilitating group process.

Psychiatric And Medication Treatment

Psychiatric and medication treatment is an integral component of the MH/MR service. Psychiatric involvement begins with the assessment process. The psychiatrist consults with the other clinicians regarding diagnosis and makes treatment recommendations. Psycho-active medication treatment and monitoring can be an important dimension with mentally ill/mentally retarded persons as a tool to assist a person toward instructional control (Menolascino, 1988) and appropriate human engagement (Menolascino, 1989). Our experience has shown that psychoactive medication treatment has been very effective with this population particularly for clients who suffer from a clearly defined and drug-responsive psychiatric disorder. For example, we have found judicious use of neuroleptic medication to be effective in mentally retarded persons who suffer from schizophrenia, depression with psychotic symptoms, or organic brain syndromes with psychotic features. A rational use of anti-psychotic drug therapy can help some individuals to achieve a psychological state in which their ability to learn and to mature emotionally is greatly enhanced (Sovner, 1989).

Psychoactive medication treatment can be used as one important aspect of a multidimensional treatment approach. In our model this treatment modality may be a condition of, but not sufficient for, a balanced approach to care and treatment. The psychiatrist and the other clinicians need to communicate on a regular basis in order to promote continuity and coordination of services for the persons we serve.

Case Management Services

Most mentally retarded/mentally ill clients require varying degrees of case management services. They typically need assistance in identifying community resources, linking up to services and providing ongoing monitoring. Case management also means being the client's advocate. In the MH/MR model at UCMHS case management is an integral part of the overall services provided. It is crucial to work with all aspects of the client's life. This may mean assisting the client to access appropriate residential and/or vocational services. It may be helping a client move toward a more independent life-style by assisting the client in finding an apartment or competitive employment.

Inter-organizational coordination and integration

Mental health services cannot be done in a vacuum and must be part of a larger comprehensive support system involved with the client. This notion is born out by the fact that the emotionally disturbed/retarded clients require various services to address the multiple problems. The components of residential, vocational, family, case management and psychotherapy need to interact in a process that is like members of an interdisciplinary team. The effect of which is synergistic rather than addictive (Szymanski, 1980).

The application of this principle requires a great deal of interagency coordination. Case conferences and treatment planning done in the context of an inter-organizational team approach.

Mental health clinicians, vocational counselors, residential staff, family members, and the client need to be aware of the goals that are developed among these various components, so that each can be supportive of one another. The inter-organizational team approach enable all involved parties to view the client in a holistic perspective.

In our model we have developed a shared staffing arrangement with the County Developmental Disability Service Office (DDSO), a local branch of the New York State Office of Mental Retardation and Developmental Disabilities. The case manager who is part of the MH/MR Team at UCMHS is actually employed by the New York State Office of Metal Retardation and Developmental Disability.

Conversely, a psychiatric social worker from the MH/MR Team works two days a week at a day treatment program operated by the same New York State Office.

In addition to the clinical interagency team meetings, there are administrative meetings between representative of the local mental health and mental retardation systems. The purpose of these meetings is to assess systemic issues and work in a coordinated fashion on planning and program development to meet the holistic needs of dual diagnosis clients.

Conclusion

Persons who have mental retardation and suffer from mental health problems should have a right to receive adequate mental health services. We must develop a system that would unable a person who has mental retardation to have accessibility to community based mental health agencies. It is hoped that the services that have just been described, can be used as a model for replication.

References

Bregman, S., 1984. Assertiveness training for mentally retarded adults. *Mental Retardation.* 22: 12–16.

Burton, A., October, 1971. Mental health clinic services to the retarded. In *Mental Retardation.* 38–41.

Chandler, C., Norman, V., Bahn, A., September, 1962. The mentally deficient in out-patient psychiatric clinics. In *American Journal of Mental Deficiency.* Vol. 67, No. 2, 218–226.

Chanteau, F. B., 1988. Abandoning facility – based programs: Evolving toward a "service-based" model. J. Stark, F. Menolascino, M. Albarelli, V. Gray (eds.). *Mental Retardation and Mental Health: Classification, Diagnosis, Treatment, Services.* New York, Springer-Verlag.

Diagnostic and Statistical Manual of Mental Disorders (DSM III-R), 1987. Washington, D. C., American Psychiatric Association.

Fletcher, R., June, 1984 a. Group therapy with mentally retarded persons with emotional disorders. *Psychiatric Aspect of Mental Retardation Reviews.* Vol. 3, No. 6.

Fletcher, R., 1984 b. Model day treatment service for the mentally ill population. In: *Handbook of Mental Illness in the Mentally Retarded.* F. Menolascino, and J. Stark (eds.) New York, Plenum Press.

Jacobson, J. W., 1982. Problem behavior and psychiatric impairment within a developmentally disabled population. In: *Applied Research in Mental Retardation.* 3, 121–140.

Kennedy, J. F., 1963. Mental illness and mental retardation (message from the President of the United States presented to the House of Representatives, 88th Congress, Document No. 58), Washington D.C., U. S. Government Printing Officer.

Landsberg, G., Fletcher, R., Maxwell, T., 1987. Developing a comprehensive community care system for the mentally ill/mentally retarded. In: *Community Mental Health Journal.* Vol. 22. No. 2. p.p. 131–134.

Lott, G., 1970. Psychotherapy for mentally retarded: Values and cautions. F. Menolascino (ed.) *Psychiatric Approaches to Mental Retardation.* New York, Basic Books.

Matson, J. L., and Senatore, V., 1981. A comparison of traditional psychotherapy and social skills training for improving interpersonal functioning of mentally retarded adults. *Behavior Therapy.* 12: 369–82.

Menolascino, 1989. Overview: Promising practices and caring for the mental retardation-mentally ill. In: *Mental Retardation and Mental Illness: Assessment, Treatment, and Service for the Dually Diagnosed.* R. Fletcher, and F. Menolascino (eds.). Massachusettes, Lexington Books.

Menolascino, F., 1988. Mental illness in mentally retarded: Diagnostic and treatment issues. In: *Mental Retardation and Mental Health: Classification, Diagnosis, Treatment, Services.* J. Stark, F. Menolascino, M. Albarelli, and V. Gray, (eds.). New York, Springer-Verlag.

Menolascino, F., and Stark, J., 1984. *Handbook of Mental Illness in the Mentally Retarded.* New York, Plenum Press.

Monfils, M., 1985. Work with the mentally retarded. *Social Casework.* 66: 177–84.

Monfils, M., Menolascino, F., 1984. Modified individual on group treatment approaches for the mentally retarded – mentally ill. *Handbook of Mental Illness and Mental Retardation.* New York, Plenum Press.

National Association For The Dually Diagnosed (NADD), 1989. NADD Newsletter, Vol. 6, No. 1.

President's Committee on Mental Retardation (PCMR), November, 1985. *National Stragety Conference on Mental Retardation and Mental Health.* Washington, D.C.

President's Commission on Mental Health (PCMH), 1978. *Report of the Liasion Task Panel on Mental Retardation.* U.S. Governmental Printing Office, Washington, D.C. p. 7.

Reid, A.H., 1972. Psychosis in adult mental defectives: Manic depressive psychosis. British Journal of Psychiatry, 120: 205–212.

Reiss, S., Levitan, G., McNally, R., April, 1982. Emotionally disturbed, mentally retarded people: An underserved population. In: *American Psychologist*. Vol. 37, No. 4, 361–367.

Sovner, R., 1989. Treating mentally retarded adults with psychotropic drugs: A clinical perspective – mentally retarded and mentally ill. In: *Mental Retardation and Mental Illness: Assessment, Treatment, and Service for the Dually Diagnosed*. R. Fletcher, and F. Menolascino (eds.) Massachusettes, Lexington Press.

Stark, J., Menolascino, F., Albarelli, M., Gray, V., 1988. *Mental Retardation and Mental Health: Classification Diagnosis, Treatment, Services*. New York, Springer-Verlag.

Sternlicht, M., 1965. *Psychotherapy techniques useful with mentally retarded: A review and critique*. Psychiatric Quarterly 39: 84–90.

Swanson, D., and Menolascino, F., 1983. Roles of the community mental health center in providing services for mentally ill – mentally retarded clients. In: *Mental Health and Mental Retardation: Bridging the Gap*. F. Menolascino, and B. McCann (eds.). Baltimore, University Park Press.

Szymanski, L., 1980. Individual psychotherapies with retarded persons. In: L. Szymanski, and P. Tanguay, (eds.). *Emotional Disorders of Mentally Retarded Persons*. Baltimore, University Park Press.

Szymanski, L. S., and Rosefsky, Q. B., 1980. Group psychotherapy with retarded persons. In: L. S. Szymanski, and P. E. Tanguay, (eds.). *Emotional Disorders of Mentally Retarded Persons*. Baltimore, University Park Press.

Došen, A., Van Gennep, A., Zwanikken, G.J. (Eds.) (1990). Treatment of Mental Illness and Behavioral Disorder in the Mentally Retarded. Proceedings of the International Congress, May 3rd & 4th, 1990, Amsterdam, the Netherlands. Leiden, the Netherlands: Logon Publications.

Chapter 9

Grief Therapy for People with Mental Handicap

S. Hollins

Introduction

There is one concern which parents of people with mental handicap all share: what will happen to their child when they, the parents, die. This concern encompasses several aspects including where their son or daughter will live and who will care for them. Concern may extend to other more subtle areas such as the feelings of grief their son or daughter might experience and how their expression of grief might affect their behaviour and their subsequent care. The provision of respite care to families is one commonly available contribution to planning for later permanent separation, but the flexibility required of service providers to meet individual needs at a time of bereavement is missing.

Sensitive bereavement care is also needed for people already resident in long term institutional or community residences; when relatives, friends or staff die, but also following other losses such as when friends or staff simply move on.

The workshop – A video called 'The Last Taboo – mental handicap and death' was shown and discussed. (Sireling & Hollins 1985)

Why The Last Taboo?

Death and mental handicap are both taboo subjects in our society – this video aims to dispel the fear and avoidance which taboos create. Based on real case histories it shows the effects of death on people with mental handicaps and on those around them. We are all affected by loss and death, yet often people with mental handicap are not given the chance to grieve... nor to grow as a result of grief. The greater the handicap, the less likely it is that the individual's grief will be recognised: care givers tend to ignore or misunderstand the effects of such losses. Normal and pathological grief are fully described elsewhere (Kubler-Ross, Ainsworth-Smith, Murray-Parkes) and this paper emphasises similarities and differences in this special population.

'The Last Taboo' provides a valuable reminder to all who work with people who have mental handicaps that lack of speech and awkward manner do not preclude emotions as sensitive as in the rest of us. Families and professionals can easily misinterpret grief reactions: the video shows how, once there is an understanding of grief, reactions become understandable and attitudes change. Sympathetic understanding coupled with practical actions can facilitate rather than inhibit the grief reaction.

What is 'The Last Taboo' about?

The opening sequences show Anthony, who has mental and physical handicaps, buying some food for a friend dying on the ward where they live. Some time after the death Anthony takes to his bed, injuring himself and refusing to eat. At hand-over the nurses discuss what they should do: one favours sedation but the other wonders – for the first time – if this regressed behaviour could be related to the recent death. The trouble is, how can he tell unless he is familiar with the healthy grief reaction and how it can appear in people who have a mental handicap? These areas are explored in a studio interview with a young woman who talks about her reaction to her father's death.

Returning to Anthony's needs, the next sequence suggests ways in which his carers could have helped prepare him for the death, and later encourage him to grieve in a healthy way. The techniques shown at the graveside and in the home surroundings are simple and practical. Relatives and professionals will find them useful.

The final section deals with the later stages of grief and its resolution. A group of mentally handicapped people return to the crematorium six months after the death of a friend, to adopt a rose bush in his name. The film closes with Alex, who has no speech and is wheelchair-bound, fixing a name plaque to the rose bush.

Who are the actors?

The cast are not professional actors. The nurses are real nurses, the vicars are real vicars – and the handicaps are real handicaps. Because the case and the events of the video are so close to reality, it is not a slick professional production: 'The Last Taboo' was written, filmed and edited by two psychiatrists who chose video as a powerful way to get across their message.

Who should see 'The Last Taboo'?

It is directed towards care staff in hospitals, and in local authority and voluntary community settings. It is also of interest to members of community mental handicap teams and to bereavement counsellors. Showing it to families and clients is a useful way of initiating discussion with those who find this area worrying.

For Discussion: Some of the questions raised by 'The Last Taboo'

1) Do all people with mental handicap have feelings/ How can you tell?
2) Do people with mental handicap suffer more losses than other people?
3) What extra problems do people with mental handicap face after a bereavement?
4) What additional strengths do people with mental handicap have to help them cope?
5) Is it kinder to tell the person with a mental handicap that his father has died, or to say that he has gone away? Is it our responsibility to protect others from painful experiences?
6) How do staff cope with their own feelings of loss? Is it too stressful for staff to have to worry about the emotional needs of people with mental handicap as well as their physical needs? The nurse found it difficult to talk about death to Anthony and said although he could do it in a film, he would find it hard to do in real life.
7) When people are upset it helps to share it. What is your reaction when you detect emotions like anger and despair, in someone with a mental handicap?
8) What special arrangements do you make when someone with a mental handicap in your care is bereaved? Would you like to do anything else?

Other resources

Death education and counselling resources were shared in the workshop, in particular two full colour picture books designed to tell the story of the death of a parent to an adult with learning difficulties (Hollins and Sireling 1990). The use of colour to express emotion and the importance of gesture and other media of non-verbal communication are often overlooked. Communicating about feelings must not rely on language alone – although words and signs can be helpful they are never enough on their own.

Guided mourning approaches are useful either individually or in groups, and mainstream bereavement counselling services are an invaluable source of expertise.

Conclusion

This paper offers a brief introduction to the area of bereavement and people with mental handicap and other relevant work includes papers by Oswin, Lipe Goodson, Kloeppel & Hollins and the novel 'Walter' by David Cook. It does not look at the experience of dying for the person with mental handicap although many of the issues discussed are relevant. A community therapist told me that none of her clients had died, and she did not see any need for special knowledge about death and dying for specialist staff working in the field of mental handicap. She had failed to realise that all of us share one thing in common – we are all going to die.

References

Ainsworth-Smith, I. & Speck, P. (1982). *Letting Go. Caring for the Dying and Bereaved.* SPCK London.

Cook, D. (1978). *Walter.* Penguin

Hollins, S. & Sireling, L. (1985). *The Last Taboo – Mental handicap and death.* St. George's Hospital Medical School, London.

Hollins, S. & Sireling, L. (1989). *When Dad Died and When Mum Died* (2 books). Silent Books, Cambridge.

Hollins, S. & Sireling, L. (to appear). *When Dad Died – Learning Disability and Death. A professional learning resource.* NFER Nelson.

Hollins, S.C. & Kloeppel D.A. (1989). *Double Handicap: Mental Retardation and Death in the Family.* Death Studies 13: pp 31-38

Hollins, S. & Grimer, M. (1988). *Going Somewhere: People with mental handicaps and their pastoral care.* SPCK, London.

Kubler-Ross, E. (1981). *Living with Death and Dying.* Souvenir Press.

Lipe-Godson, P.S. & Goebell, B.L. (1983). *Perception of age and death in mentally retarded adults.* Mental Retardation, 21, 68-75.

Murray-Parkes, C. (1986). Bereavement. *Studies of Grief in Adult Life.*

Oswin, M. (1985). Bereavement. Chapter 17 In *Mental Handicap – A multi-disciplinary approach.* Edited by Craft, M., Bicknell, J. and Hollins, S. Bailliere Tindall.

Došen, A., Van Gennep, A., Zwanikken, G.J. (Eds.) (1990). Treatment of Mental Illness and Behavioral Disorder in the Mentally Retarded. Proceedings of the International Congress, May 3rd & 4th, 1990, Amsterdam, the Netherlands. Leiden, the Netherlands: Logon Publications.

Chapter 10

Therapy for people with dual diagnosis: treating the behaviors or the whole person?

N.T. Baum

Introduction

In the past various psychotherapeutic schools held the belief that people who suffer from mental retardation were incapable of benefitting from in-depth psychotherapy. As a result, treatment of developmentally handicapped individuals was mainly focussed on managing and modifying extreme behaviors in order to aid such persons to better adapt to behavioral norms of society. Very little attention was given to the emotional needs of such individuals.

In order to understand some of the causes for this approach, one needs to explore relevant issues such as (a), the commonly perceived nature of in-depth psychotherapy and the seemingly necessary level of intellectual functioning required for a successful psychotherapeutic process; and (b), the issue of the frequent lack of professional recognition of the existence of emotional or psychiatric difficulties of people with retardation.

When we talk about "psychotherapy", what do we mean? Are we talking about a mere behavioral change to a more adaptive mode of appropriate behaviors? Or are we taking about a change in the perception of the Self and in the way a person experiences him/ herself in inter- and intra-personal relationships? Is the outcome of a psychotherapeutic process solely a change in conduct or is it a fundamental change in a person's quality of life?

Regardless of existing differences between various schools of therapy, most psychotherapeutic approaches put emphasis on the therapist-therapeutee relationship. For instance, processes such as transference and countertransference, changes in attitudes based on the correction of primary experiences, internalization of new models of behavior based on a different care giver figure, and an emergence of a more confident and solid ability to cope due to unconditional acceptance can be seen as a direct result of this intensive relationship. These are qualitative changes which occur on the level of the emotional needs of the therapeutee. They are expressed in a re-constellation of a stronger Self and in the development of a deeper understanding and a higher level of consciousness.

That is, such changes result not only in a different, more adaptive behavior but, most importantly, in a different inner emotional system which no longer need to express itself in a disruptive behavior. The person becomes more autonomous and less dependent – emotionally – on constant external approval.

All of the above seems to us to be obvious when talking about "normal" people. But our perception changes drastically when we talk about people with retardation. Usually, when treating people with retardation, we become extremely concerned with the clients' behaviors and the focus of our treatment becomes the striving for behavioral change. We tend to perceive the notion of a deep psychotherapeutic process to be irrelevant and non-applicable.
If, in addition to retardation, the client also suffers from severe emotional or psychiatric disorders which are expressed in extreme behaviors, the tendency to focus on modifying the behaviors and to ignore the emotional needs expressed by these behaviors become even stronger. Dual Diagnosis, because of its severity and complexity, often creates feelings of helplessness and anxiety in the care givers. They tend to become more rigid, restrictive and controlling, and try even more forcefully to change the external manifestations of the problem, i.e., the disruptive non-compliant behaviors.

The result of such complete focus on behaviors prevents care givers from giving attention to the clients' emotional needs and emotional difficulties. The clients then cease to be human beings in the eyes of the care givers and become their behaviors.

On the same continuum, the system and its representatives, the care givers, tend to be extremely patronizing in making decisions for the clients and in controlling their lives. Frequently, people in care are denied the freedom to make decisions in even simple day to day things (e.g., to eat or not to eat breakfast). Their freedom to choose and make significant decisions is even more restricted. For example, in the process of integrating a 42 year old man, who lived in an institute for 25 years, he was sent to live in a group home in another city. This occurred in spite of his desperate pleas to be placed in a different setting together with his girlfriend of the last 10 years. Both clients were forced to suffer a lifetime separation because the system and the workers made these life decisions for them. The man and his girlfriend were not perceived to have the right to choose for themselves. No consideration was given to their wishes, their needs or their pain.

In such a system-centred approach, the individual is less important than the bureaucratic order and regulations. It is no wonder that in a system like this the "flag" of integration and repatriation (i.e., the return of a client to his/her original city regardless of the life and the relationships they have been involved in and developed during years of institutionalization) is more important than the people it integrates.

If this is our approach to clients with retardation, it is natural that our focus will solely be on the modification and management of behavior. Such a system promotes methods of treatment that determine and define a developmentally handicapped person according to his/her behavior or level of intellectual functioning, similarly to Reiss' (1982) concept of overshadowing. Accordingly, psychotherapy which puts emphasis on the person as a whole cannot become a modality of choice.

A "system-centred" approach seems to be in contradiction with basic principles of psychotherapy in which individuals are more likely to be accepted as human beings regardless of what they can or cannot do (Rogers, 1951) and regardless of the appropriateness of their behavior. In a client-centred approach the clients have the right to effect decisions concerning their lives and their wishes are respected and taken into consideration. Support is given so that they can be empowered rather than become helpless, dependent and powerless.

Multi Focal Approach

From experience gathered at the programs provided by the Muki Baum Association[1] during the last 11 years, it became evident that when an individual is treated as a person rather than as his/her retardation or inappropriate extreme behavior, most of the severe behavioral problems presented at admittance disappear after a short period of time (usually between 3-4 months). This might suggest that many such behavioral problems are actually expressions and communication of what can be called "survival mechanisms" that evolved out of emotional necessity. Exposure to an environment that provides respect and individualized humanistic attention and treats the emotional issues, i.e., treatment on the process level, rather than solely the behavioral problems, i.e., attention to the product level, very often eliminates the clients' needs to express themselves in such extreme ways.

The use of the Multi Focal Approach (Baum, 1980) creates such an environment. In it a variety of psychotherapeutic modalities are incorporated. They include expressive art therapies (i.e., art, music, movement and drama), play therapy, individual Rogerian verbal therapy, group therapy and sandplay therapy. Individualized treatment plans are developed for each client according to their needs. As a result, a client might be involved in a variety of therapies with a number of therapists.

However, since all the therapies occur within the framework of the Multi Focal Approach, the principles and dynamics of the various therapies correspond with each other, thus, enriching the therapeutic process for the benefit of the clients.

The use of in-depth psychotherapy methods with people with dual diagnosis raises various theoretical questions: questions in regards to the evolvement and constellation of the Self; the development of ego-consciousness; the effect of intelligence on the appearance of insight, etc.

Some of these questions deal with the issue of symbolic representation: Can behavioral and/or verbal manifestation which occur in the course of therapy be interpreted on a symbolic level? Do people with retardation express themselves symbolically or solely on a concrete level? Is an interpretation on the symbolic level a mere projection of the therapist's unconscious or is the symbol a real expression of the retarded client's unconscious? Is there a similarity and a universality in symbols used by people with retardation and by people with normal intellectual development?

Through extensive psychotherapeutic work data can be gathered to find answers and clarifications to these and other theoretical questions. For our purposes, sandplay pictures will be used to explore some of the aspects of symbolic representation in the therapeutic process of people with dual diagnosis.

Sandplay Therapy

Sandplay therapy was developed by Dora Kalff with the encouragement of Carl Jung. It is a Jungian based psychotherapy in which figurines are used to create a picture in a sand box with prescribed dimensions. This, as Kalff (1980) states, provides the client with free and protected space. The client has the complete freedom to choose from hundreds of figurines the ones (s)he needs for the creation of a picture. Interpretations are not provided at the time the picture is created. They are delayed until a level of ego stability has been achieved and at times, as Kalff recommended, this may even take place a few years after the therapy has been finished.

An example of what a sand picture looks like can be seen in Figure 1.

This is a sand picture of a non-handicapped professional woman in her late 40s. In the verbal explanation, she said that the various women figurines are in the picture to express different aspects of herself. The little creature, she added, was a monster symbolizing her fears. She completely ignored the angry fire figurine which she had placed at the centre. The picture expresses her struggle with a tremendous amount of anger and her need to ignore it. It also expresses the central place that anger has in her life. However, recognition is given from the unconscious to the existence of healing agents (the various feminine parts) that will aid her in her process.

Figure 1

A fundamental belief of sandplay therapy is that deep in the unconscious of every person there is an autonomous tendency for the psyche to heal itself given proper conditions. This tendency transcends gender, race, or age and, as I believe, also transcends intellectual capacity.

Because sandplay creates tangible three-dimensional expressions of unconscious content, it seems to be most appropriate for developmentally handicapped people who frequently find it difficult, if not impossible to express themselves.

Weinrib (1983, pg. 2) says that, "Sand pictures represent figures and landscapes of the inner and outer world, and they appear to mediate between these two worlds and connect them." As such, sandplay therapy is both the therapeutic process and the expression of this process and, therefore, can prove to be a most powerful therapeutic modality for people with dual diagnosis.

From the data gathered at the Muki Baum Association for the last 3 years, it is suggested that sand pictures of people with dual diagnosis are expressions of the various levels of the person's life. They might be a concrete depiction of an event that occurred recently. They might be a direct expression of emotion, as seen in Figure 2.

Figure 2

This picture (Figure 2) is a spontaneous angry expression of the youth (14 year old boy) which occurred during the session. He "killed the therapist" with his anger.

The pictures might reflect an inner process such as the strengthening of ego boundaries. This can be clearly seen in the sand pictures of a 13-year-old boy. The three pictures shown here were chosen from a process which occurred over a period of eight months. In the process of making the pictures, this youngster would enter the sand therapy room and, in an extremely hyper and speedy way, create his picture. He never gave any explanation to his creation and his only verbalizations were some words and noises he generated during the play with the figurines.

Figure 3

This picture was made by him about six months after the beginning of sandplay therapy. In previous pictures, he had manifested again and again that no ego boundaries existed. This fully corresponded with his extreme acting out behavior in which he would lose control to the point of disintegration.

In the picture (Fig. 3), one can clearly see the loss of control, the fragility of the boundaries held only by the perimeters of the sand tray, and the flooding of unconscious material. The picture started with the construction of the inside of a house and with healing symbols like the tree of stars. However, immediately afterwards, the flooding started to occur and he lost control. This was expressed in the speed and nondiscrimination with which the dumping of the figurines occurred. He took everything in sight and threw it in the tray. There was no discrimination, no differentiation and no choice.

Figure 4

This picture was made a couple of months later. In it one can still see how difficult it was for him to contain himself. But it also becomes clear that some differentiation had started to occur and that in spite of still having to fill up the tray, he was very careful to only choose, put in and organize the figurines he needed. He said that "all these people came to this place to see the fire crackers". He used 93 vehicles to symbolize the large number of people who came to the event.

Figure 5

In this picture (Fig. 5) which was made eight months after the flooding picture, one can clearly see the emergence and solidification of his ego boundaries. Most of the vehicles used are working trucks and order-preserving vehicles. He even integrated a house and trees to express the presence of his ego and the emergence of his Self. He said that "the man who lives in the house is the owner of all the cars and trucks. They are working for him."

Sandplay can also help a person to re-live early traumas in a safe and protected way. It provides a container in which such traumas can be dealt with. According to Weinrib (1983), sandplay occurs on the matriarchal level which creates the safe environment for such a process. This is why it can be very effective in healing deep wounds that are a result of damaged mother-child relationship.

Jung (1969) speaks about archetypes that are stored in and come from the collective unconscious. He says that these archetypes are universal and therefore inner, unconscious conflicts and complexes will be expressed by different people in similar symbols.

Hurts from traumatic mother-child relationships are experienced by people both with or without retardation. Our experience demonstrates that the sandplay process transcends I.Q. boundaries not only in the existence of the process but also in the symbols used for it.

Figure 6

Figure 6 is a sand picture made by a non-handicapped professional woman in her early thirties. She is an expressive arts psychotherapist and is most verbal in her expressions and explanations. In her personal therapy she has been dealing with the traumatic devastation of her relationship with her mother and the effect this has on her life.

In her picture one can see the girl lying in the sand as if dead (bottom right) and diagonally, across from her (top left), the five babies with all the treasures around them. At the bottom left corner one can also see the existence of the wise old woman. At the centre of the picture she used a blue bird, which she said "is somewhat like me", and spiders and a snake climbing on a "single breast". The bird is wounded and the knight in shining armour cannot save her because "he is from a fairy tale and I don't believe in fairy tales".

These archetypal symbols express her wounded soul (the bird) and her devouring mother (spiders). They are at the centre of her existence, pushing everything else in her life to the corners.

Figures 7 and 8 are pictures chosen from a sandplay therapy process of a 23 year old woman with dual diagnosis . She had been placed in a group home at a very young age. She is a low functioning person with extreme violent behaviors. Her violence has usually been directed toward female staff, causing them, at times, severe injuries. This discriminatory choice might suggest that, through her violence, she is acting out her mother-child trauma and is expressing her inner conflict, i.e., the need and wish to be loved by a mother figure and the fear of further rejections by her.

She is hesitant in her verbal expressions and, until recently, has not allowed herself to be engaged in any verbal exchange during sessions. She usually comes to the sandplay therapy room, makes a picture and leaves.

The picture in Figure 7 was made by her a couple of months after the beginning of her therapeutic process. In it she used a the lioness and cub which she used previously. It is a statement of the issue of mother-child relationship in a clear way. At the centre of the tray she placed "the magic blue bird" and on both sides the spiders, symbols of the devouring, negative mother.

In her process she continued to use only animals. However, she related to some of them in a personal way that made it clear that they were expressions of various parts of herself. The animals she repeatedly used – in addition to the blue bird, the spiders and the lioness – were seals, especially a small white seal which she always kissed gently and called "baby", as well as a baby squirrel in a container.

In a more recent picture (Figure 8), she placed the white "baby" seal not with the other seals but at the edge of the tray. The baby seal is separated from the rest of the seals by the huge spider. Thus, its separation from its kin and from the blue bird (the soul) and the squirrel (another image of her Self) is complete. The negative mother is creating the isolation of the baby from the rest of the world.

Figure 7

Figure 8

Both women used the same figurines (the blue bird and the spiders) to express the same issues. Confirmation of this was provided recently by the latter woman. In her last few sessions, she allowed herself to stay in the therapy room after the completion of the picture. She used this time for some physical closeness with the therapist and some verbal communication in regards to the pictures. In one such verbal response, she said that "the spider is mom and the grasshopper is dad". Both were identified by her as the parents of the white "baby" seal.

It is also interesting to note that the appearance of these archetypical symbols in both women's sandplay pictures occurred at a similar time in their process. This might suggest that not only are the symbols universal but also the nature of the process.

Discussion

In spite of the fact that this work is only at its beginning, it seems as if its potential is tremendous. In addition to its psychotherapeutic value, sandplay therapy may also provide data to substantiate answers to the more general theoretical questions raised in this paper. But mainly, it might strengthen the argument that people with retardation also have mental needs and that they, like people without mental handicaps, can benefit from in-depth psychotherapy. Dora Kalff (in conversation, 1972) said that "we don't necessarily have to make something conscious that is unconscious in order to heal" (in Weinrib, 1983). Therefore, the argument that people with retardation do not have the intellectual capacity to understand the therapeutic process is not valid.

We, as therapists and care givers, have to be flexible enough to change our methods and modality of treatment according to the needs and abilities of our clients. If we use our creativity and grant the clients with dual diagnosis their humanity, we will stop "blaming" them for not being capable of benefitting from in-depth therapy. Instead, we will take it upon ourselves to search for the appropriate modality that will enable us to provide the most suitable and necessary treatment.

Note

1. The Muki Baum Association offers two day programs (children and adults) in Toronto. It provides treatment to clients with dual diagnosis and extremely severe behavioral problems. It is a psychotherapeutic setting in which behavior modification or management are not used. The approach used in the programs for the last 11 years is the Multi Focal Approach which is a psychodynamic,

humanistic and client centred approach. It has been developed and practiced over the last 25 years by the author (Baum, 1980).

References

Baum, N.T., A Multi-Focal Approach in the Assessment and Treatment of Multi-Handicapped Adolescents: An Individual Case Study, University of Toronto, Toronto (unpublished doctoral dissertation), 1980.

Baum, N.T., The Multi-Focal Approach, presented at the C.E.C. conference in Toronto, 1985.

Baum, N.T., Sandplay with Dually Diagnosed Children: Its validity for the Development of the Self: Questions and Issues, submitted to the International Society for Sandplay Therapy, 1988.

Jung, C.G., The Archetypes and the Collective Unconscious, Second Edition, Bollingen Series XX, Princeton University Press, Princeton, N.J., 1969.

Kalff, D.M., Sandplay: A Psychotherapeutic Approach to the Psyche, Sigo Press, Santa Monica, Ca., 1980.

Menolascino, F.J., Bridging the Gap Between Mental Retardation and Mental Illness. Overview in: F.J. Menolascino and B.M. McCann (eds), Mental Health & Mental Retardation: Bridging the Gap, University Park Press, Baltimore, 1983, pp 3-64.

Reiss, Steven; Levitan, Grant W.; and Syszko, Joseph, "Emotional Disturbance and Mental Retardation: Diagnostic Overshadowing", American Journal of Mental Deficiency, Vol. 86, No. 6, 1982, pp 567-574.

Reiss, S., "The mentally retarded have feelings, too: Personal View", Media Release, Chicago, Il., 1987.

Rogers, Carl R., Client-Centred Therapy: Its Current Practice, Implications, and Theory, Houghton Miffin Co, Boston, 1951.

Weinrib, E.L., Images of the Self: The Sandplay Therapy Process, Sigo Press, Boston, 1983.

Došen, A., Van Gennep, A., Zwanikken, G.J. (Eds.) (1990). Treatment of Mental Illness and Behavioral Disorder in the Mentally Retarded. Proceedings of the International Congress, May 3rd & 4th, 1990, Amsterdam, the Netherlands. Leiden, the Netherlands: Logon Publications.

Chapter 11

Portrait of small psychotherapy group with violin

A. Stammler

Introduction

As a psychiatrist I work in a medical cum teaching centre that deals with multi-handicapped children who suffer from severe mental deficiency. The Centre can deal with up to 120 children. The quantitative factor is important, but the Centre is broken down into subsections A.B.C. in different places which (as it is) are twelve bed dormitories in turn defined essentially by age and motor capacity.

Medical helpers' take part in daily life in the Centre; "educaters" ((low paid, little qualified helpers) take responsibility for the children individually or collectively for a certain amount of time on.

Over the past few years "music groups" have blossomed here, and in institutions of this type various pieces of recorded music are listened to whilst adults take note of the reactions. There are groups that gather child and adult around percussion instruments. A flute – or more rarely a guitar – is introduced by a musically minded adult who will play it in a dorm or games room.

Rather than go into an umpteen number of examples I'll give one that struck me. As a trained analyst I had a young boy diagnosed as suffering from Epileptic Encephalopathy in therapy. He was severely handicapped – some sessions were interesting, others brought mo to the verge of despair – he would for example go through stereotyped actions over and over again whilst dribbling and repeating the same words. Having reached the age limit (10) this child had to leave the Centre, the eve of his departure coincided with the last night before the summer break. I had played the violin in the games room, he'd run wide eyed to join us in a rush of attentive enthousiasm that differed from his usual modus vivendi as his attention remained constant.

It was then that I wished I had brought the violin earlier – I planned to use the violin as the center piece for a group of severely handicapped children (motor, psychological and sensory handicaps). In this manner Nadine A. (educater) and I started our group (3 children) between 4 and 6 in September 1988.

After this introduction I'm going to define the setting in which the group gathered once a week at the same time, and say a few words about each child and relate the key moments of their evolution.

The process

The group takes place in the "music room" on the ground floor of a building called the "teaching block". It's a large sombre room with bay windows that overlooked a tree lined park. A floor mat occupies the centre of the room.

The group took a certain amount of time to come together. Perhaps because the children come from different sections, as we so desired.

Two children have been there since the beginning. I'll call them say Oscar and Amelia, they are 4 and 4 1/2 years old. They have been here for 2 years in the same dormitory the – "babies dormitory".

Louis, the third child, arrived 2 months later; till then, our attemps had been fraught with difficulty: one agitated child was very often in hospital. Another child, bedridden, was too afraid of the other children...

Oscar's medical record was ominously thick: he'd been hospitalised at birth for septicemia; at five months, he'd suffered from West's syndrome; the diagnosis after hospital observation was of Hypoxy-ischemic encephalopathy. Eyesight, and even more his audition, had been tested and explored umpteen times; one can no longer meet his gaze for an intermittant strabism; he doesn't react to noise or to voices; he was diagnosed as deaf; after the examinations he was still considered deaf; after these tests hearing aids that he could never tolerate were tailor-made just before his admission. Nadine A. doubted this diagnosis of deafness early on.

On his arrival the endless phases of agitation seemed to dominate. One had the impression of a ceaseless "angst". He is still very hypotonic but bangs his head against the bars around the bed and rips fistfulls of his hair out. That said, by the time we started the group Oscar had already changed a lot, he was calmer – often he could sit down.

Amelia's medical record points out that encephalopathy runs in her family (she has two brothers, one in this Centre – both have similar conditions with microcephaly, dysmorphia and psychotic type of behaviour; she rocks to and fro; from time to time, she regurgitates her food and reswallows it (merys-cysm?); her file states twice over that she cannot hear human voice; it states that she is indifferent to the "world of sound" she must be touched in order to react.

Louis is a bit older, he was six when he joined the group, his file indicates severe mental handicaps with microcephaly. Because of tendinous contractures his legs are contained in walking devices.

Unlike the other two children he had been able to stay longer in his family; he has always shown an interest in the musical instruments played by his older brother (mainly percussion).

He joined the group a few weeks late but there were some crucial moments in the very first weeks that I wish to relate.

The therapy

The first meeting took place in September 1988. It's an introduction; the children have been brought by pram; we sit them down on the rug. Nadine A. is also seated; we've brought percussion, we give our names and name the children; I show them the violin and the bow as I sit on a chair by the rug, I play, they seem attentive.

Exceptionally, we met for a second time two weeks later. I remember having played a simple piece of music again – it was an exercise whose main feature was to use all 4 strings of the violin. The bass sound of the G strings had an unexpected effect on Amelia; scared out of her wits she skitted off at high speed on all fours towards Nadine who sat on the rug. Of course, I stopped playing, stood up, went towards Amelia; I alluded to a masculine voice that might have caused such terror. Her father's voice perhaps?

I returned to the violin to play another piece – "the swan" by Saint Saens – but Amelia's panic attack obliged me to stop.

At the next gathering she immediately identified the object of her fear; she moans, becomes agitated, approches Nadine as if taking shelter having nonetheless furtively touched the music stand.

I play further away from the children who are are seated in the middle; Amelia screams, is then silent, taking at the same time a muslin position of worship and covering her eyes.

I had brought a selection of Irish tunes, I played a jig; her shouting brought this to a halt, I went towards her – I asked her again did the violin remind her of a scary voice?
When? When she was small, perhaps when she was a baby?

She sat down and looked at me silently; she repeated the word "baby", the first spoken word till then. Back to the violin and I replay the tune. She's on her knees again head on the floor, she moves a hand away from an eye and gazes at the devil's instrument for a second; she is still close to Nadine, but less so than before.

We can then observe Oscar (the third child was in hospital); he's moved away from the mat and seems impatient, as soon as I return to the Irish jig Oscar beats time whilst sitting straight with a jubilant expression, when I stop we hear a number of vocal sounds.

During the next two meetings I can play more, Amelia allows herself to gaze more and more; she no longer shouts. For a few moments I sit on the rug and each child can touch the violin. Amelia plucks the strings as if they were harp strings.
Nadine pointed out that she regurgitated and swallowed her food several times when I played the next tune.

At this time in an institutional work group we spoke of Amelia with her "educater" Françoise D.; Amelia who usually made inimitable mouth noises, started using words like "here" and "give" as objects were exchanged, she also said "mummy" .

Two months went by before Louis arrived – he's rather rigid and dribbles a lot; Oscar is fascinated by his mouth and despite the fact that he'd stopped dribbling a long time ago he lets some saliva run down his mouth... Amelia makes sucking sounds.

Louis is very attracted by the violin; he puts his hand out towards the bow and strings. Amela can't stand my talking to him, she comes towards me on the carpet, takes the bow with authority; guided by my hand she draws the bow over the strings. From here on (8th session) she will no longer fear the violin; she will only have in sessions after periods of separation (holidays) occasional phobic reactions of incomparably less intensity than those seen previously.

Over the next sessions Amelia came towards me to touch the violin, remarkably she no longer bumped into things; now she sits almost upright to draw the bow over the strings producing a long shrill sound which drives her away. She returns immediately.

Louis' arrival brings change to Oscar who as we knows was mesmerised by his mouth.

On the floor mat near the children are two sets of round percussion instruments, bongos, that will be used in a very particular manner. As I start to play Oscar begins to "feed" from the edge of the bongos whilst making sucking sounds; he behaves as a baby would with a breast, his fingers draw over the white surface of the bongo (English analysts use the verb "to fiddle" to qualify this manual activity – a verb which also signifies playing the violin).

Oscar was taken away from his mother at birth to be placed in an a reanimation ward; he was drip fed; then he was unable to breast feed or even suck a bottle; between tunes I talk to him of what I know of his early history and of his handicap: he goes towards Nadine A., sucks her sleeve, her hand, the trouble is he bites her; as she objects to this, ("he'd have eaten me" she says) he goes off very worked up towards his pram whose wheels he sucks. He has to be removed from this.

During the next group, Oscar sucks the edge of the bongos and a xylophone hammer. He's calmer, sits up wide eyed when I replay an Irish jig; evidently he recognises the tune; he comes to huddle against my legs with an admiring expression, his eye no longer wanders : "he listens with the passion of a connaisseur" Nadine tells me.

End of January 1989 – 14th session – given the interest the children have in strings and because I'm obliged to protect my violin we decide to introduce a guitar. It's a battered tatty thing that Nadine no longer wants – it has three strings though!

Louis, immobile up to now, grabs it and places it vertically in front of him thereby reproducing what I do with the violin before using it. Amelia pinches the strings then approaches me to draw the bow across the violin. Oscar bites Louis' shoes who becomes rigid and begs Nadine for help. The rumpus looks like spreading and Nadine has to intervene. Two simple new tunes are played twice over (Blanchet's Carillon and E. Bozza's "La gavotte des Damoiselles"). This restores calm. Oscar and Amelia beat time by rocking their bodies. Louis bangs the drum out of time...

Sadly, Amelia is then absent for three weeks, she has chicken pox and on medical grounds is not allowed out of her dormitory; the pediatrician is anxious, because of her encephalopathy, about the risk of complications. Contact was maintained but the opening towards language was stopped dead in its tracks.

Over the following weeks we add three identical Irish flutes to our instruments. Louis uses his to hit Amelia on the head whilst looking at Nadine with a playful expression. He then blows into the flute twice unobserved whilst I play. In that same session – the 26th – we hear the voices of Oscar and Amelia.

We also note that Oscar and Amelia now always bring an object, some kind of toy found in the dormatory picked up before coming to the music room. Previously they didn't keep it in hand, they used to drop it. Several times Nadine had forcefully extracted a tambourin from Amelia's grip – she insisted on trying to leave the session with an instrument. It might have been useful to follow the tracks of that object; here a tambourin, or bells, around the dormitory.

Whilst on the subject of objects, a meeting with Louis' parents sheds light on his modus vivendi; he had a growing tendency to collect instruments without doing anything with them. Well, his home was a veritable museum – with a quantity of toys that according to the parents surprised their entourage. We spoke of this during a session, and, as he was banging on the guitar noisily with a flute we removed the lot and heard, after a moment of surprise, his voice, and this for the very first time!

Around this time I met Amelia's mother in a corridor; she was very evasive and rarely came to appointments. We were able to exchange a few words : "we hardly believe it", "she's like a baby of five-six months age – and she says words – mummy – baby – stop. We shouldn't talk about it". She quickly left.

As for Oscar's parents, for professional reasons they moved to an atlantic island with their 3 other children. Oscar often goes through periods of "angst" during which he is agitated and bites or hits himself. This anxious agitation was to disturb the group often until the summer of 1989 – there are periods of calm when I play our "golden oldies" for example – Amelia tries to sing along to slow lullabys.

Our return to the Centre (September 1989) is marred by the prospect of Nadine's extended sick leave. I'm face to face with the expectation of the children. I find Oscar and Amelia huddled together in their dormitory; Louis holds out his arms as if begging. With Nadine's agreement I decide to restart the group with another adult. A medical helper, an accomplished pianist who sometimes uses a flute, will be able to come at the beginning before leaving to have a baby. The head educater of Louis' section – Madame B. – a trained musicotherapist then replaced Nadine on a regular basis.

This reorganisation is hard; Amelia again resorts to stereotyped rocking and shouts as if roaring; Louis, already motionless, is stiffened even more by theses shouts; he dribbles more. As for Oscar he blocks his ears when I mention Nadine A., bangs his head against the pram and bites his arms through his clothes.

Despite all that, things now move along quite quickly – contact gets better session by session. They are in time – use the instruments or their voices.

One session at the beginning of the year was remarkable; Oscar and Amelia were both ill, Louis was the only child. He moved the guitar around without doing anything with it, we decided not to watch him. After some hesitation he pinched the strings whilst looking at a brushed steel fire plate that adorned the door opposite him. These steel sheets produce a mirror effect; his gaze was lively, he smiles; makes more and more notes with the guitar. I decide to follow his musical lead by bouncing the bow on the fourth string – this pleases him.

He looks at me; he's another child; he no longer dribbles; he moves; suddenly one has the impression that his body belongs to him. When he is again with the two others the following week he allows himself a greater use of the instruments; he again plucks the guitar strings with curiosity and is jubilant when my violin answers his guitar.

The nature of the group has changed of course, at the moment I go and get Oscar and Amelia in their dormitory; for Amelia the atmosphere is a happy one – she expresses her joy.

Oscar is less direct in his expression, he dances about and blushes, his eye sometimes wanders a little more. Louis holds his hand out to me and to the door of the dormitory when I go there for other reasons. Since September 1989, Mme B. goes to collect him. At the end of a session he turns to the two other children as we leave whilst waiting for the prams.

Conclusion

To conclude – the most unexpected thing was Amelias's panic, started by the violin. In the following sessions it was obvious that this very withdrawn young child experienced a manifestation of archaic phobias and an opening to language that was not mere echolalia (unlike language often heard in institutions like this). We have seen an opening towards language and a fragile tentative structuration of the subject. Archaic phobias dealt with, the violin is no longer representative of a terrifying archaic super ego as the adults discourse can be; the possibility of access to a language other than that of terror must therefore exist.

Regarding Oscar – this is neither the time nor place for a study of diagnoses; doctors never have an easy life – and working with mentally handicapped children makes our task ever harder; the violin was nonetheless instrumental in bringing to doubt the idea of deafness, a diagnosis that the mother has not yet recovered from.

I wonder about this question in relation to the depth of the world in which the child repeatedly finds himself. In the mother's discourse Oscar is still her baby, he rubs up against her as he does with other adults, legs in foetal position, gets excited and falls over backwards. Is Oscar even born? This is sometimes the question he brings to mind; of course he sits up more and more but he often lies down, legs against his stomach, sucking his big toe as others suck their thumbs; he is far from everything. The violin, that he reacts to, what's more he adores the thing – he gets impatient and worked up when I don't play. He dances jubilantly when listening to up tempo numbers.

Even if he experiences moments of great distress underpinned by the absence of Nadine – even if he bangs his head against the pram cover, he has undeniably changed. In the Centre he is more present, more visible, more audible; he produces sound phonemes : "Ni" and "Vi" (1).

As for Louis, petrified by the gaze of the other, the violin has allowed him and Amelia to lighten the burden of archaic phobias. Amongst other things bouncing the bow allowed him to look on, to smile, produce his own music.

We saw him metamorphosised, become alive; he's no longer terrorised by the other (at least not here).

Obviously, there'd be other things to go into – but I wanted to focus on the violin that allowed, in this small group, the opening of a space for each child and a movement on the road to simple humanisation for the three of them.

Note

1. The sounds if heard by a french speaker might conceivably be understood as resembling "neither" and "life". His christian name contains the "Vi" sound.

Došen, A., Van Gennep, A., Zwanikken, G.J. (Eds.) (1990). Treatment of Mental Illness and Behavioral Disorder in the Mentally Retarded. Proceedings of the International Congress, May 3rd & 4th, 1990, Amsterdam, the Netherlands. Leiden, the Netherlands: Logon Publications.

Chapter 12

Some trends in psychoanalysis and their relevance for treating people with mental retardation*

R. Ruth

This paper will review some contemporary developments in psychoanalytic thinking and explore their implications for the treatment of persons with mental retardation. The attempt will be to first engage the discussion on the level of theoretical shifts as such, and how these inform conceptual notions of mental retardation, and proceed only subsequently to clinical material. Hopefully, this will enable the containing to some extent of the deductive, minimally theoretical logic of the anecdotal case, which has characterized, and constrained, much of the psychodynamic literature on mental retardation.

A note on historical context is in order. While the study of mental retardation has never been central to psychoanalysis, from the earliest beginnings of the field parents of mentally retarded children have consulted analysts and therapists, begging us to cure their children (Jelliffe, 1914), and analytic thinking has impacted the life course of generations of people with developmental disabilities, at least in the US. In the positive case, this is because psychoanalytic notions that an unconscious with meaningful dynamics underlies daily life, and that the unvoiced can be perceived, helped create the first sense, historically, that mental retardation could be understood within the categories of science, and not just religious, moral, cultural or mythological categories. On the negative side, an uncritical application and generalization of the paradigm that symptoms are derived from analyzable conflicts, an undervaluing of biology and constitution, and a belief that that which cannot be analyzed in the traditional, mutual, predominantly verbal exchange between analyst and patient cannot be helped through psychodynamic methods have shaped a service philosophy that has had many destructive facets. It is not the purpose of this paper to explore these fully, but it is worth brief mention that traditional psychoanalytic thinking has tended to overtreat and mistreat parents

* I would like to thank Mary Ann Blotzer, LCSW, in collaboration with whom I have developed many of the ideas presented in this paper.

of mentally retarded persons (Kysar, 1968), while viewing developmentally disabled persons themselves as largely lacking meaningful inner lives, and therefore capacity to benefit from psychotherapy. Although a rich literature of case reports of (at least partially) successful psychoanalytic psychotherapy with mentally retarded persons exists (Chidester and Menninger, 1936; Smith et al., 1976; Hayes, 1977; Gair et al., 1980; Symington, 1981; Spensley, 1985; Bernstein, 1985; Mawson, 1986; Sinason, 1986), its impact on both psychoanalysis and the mental retardation service system has been very limited. Thus, there is a work of theoretical deepening, integration and renewal to be done.

Five theoretical notions – the coexistence of conflict and deficit, active agency in primitive mental life, developmental unevenness in trauma, the relational vs. the autarchic self, and the relationship between empathy and insight – will be explored here as a contribution to this process.

Theoretical Formulations

The discovery that conflict underlies neurosis was one of Freud's most powerful, liberating and defining contributions, and simultaneously one that has been deeply dissatisfying to following generations of clinical workers, particularly those who have struggled to extend psychodynamic thinking to understandings of the psychoses and character disorders. Kohut's (1971) thinking on early narcissistic failure has helped generate a rich profusion of theory, which has described a primarily non-libidinally-determined line of development that can nevertheless be replicated through transference in the analytic setting and observed in developmental history. While some theorists in Kohut's tradition have collapsed structure and libido into categories of relatively nonconflictual self-experience, others have embraced a dialectical and constructivist view of conflict and deficit, similar to the view in modern physics that describes light as both particle and wave. Fajardo (1987) has usefully applied this perspective in elucidating the experience of parents of retarded children; as yet, an application of psychoanalytic deficit theory to a systematic understanding of mental retardation has not been attempted.

The desirability of this seems clear. Both classic and contemporary (Sinason, 1986) clinicians have described an aspect of cognition and intelligence, especially in relatively mild mental retardation, that is a compromise product of drives and defenses. This construct seems necessary but not sufficient for a full understanding of mental retardation. It does not satisfactorily explicate the dynamics of more serious cognitive deficiency, the phenomenology of cognition in mental retardation (such as the preference for the concrete over the abstract), or the inner lives of relatively well functioning persons with mental retardation who nevertheless experience emotional conflicts, dynamically autonomous from their cognitive deficits, and who present a clinical picture more in line with symptom than character neurosis.

The more useful framing of the questions seems to be: which aspects of cognition, in a mentally retarded person, are conflictually determined, and which are products of deficit; under what conditions do the various facets develop and express themselves; and what are the laws of motion of each? Once viewed in this way, the relevance of psychoanalytic thinking and therapy to an understanding of mental retardation takes on new salience, with the implication that we can in fact help even when we cannot erase the cognitive deficit.

A large contingent of contemporary psychoanalytic thinkers lays greater emphasis than earlier generations on the vicissitudes of preoedipal life. Psychoanalytically informed infant observation (Stern, 1985), the ongoing generativity of Kleinian work (Segal, 1974), and the emergence of so-called post-Kleinian thinking (Ogden, 1986, 1989) all have had great general influence, though, with the exception of the work of the Tavistock group (Symington, 1981; Sinason, 1986), only scattered and marginal direct impact on the mental retardation field.

This is unfortunate in the general, in that – to the (partial) extent to which the phenomenology of mental retardation is that of developmental blockage at a primitive stage – dynamic descriptions of early psychic life are highly relevant to an understanding of the inner experience of mental retardation. More specifically, however, there is a commonality to much infant-observational, Kleinian and post-Kleinian work in emphasizing the active agency of the preoedipally organized psyche. Far from being passive, unproductive, helpless, stuck, uncomplicated, rigid or incapable of dialogue or insight, there is a powerful and growing body of evidence that the primitively organized person, whether as infant, child or adult, engages in mental life and social interaction as fully describable, meaningful and interpretable as the oedipally organized individual, though of a different qualitative variant. Interestingly, this evidence emerges as much in social anthropology (Edgerton, 1984), neurology and neuropsychology as in psychoanalysis, psychiatry and clinical psychology.

As with the understanding of the oedipal complex, the shift toward greater illumination of preoedipal life parallels, flows from and interfertilizes a trend toward depathologizing. Ogden's (1989) notion of an autistic-contiguous mode, developmentally prior to the paranoid-schizoid and depressive modes yet co-existing with these, in both health and pathology, in dialectical interplay, seems especially helpful in understanding what might be termed the "life of the void", that is, what is going on in what an external observer sees as cognitive deficit. (Feminist psychoanalysts, *passim*, have made intriguingly similar observations about the vagina as an organ vs. an empty hole (Schlesier, 1984).) From outside psychoanalysis, the neurologist Oliver Sacks's (1985) notion of the concrete as a mode of cognition and psychosocial operation different from, but not inherently inferior to, the abstract, would be another useful example of this kind of thinking.

The Latin American psychoanalytic tradition has, since the early 1970s, become greatly occupied with deepening an understanding of the impact of trauma, in no small part as a way of making productive and reparative use of analysts' own experiences of loss, dislocation and state terror. A salient lesson of this work (Langer, 1971, 1973, 1989; Lira et al., 1984; Grinberg and Grinberg, 1990) has been that trauma produces regression, not in the linear sense of going backward along a line, but in the more complicated sense of developmentally primitive moments co-existing with more sophisticated structural and defensive evolution.

The interplay between the dynamics of trauma and mental retardation have long been appreciated, though in varying ways. Mental retardation has been conceptualized as a product of very early pathology in the mother-infant emotional dyad (Symington, 1981; Spensley, 1985; Sinason, 1986) or as a primarily constitutional phenomenon likely to produce secondary trauma as parents and children attempt to grapple with feelings of damage and loss (Solnit and Stark, 1962). Less appreciated in the psychoanalytic literature, but well understood by sociologists, is the tendency of mentally retarded persons to be vulnerable to sexual, physical and emotional assault, in a society where they are not only often poorly protected, but readily projectively identified with as containers for the projections of the inadequacies, fears and vulnerabilities of the non-retarded. (See Haffter, 1968, for an interesting folkloric variation of this, in the theme of the changeling.)

Lessons from psychoanalytic work with traumatized persons (Lira et al., 1984; Grinberg and Grinberg, 1990) can help understand that retarded persons can be simultaneously successful in work, love and friendship and regressively pushed to more primitive inner coping mechanisms. This enables a therapist to avoid the equal risks of viewing functional competence as an adequate therapeutic endpoint and viewing primitive, traumatically induced regression as the totality of a mentally retarded person's psychic reality.

In that social prejudice and discrimination define a type of chronic trauma, it is cogent to observe that mentally retarded persons are among other things a minority group. As regards therapeutic process, then, this aspect of contextually determined experience cannot remain unanalyzed, any more than the treatment of a Black person could be viewed as complete without a thorough exploration of their experience of being Black. Indeed, this may be especially relevant in the case of mental retardation, which is defined primarily by reference to the intellectual majority.

Current feminist psychoanalytic thinking has made significant advances in elucidating a gendered facet of self-concept (Belenky, 1988; Benjamin, 1988; Chodorow, 1989). In particular, the relationship between the hegemonic psychological ideal of an autonomous, individuated self and the patriarchal notion of an autarchic ideal has been challenged, and the notion of a relational self (Belenky, 1988), dynamically closer to the historically female pattern that locates meaning and identity primarily in a relational matrix, has been counterposed.

This construct seems relevant to a dynamic understanding of mental retardation in two distinct ways. First, in a society with strong patriarchal tendencies, mental retardation itself may be viewed as a gendered concept, with mentally retarded persons seen psychodynamically in many ways as demasculinized, e.g., impotent, passive, sweet, dependent, affectively as opposed to cognitively oriented. If this is so, then it could be positted that the self-concept and self-experience of many mentally retarded persons may well organize themselves in traditionally female categories, and respond to their exploration and clarification as such in therapy.

Second, the frequent psychotherapeutic goals for persons with mental retardation of residential independence and vocational self-sufficiency – so overdetermined that they are often presented and perceived as axiomatic – may also need to be reconsidered. For the same reason that the tendency of a female patient to deny, repress or decathect maternal and affiliational strivings would not be supported, it may be found that there is something in the fundamental nature of mental retardation (at least in its character as a socially constructed category of identity and social role in Western society) that is intrinsically, i.e., quite primally, defined by embeddedness within, as opposed to relative autonomy from, a relational matrix.

Finally, the role of empathy and empathic attunement in psychoanalytic treatment bear mention. Psychoanalytic writings on the early relationship between parent and mentally retarded child (Solnit and Stark, 1962; Stott, 1962a, 1962b) emphasize the profound sense of loss, guilt and rage parents typically experience. Less frequently discussed are the impact this may have on the child, who may experience the parent as empathically failing in attunement and availability for bonding – affectively ordered functions, for which mentally retarded persons are in no way incapacitated by virtue of their cognitive disability, as studies of severely retarded persons amply demonstrate (Wing and Gould, 1977; Whittaker, 1980). It is in this specific sense that emphasis on therapist empathy with mentally retarded patients becomes something other than a generic imperative of good "therapeutic hygiene" applicable to all patients.

Further, empathy with a mentally retarded patient is not simply a kind of corrective emotional experience. Empathy is in large part a primitive order of interpersonal experience, pre- and supracognitive, and thus uniquely capable of generating an attuned and workable therapeutic space for the analytic perception and transformation of disorders of narcissism, attachment, and developmental autism and symbiosis – all aspects of development and adjustment of specific relevance to persons with mental retardation, who live closer to primitive experience. It is only from an empathic vantage point that a therapist can understand the uniqueness of the inner life of a mentally retarded person, which often – similar to that of a psychotic in being more affectively than cognitively centered, but different from it in both extent and quality of pathology – is both too horrible and too sensitive to survive projection onto the classical blank screen.

Clinical Material

Two clinical examples will be offered, one from a consultation situation and one from an on-going therapy, to illustrate the application of these theoretical notions.

A., a 26-year-old woman, was seen for initial consultation in a clinic. Referral materials noted she was moderately mentally retarded, and that she had recently separated from a violent, alcoholic husband. She lived with her youngest son, 14 months; her sister; and the sister's four children, ranging in age from preschool to preadolescent. An older son, 5, was kept by the husband and not allowed to live with or visit A. A. had received only the legal minimum of special education and had no serviceable job skills. From a medical perspective, she appeared pale and poorly nourished, with an uncomfortable, collapsing-inward posture and only four teeth, all of them rotting.

The community worker who brought A. to the clinic mentioned that A.'s family was Appalachian, which was also identifiable by her accent. She lived within a clan rather than a nuclear-family frame of reference, and her clan and the former husband's were engaged in a longstanding blood feud. A. was referred to the clinic by the local social services department, who were investigating whether the child living with her was being neglected.

I began the interview by asking A. how I could help her, and by telling her that I thought I could do best if she would just tell me whatever she was feeling or thinking. After some sparse, concrete comments about what had happened earlier in the day and some awkward silences, in which my observations of A.'s nonverbal communications suggested that she was oscillating between autistic and paranoid-schizoid experiential moments, A. began to talk about a series of miscarriages that she had suffered some years ago. She went on to spend the bulk of the hour talking about this material.

My sense was that several things were involved. A. was making use of an interpersonal space experienced as attuned and empathic to metabolize a focal memory of trauma, to which she simultaneously kept hold as a critical and reparative aspect of her identity. In being a *potential* (good) mother, even more than in being a real (imperfect) mother, A. was at her most effective, most affect-rich, most competent and developmentally advanced moment, and perhaps the moment in her psychologically accessible history in which her desires had had most ample play. At the same time, she projectively identified with the damaged fetuses, as symbolizing her own self-experience as an imperfect, nonviable and discarded being. By holding the dead fetuses in memory and in remembered affect, and almost caressingly telling me about them and about her experience giving birth, there was both retreat to a moment of critical (almost diagnostic) developmental blockage, and a present moment of repair. The tremendous, virtually intolerable anxiety A. had experienced in the waiting room and in the first few minutes of her meeting with me became bound, and availability for therapeutic dialogue was established. Neither a functional nor a social view of A.'s psychological state could have yielded this kind of intimate understanding of her life course and current situation, nor generated this type of availability and potential for change.

B. is in his second year of therapy. He lives in a group home. At the beginning of treatment, he attended a day habilitation program, where he was long plateaued at a prevocational level. He currently works competitively half-time, and attends the program a few mornings. B. has a seizure disorder as a consequence of a neuroanatomical abnormality, well but not completely controlled pharmacologically; mild cerebral palsy with right partial hemiplegia with minimal effect on speech and ability to ambulate; and intelligence measured in the mildly mentally retarded range. Qualitatively, he is almost completely lacking in abstract capacity and has a savant quality in his recollections of television trivia. His psychological functioning in childhood was characterized as angry and withdrawn, with poor social skills. In adolescence, B. experienced several years of psychotic functioning, though without character fragmentation or major loss of global ego strength, and spent several years in residential and in-patient settings. He completed secondary special education at a public high school for moderately retarded persons, in which he was placed because of his demanding and poorly controlled behavior.

B.'s social skills are still little evolved. He has no friends, in the sense of friends he spends time with or does things with outside of structured settings. He is deeply if passively invested in his relationships with sales clerks and people he meets incidentally in his wanderings through the community. His favorite pasttime is to stay in his room with multiple electronic media going at the same time.

B.'s parents (based on consultation, reconstruction and review of clinical records from B.'s hospitalizations) never worked through their own sense of loss and outrage at his disabled birth. B. was an unplanned child, 11 years younger than his next oldest sibling. He was simultaneously unwanted, disabled or not, and seen, in a negative case, as the flickering and extinguishing of a magical phantasy for a different, richer, more generative life for the parents. Instances of parental emotional neglect and emotional and physical brutality toward B. are legion; and suffice it to say, throughout his life at home, B. gave as good as he got. A bit over a year into treatment, B.'s parents relocated from the home they had lived in all his life, near the group home, to a distant state, telling B. only after they had made the move. This left B. emotionally enraged, but more than this devasted, for months.

B. came into intensive psychoanalytically oriented psychotherapy with me because a dynamically oriented social worker/nurse team involved with him identified a capacity to benefit from therapy.

The foregoing makes the point that there are indeed identifiable, rich and meaningful psychodynamic themes in B.'s life, that he is not a simply organized or passive person. The connection between B.'s case and the themes described in the first part of this paper can be deepened by focusing on a critical incident that took place a few months ago.

B. typically arrives several hours early for his sessions. Perhaps because his social life is so limited, he likes to spend time in the clinic waiting room and chat with other patients. Both the children and the adults seem to enjoy his company; he seems to visibly relax them.

I usually arrive at the clinic several hours before B.'s appointment. I have been aware that he watches me come out between patients, communicate briefly with the secretary, go to make a note in a chart and the like. These observations of me in a non-therapeutic role make me somewhat uncomfortable, particularly because B. tracks me in a close, hypercathected way.

One day I did not arrive at my usual time, because the earlier patients had cancelled; I arrived 15 minutes before B.'s appointment. B.'s visible distress was intense, and went beyond what could be attributable to a violation of routine. His initial productions in the session were anxious, less organized than usual, and reflected undercurrents of anger quickly dissipating into experiences of existential loss and both pathetic and touching attempts at repair. B. told me that, if I had been late, he would have waited for me until 6:09. The meaning of this, he went on to explain, was that usually he only would wait for five minutes if someone were late, but in this case – my case – he would wait until nine minutes had gone by.

On a cognitive level, B. knew, understood and accepted that I was not really late, but – very much as would be the case with a non-retarded person well engaged in an analytically oriented therapy – that was neither his experiential focus nor his point. He experienced the momentary loss of me, and it evoked a long developmental moment, now superseded but still powerfully remembered as a phantasy-state of disorganiztion, when his parents had been similarly non-present. The processing of this material reflected a softening in B., compared to his initial stance in therapy. In the working through in subsequent sessions B. maintained this softened, affectively warmer and more available stance, and used humor, metaphorical and richly layered language that was new for him. He commented on how well I knew him, that he liked me, and that he "knew who he was" since he began coming to therapy (relational self). Group home staff noted a change in B. in this period, describing him as "nicer, more interesting and easier to get along with."

Summary

This paper has described some theoretical developments in psychoanalysis and attempted to extrapolate their relevance for treating persons with mental retardation using psychoanalytic psychotherapy. It is argued that some of these newer views, particularly psychoanalytic understandings of development and identity formation and the conceptualziation of how therapeutic process works, enable a better therapeutic fit between developmentally disabled persons and the dynamic model than was possible in earlier periods. Case examples have illustrated the application of this thinking in both diagnostic consultation and on-going psychotherapy.

In many ways, the story of the inner lives of persons with mental retardation remains to be told. If there is a metacommunication in this paper, it is that – not unlike what happens with many psychoanalytic recountings – these stories cannot be recorded without being transformed.

References

Belenky, M.F. *Women's ways of knowing: the development of self, voice and mind.* New York: Basic, 1988.

Benjamin, J. *The bonds of love.* New York: Pantheon, 1988.

Bernstein, N. Psychotherapy of the retarded adolescent. *Adolescent Psychiatry,* 1985, *12,* 406–413.

Chidester, L., & Menninger, K. The application of psychoanalytic methods to the study of mental retardation. *American Journal of Orthopsychiatry,* 1936, *6,* 616–625.

Chodorow, N. *Feminism and psychoanalytic theory.* New Haven: Yale University Press, 1989.

Edgerton, R.B. Anthropology and mental retardation: research approaches and opportunities. *Culture, Medicine and Psychiatry,* 1984, *8,* 25–48.

Fajardo, B. Parenting a damaged child: mourning, regression and disappointment. *Psychoanalytic Review,* 1987, *74,* 19–43.

Gair, D.S., Hersch, C., and Wiesenfeld, S. Successful psychotherapy of severe emotional disturbance in a young retarded boy. *Journal of the American Academy of Child Psychiatry,* 1980, *19,* 257–269.

Grinberg, L., & Grinberg, R. *Psychoanalytic perspectives on migration and exile.* New Haven: Yale University Press, 1990.

Haffter, C. The changeling: history and psychodynamics of attitudes toward handicapped children in European folklore. *Journal of the History of the Behavioral Sciences*, 1968, *4*, 55–61.

Hayes, M. The responsiveness of mentally retarded children to psychotherapy. *Smith College Studies in Social Work*, 1977, *47*, 112–153.

Jelliffe, S.E. Technique of psychoanalysis. *Psychoanalytic Review*, 1914, *1*, 63–75 et seq.

Kohut, H. *The analysis of the self.* New York: International Universities Press, 1971.

Kysar, J.E. The two camps in child psychiatry: a report from a psychiatrist-father of an autistic and retarded child. *American Journal of Psychiatry*, 1968, *125*, 103–109.

Langer, M. *Cuestionamos I.* Buenos Aires: Granica, 1971.

Langer, M. *Cuestionamos II.* Buenos Aires: Granica, 1973.

Langer, M. *From Vienna to Managua: journey of a psychoanalyst.* London: Free Association, 1989.

Lira, E., et al. *Psicoterapia y represion politica.* Mexico City: Siglo XXI, 1984.

Mawson, C. The use of play technique in understanding disturbed behavior in school. *Psychoanalytical Psychotherapy*, 1986, *2*, 53–61.

Ogden, T. *The matrix of the mind.* Northvale: Aronson, 1986.

Ogden. T. *The primitive edge of experience.* Northvale: Aronson, 1989.

Sacks, O. *The man who mistook his wife for a hat.* New York: Harper & Row, 1985.

Schlesier, R. On the alleged demise of vaginal sexuality. *Telos, 1984, 17*, 101–118.

Segal, H. *Introduction to the work of Melanie Klein.* Revised edition. New York: Basic, 1985.

Sinason, V. Secondary mental handicap and its relationship to trauma. *Psychoanalytical Psychotherapy*, 1986, *2*, 131–154.

Smith, E.; McKinnon, R.; & Kessler, J.W. Psychotherapy with mentally retarded children. *Psychoanalytic Study of the Child*, 1976, *31*, 493–514.

Solnit, A., & Stark, M. Mourning and the birth of a defective child. *Psychoanalytic Study of the Child*, 1962, *17*, 523–537.

Spensley, S. Mentally ill or mentally handicapped: a longitudinal study of severe learning disorder. *Psychoanalytical Psychotherapy*, 1985, *1*, 55–70.

Stern, D. *The interpersonal world of the infant.* New York: Basic, 1985.

Stott, D.H. Abnormnal mothering as a cause of mental subnormality – I. A critique of some classic studies of maternal deprivation in the light of possible congenital factors. *Journal of Child Psychology and Psychiatry*, 1962, *3*, 79–91.

Stott, D.H. Abnormal mothering as a cause of mental subnormality – II. Case studies and conclusions. *Journal of Child Psychology and Psychiatry*, 1962, *3*, 133–148.

Symington, N. The psychotherapy of a subnormal patient. *British Journal of Medical Psychology*, 1981, *54*, 187–199.

Whittaker, C.A. A note on developmental trends in the symbolic play of hospitalized profoundly retarded children. *Journal of Child Psychology and Psychiatry*, 1980, *21*, 253–261.

Wing, L., & Gould, J. Symbolic play in severely mentally retarded and in autistic children. *Journal of Child Psychology and Psychiatry*, 1977, *18*, 167–178.

Došen, A., Van Gennep, A., Zwanikken, G.J. (Eds.) (1990). Treatment of Mental Illness and Behavioral Disorder in the Mentally Retarded. Proceedings of the International Congress, May 3rd & 4th, 1990, Amsterdam, the Netherlands. Leiden, the Netherlands: Logon Publications.

Chapter 13

Indications and goals for play therapy with the mentally retarded

J. Hellendoorn

Introduction

Psychotherapy has only recently been acknowledged as a viable form of treatment for emotionally disturbed mentally retarded persons. It is often argued that for retarded children and youth *play therapy* might be particularly suitable, because play provides them with a relatively free and safe environment to express experiences and problems, and because play is tuned to their mental age range (e.g. Roskam, 1980). In the Netherlands, different theoretical frameworks are in use, especially client centered play therapy, relationship therapy and hermeneutic imagery therapy. Psychoanalytic play therapy for the mentally retarded is rare. In a survey of the field, Lamers & Van Santen (1985) found that in about 40% of the residential centers in this country play therapy was practiced, with children as well as with older mentally handicapped persons. However, most work in this field is still at the pioneer stage, and as yet very little is known about its process and effects.

Unfortunately, this reflects the general picture (Bernhardt & Mackler, 1975; Li, 1981). Publications usually are clinical reports and single case studies. And although these are often most interesting, there is a sad lack of outcome research. I could not find a single effect study on play therapy with retarded persons after 1975! And the results of the few existing studies are ambiguous. Mehlmann (1953) and Subotnik & Callahan (1959), for instance, found no significant improvement after play therapy. Others (such as Leland, Walker & Taboada, 1959; Morrison & Newcomer, 1975) observed some improvement in cognitive but not in social functioning. These studies all use standard tests as outcome measures. Since case studies *do* show positive effects in single cases (e.g., Goessens, 1985), it may well be that more individual goals and outcome measures are needed.

Since so little is known empirically about the indications for treatment and about treatment goals with regard to play therapy with retarded clients, we turn for a moment to the aims and effects of play therapy with *nonretarded* children. Usually, these are phrased in terms of rather unspecific goals, often related to the theoretical framework of the therapist. For instance:

- therapy should lead to more or better adaptive social behavior;
- the client should develop better insight in his or her personal problems;
- emotional blocks to developmental growth should be removed;
- the client should build up better work or learning behavior, better concentration, more adequate coping behavior;
- excessive anxiety, bad dreams or obsessions should be reduced or disappear.

In their meta-analysis of 75 controlled outcome studies on psychotherapy with children, Casey & Berman (1985) found the largest effects for non-behavioral treatment in cases of somatic problems and social maladjustment. Play therapy was found equally effective as other methods. In a comparable meta-analysis of 108 studies, Weisz, Weiss, Alicke & Klotz (1987) concluded that in general behavioral methods show greater effects. However, even though many outcome studies were published, specific indications and goals for different therapeutic methods are still unclear.

In his comprehensive work on therapy with children, Schmidtchen (1978) emphasized that goal-oriented, targeted therapeutic action is only possible on the basis of a clear statement of the indications and goals for treatment. He distinguished *substantial, functional and intermediate goals*. Substantial goals pertain to general ideas about more healthy ways of being, such as: being able to make choices, forming a personal identity, ability to formulate you own life goals, ability to work with others cooperatively and effectively, finding adequate role behavior in different social roles. These goals are all part of what we usually call: psychosocial health, which may have a personal or a social accent, depending on one's view of man. Functional goals pertain to the way persons cope with everyday problems. The third category, "intermediate" goals, are those that support or facilitate the therapeutic process, in particular: establishing a relationship and a therapeutic climate. Schmidtchen is a strong advocate of individual goals and outcome criteria, tuned to the individual case. And not without reason: In their study of play therapy in practice, Loeven & Harinck (1985) found higher success rates with therapists who prior to treatment systematically formulate goals and strategy for their individual clients.

Although there has been some research done on play therapy with nonretarded children, this has not resulted as yet in clear guidelines about indications and goals. But it seems at least worthwhile to systematically think them through in each individual case. The same may be true, and the same kind of goals might be valid, in therapy with retarded clients. In the Lamers & Van Santen (1985) survey, play therapy for retarded children was defined as "a form of psychotherapy, in which play is used as the medium to bring about changes in experiencing and in behavior, and to remove emotional blocks to development". This definition at least gives no reason to suppose that play therapy with retarded people is essentially different from that with nonretarded children.

Research problem and method

Recently, as a first step to fill the startling lack of knowledge in the field of play therapy with the mentally retarded, we started an evaluation study in Dutch special schools, day care and residential centers. Research questions for the project as a whole are:

1. What indications for play therapy are used by the therapists?
2. What (therapeutic) goals are formulated?
3. What specific features characterize play therapy with the mentally retarded?
4. On what grounds and in what ways do therapists plan their interventions?
5. What results and developments can be perceived in the client, short-term as well as long-term?

Participants to this evaluation study are thirteen female play therapists, working in special schools, day care and residential centers, all with a professional training in special education and most of them with some additional training in play or play therapy. None of them is a specialized or registered therapist, and doing therapy is usually a small part of their duties.

Since so little is known, even about simple questions such as: what exactly happens in play therapy?, a descriptive process approach was chosen, in the form of a multiple case study. To this purpose, the therapists were asked to keep a detailed record file of their clients. Standard forms to record different aspects of therapy were constructed by us, in close cooperation with the therapists. These forms should be completed according to the following procedure:

Before the start of therapy, forms are filled out on personal data and on indications/goals. In addition, a list of behavioral symptoms at referral is completed by one or more primary caregivers. This list contains 48 behavioral symptoms, to be scored on frequency of occurence (often, occasionally, rarely) and on problem value. All other forms consist of open-ended questions, in order to minimize experimental constraint on the natural situation of a therapist reporting about clients.

During therapy, all play sessions and interviews with caregivers are recorded. In addition, every second month the therapy process is evaluated by the therapists. Every 6 months, the behavioral symptom list is repeated, as far as possible by the same scorer(s).

At termination, the results of therapy are evaluated by the therapist and the caregivers, as well as the referents.

Lastly, *one year after termination*, caregivers and referents are again asked to evaluate the client's functioning.

This paper focuses on the first two research questions, about indications and goals. For this report, the completed forms on personal data and on indications/goals were used. Because of the qualitative nature of the responses, a content analysis of the answers was performed by two judges. The categories they inductively and independently formulated showed remarkable similarity, and their agreement on the scoring of separate goals in these categories was about 80%.

Personal data

For the purpose of this paper, data about indications and goals were available on 16 clients (in the near future, a further expansion of the number of clients is foreseen). The group of clients consisted of

- 5 males, age range 5 to 25 yrs, MA range 2,2 to 7 yrs,
- 11 females, age range 4 yrs 6 mos to 65 yrs, MA range 3 to 8 yrs.

Half (8) of the clients were under 18 yrs of age, of which 4 were living at home. Among the 8 older clients only one was living in the parental home. These clients visited day care centers. The others were living in residential homes, usually with day activities nearby.

Results on indications and goals.

Therapists were asked to formulate therapy goals with respect to each individual client, as wel as goals pertaining to counseling of the caregivers. In general, those regarding the client were much clearer. Therefore, only these will be reported. Per case the number of goals for the client varied from 3 to 7, for the caregivers from 1 to 3. All client goals were qualitatively categorized in 13 categories, in 6 clusters, as shown in Table 1. The overlap between the clusters is shown.

Table 1
Goals for play therapy clients, as stated by therapists
(N of clients: 16)

		in nr. of cases
Intermediate:	– Establishing a therapeutic relationship	10
	– Diagnostic: clearer view of problems and symptoms	3
Behavioral:	– Promoting specific adaptive behaviors	4
	– Reducing maladaptive behaviors	5
Social:	– Better/stronger social contacts and initiatives	6
	– Learning to communicate emotional experiences	6
Emotional:	– Differentiating / better handling of emotions	6
	– Reducing anxieties	3
	– Promoting feeling of being accepted / loved	3
Cognitive:	– Coming to terms with emotional (traumatic) experiences in life history	7
	– Better dealing with daily experiences / promoting self-regard and self-confidence	6
Developmental:	– Reducing blocks / facilitating development	5
Other:		2

The intermediate goal: establishing the therapeutic relationship, was the one most frequently named. Even though this alliance should by definition be temporary, and thus cannot be a final goal of therapy, it was evidently seen as most important. Even so, in some cases it was not mentioned. This may reflect the fact that some clients established contact very easily. In these cases this is evidently not a therapy goal. The second kind of intermediate goal mentioned was more diagnostic: during therapy, therapists hope to get more insight into the problems and problem behavior of their clients. Most other goals can be categorized as "substantial": better dealing with emotions and emotional experiences in one way or another, beter coping with past and present experiences, more and better social contacts. Interestingly, no goals were formulated in terms of "better insight in own problems" or "reducing psychosomatic problems", such as might more often be found in therapy with nonretarded persons.

Table 2
Indications for play therapy (referral problems) as stated by therapists (N of clients: 16)

		in nr. of cases
Behavioral:	– Specific maladaptive behaviors	14
Social:	– Lacks social contacts and initiatives	10
	– Unable to communicate emotional experiences	6
Emotional:	– Cannot handle / differentiate emotions	11
	– Manifest anxieties	10
	– Misses feeling of basic acceptance / trust	5
Cognitive:	– Unable to cope with emotional (traumatic) experiences in life history	6
	– Cannot deal with daily experiences / low self-regard / low self-confidence	6
Developmental:	– Developmental blocks	4
Other:		7

BEFORE START OF THERAPY:
form 1: personal data
form 2: indication, goals, strategy
form 3: list of behavioral symptoms (caregivers)

DURING THERAPY, ALL SESSIONS:
form 4: play session with client
form 5: interview with caregivers

EVERY 2 MONTHS:
form 6: evaluation of therapy process

EVERY 6 MONTHS:
repeat form 3: behavioral symptoms

AT TERMINATION OF THERAPY:
repeat form 3: behavioral symptoms
form 7: evaluation by parents/caregivers
form 8: evaluation by therapist

FOLLOW-UP, 1 YEAR AFTER TERMINATION
repeat form 3: behavioral symptoms
form 9: follow-up evaluation by caregivers

Referral problems, as stated by the therapists, were classified in comparable categories (see Table 2). Some interesting differences with the goals (cf. Table 1) were apparent. For instance, the aspects pointed to in "intermediate goals" are completely missing were completely missing in the indications. Evidently, the therapeutic alliance was not a referral problem (although social relationships in general were). Uncertainty about the causes of behavior and about what exactly activates this client's problem, three times mentioned in connection with Therapy Goals, was evidently not an indication for treatment. Indeed, it might be argued that in such a case better assessment is needed, not therapy. Next, adaptive behavior was (naturally!) not mentioned as a problem. On the other hand, maladaptive behavior and manifest anxieties were a massive source of referral problems, much more so than might appear from the therapy goals as stated above. Reduced or inhibited social and emotional competence, as well as traumatic experiences, were also often considered an indication for play therapy.

What kind of diagnostic material was used to decide on play therapy as a suitable form of treatment? In all but one of the cases, the existing record files were used, including reports of parents or caregivers on present and past experiences and behavior. Twice, a case conference with other professionals was a decisive factor. Developmental or intelligence test data were used in 11 cases, one client was considered untestable. The WISC-R and the SON 2-7 (a Dutch nonverbal test for children) were the most popular developmental tests used. One to four observation sessions in the living environment or day activity group were part of the indication process for 11 clients. Not unnaturally, play observation was the favorite indicator (in 13 of the 16 clients).

In all but one of the cases, clients were motivated in the sense that they liked to come. One client was unable to take any initiative at all because of an acute crisis. In this case the therapist went to her, in order to try patiently and carefully to establish a first contact. But this was the exception. The free and easy aspect of play was generally described as a powerful stimulant for the clients to express themselves, in a way that respects their anonymity, that does not seek to break through rituatilistic behaviors, and that does not demand too much of their integrative powers. Many therapists felt they themselves could help the integrative process by initiating transfer and by informing and consulting with caregivers. Therefore, a cooperative attitude of primary caregivers was considered crucial, and in two cases an unfavorable living environment was considered a possible contra-indication for therapy. In three cases, the therapist was still unsure whether therapy might not be too anxiety-provoking. If this should be the case, one might consider terminating play therapy in favor of more structured ways of working with the client. Other contra-indications mentioned were: uncertainty about the suitability of *play* techniques in two cases (too little imagination? play too childish?), or possible organic causes for client's maladaptive behavior (one case). Of course, since all these clients were already admitted to therapy, the possible contra-indications should be regarded more as a warning than as a reason to reconsider the decision for treatment.

The therapist's prognosis for duration of therapy ranged from 6 months to several years, but for most cases between 1 and 2 years. One might think that younger clients might be easier to help. However, no clear relation between estimated length of treatment and client age was found.

Concluding remarks

In this first report of an ongoing evaluation study on play therapy with mentally retarded clients, indications and goals as stated by the therapists on their individual cases were discussed. It appeared that although maladaptive behavior was the main cause for referral, the play therapists – as opposed to behavior therapists – were primarily concerned with the establishing of a therapeutic alliance, with the working through of emotional and social problems and with the advancement of emotional development. However, emotional growth does not take place in a vacuum. The emotional climate of the client's living environment should provide a background for this kind of develoment. In view of this, one wonders whether parents and caregivers should not have a larger place in treatment. Goals and indications were mostly tuned to the client. Goals towards parents and caregivers were often rather vaguely phrased as: giving and receiving information, providing more insight. In some cases, contact of the therapist with the caregivers was reported as very limited indeed. More participation of parents and caregivers, both in terms of co-formulating indications and goals, and in terms of being counseled during the therapy process, might, in our view, contribute essentially to the therapeutic process (see also Brack, 1982).

This evaluation study is now continuing with the gathering of data about the process of therapy. Firstly, to see in what ways these goals are tackled in the therapy process. Secondly, to ascertain whether and in what ways the goals are met at termination. Overviewing the files of all cases up till now, we have not succeeded as yet to discern patterns or subgroups. Instead, the diversity of problems and goals in these cases was striking. At least in our material, *the* mentally handicapped play therapy client did not emerge. In fact, they seemed as heterogeneous as nonretarded persons, requiring the same individual approach.

References

Bernhardt, M., & Mackler, B. (1975). The use of play therapy with the mentally retarded. *Journal of Special Education, 9*, 409-414.

Brack, U.B. (1982). Eltern als Co-Therapeuten von retardierten Kindern: Probleme des Anleitung und Motivierung. *Psychologie in Erziehung und Unterricht, 29*, 41-48.

Casey, R., & Berman, J.S. (1985). The outcome of psychotherapy with children. *Psychological Bulletin, 98*, 388-400.

Goesse Goessens, T. (1985). Beeldcommunicatie bij zwakzinnige kinderen. In J. Hellendoorn (Ed.). *Therapie, kind en spel: bijdragen tot de beeldcommunicatie* (pp. 188-204). Deventer: Van Loghum Slaterus.

Lamers-Osterhaus, M., & Santen, M. van (1985). *Spelend werken aan bevrijding: speltherapie in de zwakzinnigenzorg*. Utrecht: NGBZ, publicatie nr. 38.

Leland, H., Walker, J., & Taboada, A.N. (1959). Group play therapy with a group of post-nursery male retardates. *American Journal of Mental Deficiency, 48*, 53-60.

Loeven, L., & Harinck, F. (1985). Praktijk in beeld: werkwijze en meningen van beeldcommunicatie-therapeuten. In J. Hellendoorn (Ed.), *Therapie, kind en spel* (pp. 257-273). Deventer: Van Loghum Slaterus.

Mehlmann, B. (1953). Group play therapy with mentally retarded children. *Journal of Abnormal and Social Psychology, 48*, 53-60.

Morrison, T.L., & Newcomer, B.L. (1975). Effects of directive vs. nondirective play therapy with institutionalized mentally retarded children. *American Journal of Mental Deficiency, 79*, 666-669.

Roskam, A. (1980). Speltherapie juist erg geschikt voor veel zwakzinnige kinderen. *Klik*, juni/juli, 12-15.

Schmidtchen, S. (1978). *Handeln in der Kinderpsychotherapie*. Stuttgart: Kohlhammer.

Subotnik, L., & Callahan, R. (1959). A pilot study in short-term play therapy with institutionalized educable mentally retarded boys. *American Journal of Mental Deficiency, 63*, 730-735.

Weisz, J.R., Weiss, B., Alicke, M.D., & Klotz, M.L. (1987). Effectiveness of psychotherapy with children and adolescents: a meta-analysis for clinicians. *Journal of Consulting and clinical psychology, 55*, 542-549.

References

[illegible] O.R. (1982). [illegible] [illegible] [illegible] [illegible] und [illegible]. [illegible] [illegible].

[illegible] R., & [illegible], T.S. (1985). [illegible] [illegible] psychotherapy [illegible]. *Psychological Bulletin*, *97*, [illegible].

[illegible] (1985). [illegible] [illegible] [illegible]. In J. H. Bleeksma (Ed.) [illegible] [illegible]. Amsterdam: Swets & Zeitlinger.

[illegible] [illegible], M. [illegible] [illegible] [illegible] [illegible] [illegible].

[illegible] & [illegible], A. [illegible] [illegible] group of [illegible] mild retardation. [illegible] *Journal of* [illegible] [illegible].

[illegible] (1985). [illegible] [illegible] [illegible] (Ed.) [illegible] [illegible]. [illegible] Verlag.

[illegible] B. [illegible] play [illegible] [illegible] of child [illegible]. *Journal of* [illegible] [illegible].

[illegible] (1978). [illegible] [illegible] [illegible] [illegible] [illegible] [illegible]. [illegible].

[illegible] (19[illegible]). [illegible] [illegible] [illegible] [illegible].

[illegible] (1976). [illegible] [illegible] [illegible]. [illegible].

[illegible] (19[illegible]). A [illegible] study [illegible] with play therapy with [illegible] [illegible] [illegible]. *Journal of* [illegible] [illegible].

[illegible] & [illegible], M. (1987). [illegible] [illegible] [illegible] children and [illegible] [illegible] [illegible]. [illegible].

Došen, A., Van Gennep, A., Zwanikken, G.J. (Eds.) (1990). Treatment of Mental Illness and Behavioral Disorder in the Mentally Retarded. Proceedings of the International Congress, May 3rd & 4th, 1990, Amsterdam, the Netherlands. Leiden, the Netherlands: Logon Publications.

Chapter 14

Treatment of psychiatric disorders and behavioral problems in mentally handicapped persons: working with relationship therapy and gentle teaching in an institutional setting

J. van Loon

Introduction

In this presentation I will describe how in our institute we did a treatment with an eight years old mentally handicapped girl with a rather complex psychiatric problem, according to the relationship therapy of Anton Došen, and how we work with Gentle teaching.

The framework for the relationship therapy and the diagnostics it has to be based on, is to be found in the developmental approach.

As dr. Došen himself has given a lecture on developmentally-dynamic based relationship therapy in the plenary sessions (Došen, 1990), I will not repeat the theory on this theme, but just start with the case description.

Further I will compare and link the principles of relationship therapy and those of Gentle teaching by John McGee (McGee et al, 1987), as in both approaches the relationship between the caregiver and the person in need is essential.

I will do that by telling you something about Gentle teaching and about how we work with these ideas in our institute. In addition I will try to state some conclusions about Gentle teaching in relation to relationship therapy.

Developmental-dynamic relationship therapy

Case A

The case I want to present here concerns an eight years old mentally handicapped girl who at first still lived at home and visited a day care centre for children. In the past half year she was getting more and more rapidly irritated, it was difficult to make contact with her, more often she refused to eat, she hit herself, was often awake at night for hours, didn't want to go to the toilet, etc.

She came to our institution for a crisis admission. At that time she hit herself very frequently and intensively against her head, she hadn't eaten for weeks, didn't go to the toilet anymore and didn't have defecation for more than two weeks.

Her mood was sombre, even sad; sometimes she would cry and yell hysterically. She did want attention and she spoke whispering.

It was told also that when she was "allright" she was a bit strange and confused, with easily changing behaviour and changing moods.

She was admitted to De Sterre, an institute for people with mental retardation, as a crisis admission, because of the seriousness of the situation and because there were no alternatives.

To start with, we tried to get a diagnosis following the developmental approach, according to which we regarded medical and family information, problems in the development, cognitive development, emotional development, social development, milieu and the symptoms.

Medical information

At birth there was cord entanglement and An was cyanotic. The E.E.G. was unusual but not specific for epilepsy.

Family

A cousin of An is diagnosed as infantile autistic, which we regard as an important piece of information.

Problems in her development

- The development of her functions was retarded: she started walking at the age of $2^1/_2$ years and she did not develop speech until much later.
- At the age of three years she went to a child day care centre where she gradually developed behaviour problems.
- At the age of five she was described as suffering from developmental psychosis and she showed self-injurious behaviour.
- At the age of six she was admitted to a clinic for observation and treatment because she couldn't be handled anymore at home. She didn't want to eat or sleep, she only whispered and she was aggressive towards herself and others.

  After a few months the behaviour of An changed, the self-injurious behaviour disappeared and she became a cheerful, willful and attached girl.

  Seven months after her admission she went back home from this clinic.

- About $1^1/_2$ years later she relapsed again: she hit herself, it was difficult to make contact with her, she ate less etc.

Cognitive development

Her I.Q. is about 55, but her profile shows discrepancies: An doesn't have a good notion of numbers but a better spatial insight and her performance is better than her verbal ability.

Emotional development

We tried to estimate her level of emotional development by using two scheme's according to Došen.

Because of emotions of love, happiness, sadness and jealousy that we saw in her, we thought she was in the third phase: the phase of individualisation.

Also the items of the second scheme indicated that An was in the phase of individualisation, as we saw her discovering her own person and verbal communication.

However, her emotional base was so insecure that sometimes she relapsed to the lower level: she directed her aggression or anger at herself, started whispering and sometimes stopped verbal communication. The quality of her emotions became more primitive: uncontrolled fear or anger with loss, sometimes complete passivity and especially themes such as attachment, symbiose and basic security were more prominent.

Social development

The social functioning depends almost entirely on the situation.

Milieu

Her father died when An was three years old. During the first three years of An's life, mother was taking intense care of her husband.

Three years later mother and daughter moved to a completely new environment. An was very demanding and obstinate towards her mother, while on the other hand both were very close.

Symptoms

- When An is "allright" she still needs a fixed pattern.
  She has many stereotyped behaviours and is compulsive. She often asks for confirmation.
  An is always a somewhat strange and confused girl with easily changing behaviour and changing moods.
  She cannot make a clear distinction between her inner and the outer world, has insufficient ability to enter into the thoughts and emotions/feelings of others and there is a significant discrepancy between a good spatial orientation and a weak orientation in time.

In this respect it seems important to notice the fact that her cousin is diagnosed as being autistic.
In my opinion the picture of An is most in accordance with "Childhood Onset Pervasive Developmental Disorder", as it is called in DSM-III.

- The six months before admission to our institute she became more and more irritated, it was difficult to make contact with her, she was getting problems with eating, she began to hit herself, was awake at night for hours, didn't want to go to the toilet, etc..
  At the time of her admission she hit herself frequently and intensively against her head This increased with more tension, for example if someone wanted to make contact with her.
  She also hadn't eaten for weeks.
  Her mood was continuously sombre, even sad; sometimes she would cry and yell hysterically. In spite of this all she wanted much attention. An spoke whispering.

- In all this it strikes us that many symptoms were pointing towards the diagnosis of depression, such as:
  - disorders in the vitality
    - not eating
    - not sleeping
    - obstipation
  - regression
  - a need for attention remains
  - sombre/sad mood
  - self injurious behaviour.

Diagnosis

Our diagnosis was that in the first place there was a developmental psychosis of congenital nature.

Secondly there was a severe disturbance of emotional development in the phase of socialisation: allthough she is further in her emotional development when she is "allright", her emotional base is so insecure that she relapses easily when she is under pressure and then she gets stuck in the second phase, the phase of socialisation.

As such, however, one can say that An has had an abnormal development.

On this basis one understands that twice she got in a depression, which is, in view of the symptoms, the best name for the acute problem with which we got to know her.

In summary we see An as a developmentally psychotic mentally handicapped girl with a disturbance in the phase of socialisation, who under unfavourable circumstances regresses in a depression with vital signs.

Treatment

For the treatment of An the above means that when she is in an acute state of depression we have to treat her for this depression, and that when she is "allright" we have to treat her in accordance with the diagnosis of development disorder.

For the treatment of depression we based ourselves on the scheme of Anton Došen:

- complete acceptation of An as a person,
- much emphasis on basic security, and
- as much structure as possible in persons, space and time.

These were the pillars on which we builded our treatment.

Since An's admission in "de Sterre" we started treatment which mainly follows the principles of Došen's relationship therapy.

First Phase

To begin with we agreed to emphasize complete acceptation and tolerance in order that An should experience security and feel at peace.

Only minimal demands were made: she wasn't forced to do anything and the self-injurious behaviour was completely ignored. Trust, acceptation and relaxation were the main points.

The principle of structure in space, persons and time was maintained by keeping at first her *living space limited* to the unit she lived in, in which a *permanent team of caregivers*, and within this team *two explicit persons for her to trust* or put her faith in (the therapists) worked with her and in which they worked with a *fixed daily program.*

By this program we also came to meet the principle of a fixed, diurnal rhythm of activity and inactivity. As a departure from the way Došen described it we decided to use two instead of one therapist to guarantee more continuity, considering the changing working schedules. We had the feeling that An could handle this well enough.

Second phase

Then it became possible to enter the second phase of the relationship therapy: to build a warm and positive relation between An and her caregivers, especially the therapists, but also the other members of the team.

Here it was the purpose to make An realise that she was completely accepted and further to stimulate her to take initiatives in communication and to express her self-esteem: important aspects in the treatment of depression.

The living space could gradually be extended, however: within the fixed structure of the safe bond with her permanent caregivers.

Third phase

After some time it slowly became possible to make a little more demands and thus to cautiously enter the third phase.

Here we tried to help her over thresholds, which made application of some pressure on her necessary, but avoiding a real conflict and within a bond of trust.

This treatment resulted in a reasonably fast lowering of the intensity of self-injurious behaviour. After one month it stopped almost completely.

Gradually she came more out of her own and it became possible to really make contact with her. After about five weeks she started having cheerful moments, that became more and more apparent. She also started talking more, telling things and getting interested in all kinds of things.

Only after about four months she eventually started eating real food again.

Gentle Teaching

In the past year I did a one-week workshop on Gentle Teaching by John McGee.

One of the things that attracted my attention there, as well as in the literature on this subject, was that Gentle Teaching and relationship therapy have a strikingly similar basis. For this reason I would like to compare and link these methods.

In both approaches the aim is to establish a solid relation with the people one has to care for.

While however the relationship therapy was developed by Došen as a kind of psychotherapy for mentally retarded children, Gentle Teaching origininally has a broader intention: Gentle Teaching is a pedagogical process that focuses on teaching the value inherent in human presence, human interactions and human reward, and on establishing a close relationship with people who often just try to distance themselves of human interactions.

In summary Gentle Teaching focuses on:

- respect, acceptance, tolerance, affection, friendship, warmth
- a sincere desire to establish bonded relationships
- promoting mutual growth in the person and ourselves
- human dignity
- justice
- solidarity
- interdependence between the person and ourselves
- the totality of the person
- a democratic attitude
- an authentic attitude

- participation: doing things together
- liberation
- communication with the handicapped person: maintaining a dialogue
- non-contingent valuing of the person.

As such Gentle Teaching describes a sound basic attitude in working with mentally handicapped persons in general.

What I like especially in this approach is that, if handled systematically and as a process, it provides a methodology for the treatment of mentally handicapped persons with severe behaviour problems, as McGee describes it explicitly.

These persons have to be taught the same values as described above.

- We teach them friendship: that our presence equals safety and security, what the meaning is of participation, of reciprocation of valuing, of warmth etc..
- We give them non-contingent approval for who they are; warmth and authenticity are important characteristics in this matter.
- We try to get a dialogue going with the person.
- We try to establish bonded relationships between the caregivers and the persons.
- We try to reduce the number of dominant interactions and increase the interactions focused on valuing.

Especially when McGee describes the steps in this process (McGee, 1989) Gentle Teaching and the relationship therapy appear to be close:

1. *Designification of distancing context*
   The existing situation often leads more to distancing than to approach. This situation has to get a different meaning, a different load, such that the accents are nog longer on distancing:
   - you have to recognize and tolerate alienating interactions
   - and focus on the prevention or dissipation of non-participatory interactions.

2. *Restructuring the interactional context*
   - enable participatory interactions
   - provide whatever assistance is necessary
   - use errorless teaching strategies
   - save your contact for valuing
   - assume an attitude and praxis of value giving rather than compliance seeking.

3. *Resignify interactional context*
   - all caregiving interactions begin with, center on and effectuate human valuing
   - recognize the dialectical process of psychology
   - gradually withdraw special supports, but be aware of natural ebbs and flows.

4. *Co-signify relationship based on solidarity*
   - through the bonding process via mutual feelings of human presence, participation, and valuing.

5. *Communitize the interactional context*
   - through a focus on interdependence, extend personal value-based relationships throughout the basic community.

Working with Gentle Teaching

In the past year, the ideas of Gentle Teaching have been very inspiring for us in our work with the mentally handicapped.

Since I was involved in starting up two units at our institute with a special function for mentally handicapped people with severe behaviour problems, I had the opportunity to propose Gentle Teaching in formulating a basic vision for working in these units. Both units are meant for mentally handicapped people:

- with severe behaviour problems, e.g. aggression, destruction, self-injurious behaviour, severe restlessness, severe mood changes;
- who because of their behaviour problems cannot be cared for in a normal unit.

One unit is meant for profoundly and severely retarded people, the other for severely and moderately retarded young people.

In preparing ourselves and the unit team, the caregivers, for this job we broadly discussed the ideas of Gentle Teaching as stated above.

We found and still find it a good and a sound basis for developing an atmosphere of warmth and acceptance in which people are valued for who they are as a person.

In our vision for both units we have stated that we want to create for our people a home, with a good quality of a pleasant life, with better opportunities to accept them as they are and better opportunities for treatment if this is necessary.

Acceptance however means for us that we take a person as he is, without trying to change him (once again), unless there is a clear underlying problem or disorder which can be treated (e.g. a psychiatric disorder).

Therefore we focus on the individual and adjust our norms and our standards to him instead of adjusting him to our group norms and standards. In this atmosphere the caregivers try to establish warmth, friendship and a strong relationship. They are focused on non-contingent valuing of the handicapped people: they try to diminish the amount of dominant interactions and to increase valuing interactions.

Our experience with working like this until now is that everyone involved is very positive: the caregivers as well as the parents, and, deducting from their behaviour also, the mentally handicapped people, who as a group are more relaxed, less tense, more happy and show less behavior problems.

What strikes me especially is that the caregivers are highly motivated to go on working like this. However it appears to be very important that a number of conditions regarding staff-pupil ratio, accommodation etcetera are met.

Case B

Betty is a 19 years old severely mentally handicapped women who lived at home until last year.

Because of ongoing behaviour problems such as aggression, temper tantrums, severe restlessness, throwing plants and other objects etc., she was admitted to our institution for day care when she was $17^1/_2$ years old.

As her behaviour continued to cause severe problems to her family, she was admitted to live in our institution 10 months later.

As a result of our observation we found out that there was a variety of factors which could cause aggression to Betty: she was easily frustrated, she had difficulty going to the toilet, her menstruation made her more tense etc.: anything that she felt went wrong or she didn't like could cause aggression. Of course she received the necessary medical attention, but we thought it would be very important to make her feel at home, to try to make her happy and we explicitely stressed the importance of a good relationship between her and the caregivers.

To make this concrete we made a plan inspired by the ideas of Gentle Teaching, in which acceptance, tolerance, respect, friendly relationships, affection and valuing of the person etc. played important roles. We formulated our plan as follows:

1. We will have to learn Betty the meaning of friendship:
   - to make her realize that our presence means safety and security
   - to teach her to appreciate doing things together, to participate

- to teach her the meaning of mutual respect
- to teach her what mutual affection and warmth means.

2. Therefore we have to make her feel valued as a person, non-contingent: we value her, like her, give her warmth.
3. In dealing with her we shall try to diminish dominant interactions and increase valuing interactions.
4. Apart from that, we will create situations in which we explicitly try to work together with her: situations in which she can experience much warmth, attention, valuing and friendship, but in which we also expect her to participate.
5. We will try to prevent or redirect (or divert) interactions from Betty that go in the opposite direction.
   If it is necessary to interfere with her behaviour to protect ourselves or other mentally handicapped who live with her, we try to do this in such a way that it remains clear that we do value her as a person.

This approach led to a more positive way of thinking about Betty and her behaviour problems. Instead of a pressure as a consequence of trying to change her there came the relaxation of accepting her as a person.

The team also discovered more and more the other, more enjoyable, side of Betty.

Betty herself grew to like being together with other people, which at first she tried to avoid. This was even more special because as a consequence of the new approach she was allowed to be more on her own as she liked it, while before she was often sent to her room as a consequence of behaviour problems.

Relationship therapy and Gentle Teaching

In spite of the correspondence between relationship therapy and Gentle Teaching regarding the importance of establishing bonded relationships, I also see a few differences.

Especially through the emphasis that Došen puts on the principles of structure in space, persons and time, a diurnal rhythm of activity and inactivity and of gradual emotional development, relationship therapy is more focused on the treatment of psychiatric disorders than Gentle Teaching.

Also the fact that Došen proposes one therapist points in the same direction.

With these aspects one comes to meet explicitly the high vulnerability and lability of people with psychiatric disorders.

Relationship therapy, however, has to be embedded in a broader atmosphere of working with and caring for people with mental retardation.

In this respect Gentle Teaching is an interesting approach. In my opinion, with Gentle Teaching many behaviour problems can firstly be prevented, and secondly be well treated. In the case of psychiatric disorders there is, with Gentle Teaching as basic approach, a good climate for applying a relationship therapy, if necessary.

Summarizing one could say that Gentle Teaching provides a broad and sound framework for the care of mentally retarded people. In its more acuminate form it gives us a good methodology for helping persons with mental retardation and (severe) behavioural problems. The relationship therapy, while starting from the same principles with attachment as a central point, is more focused on the treatment of mentally retarded people with psychiatric disorders, but can to a great extent benefit from a climate which is fully alive to Gentle Teaching.

References

Došen, A. (1990, this volume). Developmental-dynamic relationship therapy.

McGee, J.J., Menolascino, F.J., Hobbs, D.C. & Menousek, P.E. (1987). Gentle Teaching: a non-aversive approach to helping people with mental retardation. New York: Human Sciences Press.

Došen, A., Van Gennep, A., Zwanikken, G.J. (Eds.) (1990). Treatment of Mental Illness and Behavioral Disorder in the Mentally Retarded. Proceedings of the International Congress, May 3rd & 4th, 1990, Amsterdam, the Netherlands. Leiden, the Netherlands: Logon Publications.

Chapter 15

Counseling of mentally retarded children with emotional and behavioural problems in a day care centre: a report of practice

J. Vonk
Ch. Egberts

Introduction

A day care centre supplies day care for mentally retarded children in the age of 2,5–17 years from 9.00–15.30 five days a week. The centre is not a school or a therapeutic clinic, but can be regarded as a "kindergarten for handicapped children". Stimulation of development is a very important goal. Therefore the professional workers in the groups are supported by a spectrum of therapists, including a speech therapist, fysiotherapist, play therapist, psychologist, music therapist and special educationalist.

Leaving our centre many children are admitted to a ZMLK-school (a school for children with severe learning disabilities). When a ZMLK-school is beyond reach (e.g. because of very limited learning potential) childeren remain in our centre until the age of 18. By that age they can attend a day care centre for adults, a facility that resembles our centre in many ways.

Differentiation into groups

Our day care centre provides care to +80 children, divided into 10 groups and housed in two facilities. Because of this large number of children, we are able to make an optimal differentiation into groups. It offers us an unique opportunity to develop special groups. Clustering of children into groups is mainly based on common educational needs of children (Kok 1973). We agree with Redl (1966) that mistaken grouping can be a main source of problematic behaviour. We therefore devote much of our time to the "art of group composition". This includes an optimal "fit" with relation to groups and professional workers. The group is managed by two professional workers. The size of each group varies from six to nine children depending on the educational needs of the children. The most unresponsive children are placed in the smallest groups. When the educational needs change (e.g. with the entry of new children) the size of the group can be changed. At this moment we use the following differentiation.

Name of the group	Number of children	Keywords
Entrance group	8	2,5-6 years old, care
Entrance group	8	2,5-6 years old, care and development
Special education group	9	3-7 years old, development ZMLK-school
Day care group	8	6-10 years old, care, practical skills.
Day care group	9	10-17 years old, practical/social skills, in future: day care centre for adults or an institution.
Day care group	8	8-13 years old, social/developmental skills, history of school failure.
Intermediate group	9	6-10 years old, practical/social skills, sometimes ZMLK-school.
Intermediate group	8	5-10 years old, partical/social skills.
Special care group	6	all ages, observation of mental health problems treatment.
Observation group	7	2,5-7 years old, observation of retardation (degree and nature) advice.

Theoretical notions

The developmental dynamic theory (Došen, 1983; Greenspan and Lourie, 1981) is an important aspect of our way of working. A mental handicap has three components: a social, an emotional and a cognitive component. One of the requirements of mental health is a dynamic balance between these components. Quite often we notice that the emotional retardation gets less attention than the mental retardation.

Very often these children show a history of overcharge (Kraijer, 1985). It is clear that both mechanisms can block the total development of a child. We therefore pay special attention to the development of the emotional component. Often this is already accomplished by placing a child in group clearly below its own intellectual level. If necessary we offer the child relationship therapy (see below) in which we systematically try to stimulate the emotional development. Sometimes this means regressing as far as necessary. Relatively little is known about the milestones of emotional development. There are no scales (as there are scales about self help, language, or social skills). In counseling we sometimes use the theoretical framework of M. Mahler (1975) on early social emotional development. Bugental (1985) shows that unresponsive children elicit an inconsistent and uncertain adult communication style which maintains and reinforces the initial unresponsiveness. But this interaction effect is seen only when adults have a lack of self confidence and believe that care giving succes is due to uncontrollable, situational factors. Adults with high self-perceived competence as caregivers do not alter their behaviour in reaction to the unresponsive behaviour of a child. Our experience with special groups leads to the same conclusion. Therefore a careful selection of the professional workers in these groups is particularly important.

Methods

A description is given of specific methods, both used in the special care group and the observation group.

We already mentioned the use of relationship therapy. This therapy has been developed by Došen (1984) and can be carried out by the professional group workers. The three phases Došen describes (tolerance and acceptance, meeting and growing together, and reeducation), illustrate the developmental point of view of the therapy. In our day care centre we particularly use relationship therapy when children have experienced contact problems in their early relationship with their mother. A lot of these children show disinhibitive or aggressive behaviour. Mostly the frequency of the therapy is four to five times a week (half an hour, each session) during a period of 6-18 months. An activity is chosen that makes the child feel accepted and comfortable. The professional worker only gives positive attention in a stimulating and affirming way as long as the child needs to. Changing of activity and making higher demands is possible when the child makes progress in his/her emotional development. At the same time a transfer of the therapy to the group is attempted. The final step concerns transfer to the family of the child.

We frequently use video equipment for observation of the child's behaviour and the interaction between the children and the professional workers. Video material is used for team discussion, in contact with the parents and in communication with professional helpers outside the day care centre.

Regular standardised screening of development is an important part of our approach. We use several scales such as: 'Sociale Redzaamheidsschaal Kinderdagverblijven' (a scale that measures practical skills, language and social behaviour), 'Storend Gedragschaal Zwakzinnigen' (a scale that measures verbal and nonbal aggression and behaviour) and the 'Schaal voor Extra Aandachtvragend Gedrag' (a scale that measures all kind of extra attention attracting behaviour). In addition we frequently use psychological tests to measure the mental development (including Bos 2-30; Psycho-Educational Profile, Stutsman, WPSSI, Kleuterson, Peabody, Reynell, etc.).

Twice a year a child psychiatrist is consulted. Before the consultation, written reports and prepared questions are sent to the psychiatrist. Before discussion, video material that illustrates our questions is presented.

The special care group

When we restructured the groups of our day care centre in 1987, we decided to form two groups especially for children who were experienced as difficult by the professional workers in the group. It resulted in a more homogeneous grouping in the sense of common educational needs of children. Instead of being a negative exception in their groups, the difficult children were now "normal" members in their new groups. In general this made a more positive approach possible.

Target population

Children with emotional and/or behaviour problems. Examples of emotional problems are autism or another form of disturbed contact, depression, low self-confidence, low frustration tolerance and extreme apathy. Examples of behaviour problems are negative destructive behaviour, aggression, bad tempers, and hyperkinetic behaviour.

The aim of a special care group

1. Observation: what is the cause of the specific behaviour and what are the possibilities to change a situation and the behaviour of a child?

2. Treatment: very structured day programme, consistent way of dealing with the children, (when indicated) relationship therapy. Placement into a group of normal size is attempted. For some children this will prove impossible.

Therefore the third aim is:

3. Permanent care: these children are not able to function without the structure and counseling of this special group.

Specific characteristics of the special care group (in relation to other groups):

- Very experienced professional workers who are selected because of motivation, experience and preponderance.
- Adjusted furnishing and materials in the 'classroom'. Often this means less stimulating objects.
- When indicated: use of developmentally dynamic relationship therapy.
- Extra support for the professional workers in the group (case discussions, in-service training, lectures of invited experts, theoretical discussions, etc.). These efforts are coordinated by the special educationalist who is supervising the group.
- Consultation of a child psychiatrist.

Results and experiences

We started with two groups. One group consisted only of children who had acting-out problems. In the other group these children were mixed with emotionally vulnerable children. This proved to be a difficult combination. We were able to move +70% of the children to groups of normal size. Thus two years after the start only one special care group was necessary. Besides at this moment a growing number of new children is referred by other facilities. For some children the special care groups prevented reference to a residential observation clinic. That implicates that children can remain with their parents. As a consequence of working with more or less homogeneous groups, children have to change more. This effect is strengthened by the temporary character of the special care group. Frequent change produces often commotions. However, because a new group means an improvement for the child, our experience is mostly positive. Oppenents of clustering difficult children into one group often use the argument of reinforcement of negative behaviour. In our experience dispersion had a far more negative effect.

The observation group

Many young children with unclear developmental problems are screened by doctors and psychologists. Usually these children have no regular day care until a concluding advice can be given. For some children this means that they have to wait a long time before a choice can be made. In december 1987 we decided to start an observation group for these children. It offered day care at an early moment and the possibility to integrate diagnostics in the daily routines. We expected that a more natural test situation would result in more reliable test results.

Target population

Young children with developmental problems; diagnostics had to be unclear (e.g. cause, nature and degree of the retardation). Because of their developmental problems the children need a strongly individualized approach.

Aim of the observation group

To obtain a clear diagnosis of the nature and degree of the developmental problems and advise accordingly for further day care. In principle, this means temporary observation (minimum 3 months and maximum 1 year).

Specific characteristics of the observation group:

- Professional workers are selected because of their motivation and capacity of making good observations.
- Intensive cooperation with parents is important. The same holds for the professional parent workers.
- In a short time, a lot of investigation is done by the professional workers, speech and play therapist. It requires good interdisciplinary deliberation among all professional workers. Thorough investigation of intelligence is done by the special educationalist. Psychological examination starts only after a child feels at ease in the day centre. After 3 months, the first team evaluation takes place (including the parents of the child). This is repeated after 6 or 9 months. In the last team evaluation, conclusions are drawn and advice for further day care is given.
- The emphasis on observation requires good 'public relations': cooperation with other institutes must be fluent.
- Use of video equipment to screen developmental changes precisely.
- When indicated: use of relationship therapy.

Results and experiences

Since the start of the group about 20 children have been observed. The developmental delay of half of the children proved to be so serious that further care in our day care centre was advised. The other 10 children were outplaced into a wide variety of special education schools. In our experience the developmental possibilities of some children have been underestimated by previous researchers. These children performed under their potential because the test conditions proved to be disadvantageous for them. Once they are accustomed to the routines of the day care centre, psychological testing loses its threatening character. Until now the number of children that can be observed in the group equals the existing need.

Conclusion

Because of the large capacitity of the day care centre it is possible to make a flexible differentiation into groups. For about three years two special groups exist: a special care group and an observation group. The results of both groups have proved satisfactory; it is now possible to create adequate day care for children who formerly dropped out because of problem behaviour or yet unsolved diagnostics. A specialism has been built up and is used both within our centre and by other facilities in the city. Sometimes outplacement of a child to residential care can be prevented. Working in the field means little time for reflection. We are still looking for a method to evaluate our differentiation into groups in a systematic way. We hope that our way of dealing with exceptional (mentally retarded) children will convince other day care centres to take their own initiative. In our opinion we have not presented a complex and inimitable approach. Every day centre can do the same provided a few conditions are fulfilled (e.g. enough groups to make an optimal differentiation, at least one professional who functions as initiatator and supervisor, willingness to invest energy to help unresponsive children, etc.). When the size of a day care centre is too small to permit differentiation it could be considered to form a functional union with another day care centre in the same region.

References

Došen, A., 1983, Psychische stoornissen bij zwakzinnige kinderen. Lisse.

Došen, A., 1984, Experiences with individual relationship therapy within a therapeutic milieu for retarded children with severe emotional disorders. In: J.M. Berg (ed.), Perspectives and progress in mental retardation, II; Biomedical aspects. IASSMD.

Greenspan, S. and Lourie, R.S., 1981, Developmental structuralist approach to the classification of adaptive and pathologic personality organizations: infancy and early childhood. American J. of Psychiatry, (138) 725-736.

Kok, J., 1973, Opvoeding en hulpverlening in behandelingstehuizen. Rotterdam.

Kraijer, D.W., 1985, Volwassenen zwakzinnigen van hoger niveau met gedragsstoornissen. Ruit, (11) 5-15.

Mahler, M., 1971, Symbiosis and individuation; the psychological birth of the human infant. The Psychoanalytic Study of the Child, (26) 89-106.

Redl, F., 1966, The art of group composition. In: F. Redl; When we deal with children; selected writings. New York.

Došen, A., Van Gennep, A., Zwanikken, G.J. (Eds.) (1990). Treatment of Mental Illness and Behavioral Disorder in the Mentally Retarded. Proceedings of the International Congress, May 3rd & 4th, 1990, Amsterdam, the Netherlands. Leiden, the Netherlands: Logon Publications.

Chapter 16

Ericksonian approaches to the treatment of mentally retarded human beings: hypnotherapeutic, systemic and strategic ideas

E. Hohn

Introduction

"If you are not part of the solution, you are part of the problem."
(English commercial)

Change is the subject of every kind of (psycho)-therapy; only if it means change in experiencing, behavior or in measures of adaptation observable from "outside".

Some therapies try to discover the causes as a prerequisite for intervention while others focus more on the ongoing process, silently presuming that people can change and knowing the causes is not necessary for a responsible therapeutic intervention.

Nevertheless the therapist needs a great deal of information about the client, his feelings, ideas, interactions and social relationships; in short an answer to the question: "How does the client construct her/his world?"

This is a central theme in Ericksonian psychotherapy, because Erickson states: "Every person is unique."

The illness, the disturbance or the problem (their conditions included) of a person are only an aspect, not the proper object. An Ericksonian therapist is more interested in the way a person acts, feels and contructs his view of the world/ the reality than in objective conditions, though he will not deny them.

Such a position reminds us of a word from Sartre: "It is not the point, what made us the existence we are, but what we do with this made existence." Even if we admit this would be a suitable conception for normal clients, is it a possible way for mentally retarded (m.r.) persons?

Let's consider the problem by means of a diagram:

Figure 1
External (A) and Internal adaptation

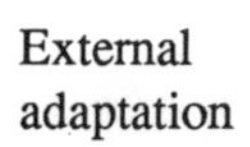

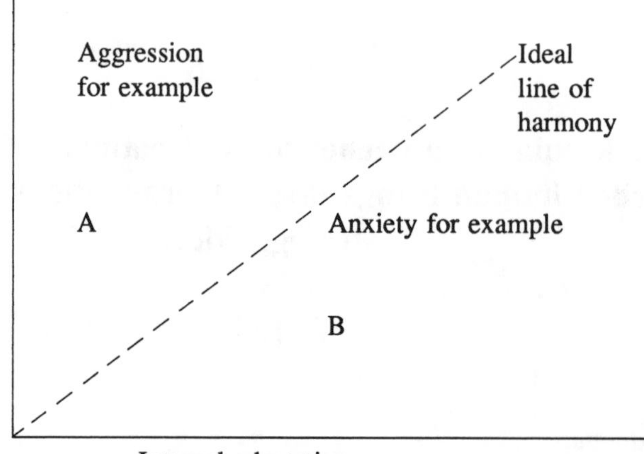

A person always has to manage demands of two types of adaptation as seen above. Disorders may fall in one of these types, for example aggression as a contravention of social norms and rules, anxiety as a disorder of the internal ecology. Of course you can imagine combinations, when a depressed person for example can't fulfill demands of achievement and simultaneously suffers psychic pain. Or in a case of alcoholic addiction, a person at first functions well socially, but later breaks down, loses his job, runs into debts and so on.

When infants are suffering more and more from allergies or "pseudo-krupp", you must ask if these phenomena are signs of the limits of external adaptability (ecological destruction) rather than simple organic weaknesses. You also may distinguish therapeutic interventions into methods which focus on internal adaptation and others which stress external adaptation. An activity program for depressive clients would belong to a strategy for external adaptation, while a cognitive therapy would deal with internal adaptation.

It is also a difference if you react to aggression with reinforcing alternative behavior and simultaneously extincting the aggressive behaviors or if you deal with the underlying grief which is constantly feeding the aggression with energy.

Both types are mutually related and dependent, of course. A therapist always should reflect the effects of combining methods, assuming she/he attaches value to the internal-external-metaphor.

A therapeutic strategy doesn't follow a "the more the better" inflation, but criteria of economy, aesthetics and ethics.

With regard to m.r. clients external strategies are clearly dominating: medication, behavior therapy to manipulate the consequences of a behavior and special institutions to banish reality, to name a few especially conspicuous examples.

This is due to a lack of experiences with internal strategies and the conviction that mental retardation hinders insight and therefore success in therapy. We are just beginning to learn that we are no longer forced such prejudices.

The way I work with Ericksonian therapy concerning m.r. clients is primary an internal, subjective (or better: constructivistic) and individual approach, which will be combined with external methods in each case.

Mental retardation is a concept for a very heterogeneous population. Usually these clients will be subdivided into groups of different intellectual levels; or special problems (aggression, self-destructive behavior etc.) will be subject to research and treatment. In West-Germany the convenience is dominating the scene, that a structural brain damage is sufficient to suppose; you hardly will succeed in discovering dynamic aspects in explanations.
The approach represented here however wants to step another way. To do this, at first four premises have to be stated, implying indeed that certainty is not possible, and that each undertaken therapy may be classified as a field experiment:
1. M.r. clients do have the ability to experience suffering;
2. M.r. clients do have the ability to change by themselves;
3. Ericksonian psychotherapy (of which hypnotherapy is a part) in a sense of an internal strategy is possible;
4. The difference between m.r. clients and ourselves therefore will be reduced (therapy as means of integration and normalization).

The latter premise becomes relevant for your hypotheses (hypothesizing) during the therapeutic process and your ability to indicate the client that you really are striving for an understanding of his unique person and his problems.

Principles

The following principles or guidelines deliver the material from which therapy can be built up. There is no difference in doing therapy and in establishing its preconditions. If attention is poor, you do therapy in a way that strengthens attention, so you establish the preconditions of therapy by doing therapy!

1. Contextualization

The therapeutic situation of the setting shows three persons,

a) the m.r. client;

b) the “Kümmerer” (someone who cares for someone, caregiver) who brings the client into therapy;
c) the therapist.

Within this setting roles and functions of the partipicants are well defined. Not the therapist carries the responsibility for change but the client.

The m.r. client will be regarded as a historical human being with a history of learned behaviors. Attributions and expectations coming from his environment where he lives, are of special interest, not so much for explanation of the problem but more because of the intended change. Diagnostic purposes don’t follow an idea of objectivity or truth but a weighing of several sources of information, which are condensed in a social agreement.

Moreover, the m.r. client is an active participant and not a mere object of investigation. Diagnostic inferences have the status of hypotheses and attributions only.

The “Kümmerer” serves as a cognitive memory for the therapist and a representative of the client’s social support system. She/he often is very engaged and feels responsible, therefore the therapist avoids valuations. He promotes rather observations than explanations. He focuses on the “Kümmerer’s” knowledge of the client’s history more than on present interactional problems.

The therapist acts as cultural agent who tries to create an experience for his client which stands out of the triviality: therapy as a cultural event.

As a therapist she/he should protect her/himself from three sins: controlling, helping and instructing.

The only thing a therapist can do is to make available a context where change becomes possible. All communications and interactions within this context potentially operate on several levels: direct-indirect, literal-metaphorical, individual-social, verbal-nonverbal and so on.

The therapist uses the concept of contextualization also to understand behavior, normal or disordered in any way. Any behavior has a context of interaction, which has a context of social organization. This requires a more functional perspective than a causal one. Change may be produced in every stage. Context as a meta-position gives meaning (sense) to a behavior. In a systemic view, the person as author of his behavior raises the question for responsibility, not for causality.

2. Historicity

There is a definition of Mental Retardation as “loss of the cultural heritage”. Everybody knows the dramatic phenomena of brain damages affecting the memory functions, especially in the case of when long term memory impairments.

Identity is that summary of constancies to understand ourselves and to have a measure of comparison between stability and change. Without identity you cannot even build expectations, you are caught by the situation only. For m.r. clients I developed some techniques to work with their history (family of origin, trauma, kinesthetic memory), but I cannot describe them here because of the restricted space.

3. Differentiation

This is a genuine systemic concept consisting of several dimensions.

a) Positive and negative feedback:

If you say: "you are anxious (positive feedback) but you feel better (negative feedback) more and more ...", you create a field of tension within which change may develop.

b) Associative and dissociative methods:

Ericksonian methods can be distinguished this way. Methaphors and the technique of seeding belong to the associative methods, while confusion, provocation and humor on the other hand are dissociative methods. Associative methods lean on the frames of reference of a person whereas dissociative ones disrupt patterns of behavior to make a person accessible for new ideas which may lie outside the habitual paths. Both methods are applied to therapy alternately.

c) Reframing: motivation vs. behavior

The technique of reframing comes from the idea that therapy is the substitution of a good idea for a bad idea. While behavior might be considered as false, disordered, not fitting, the underlying motivation is defined as positive for the individual. So you can find other ways with your client which fulfill her/his needs and desires also or even better.

d) Physiological: tension vs. relaxation

This dimension seems universally relevant for m.r. clients. They really have to learn that relaxation is followed by tension and that tension doesn't always need to produce a feeling of being threatened and impulses to actions. In hypnotherapy one works with flexible states of emotions, which pass over to each other.

e) Therapeutic cooperation strategies: pacing and leading

The therapist tries to meet a client in her/his frame of reference, she/he speaks her/his language, that means pacing. Complementary to this, leading is used to produce minimal change(s). You can imagine pacing-leading as a harmonious dance!

4. Utilization

This principle is central, and a genuine idea of M.H. Erickson. No part of the client's conduct is rejected or condemned. Symptoms are not considered as signs of a disease to be healed or as enemies to be fought against. Rather symptoms serve as a lever for change whatever the phenomena are. You can utilize any part of the client's behavior: symptoms, cognitions, motor patterns, expressive behaviors and so on. You also can combine the utilization approach with an developmental one: you use everything to stimulate development or to unblock development.

Home-tasks are good tools for utilization. A m.r. client who likes to telephone may be instructed to look for telephone booths in the village; this promotes his self-reliance and social integration.

Ericksonian language patterns are too complex a theme to deal with here. Interested readers should consult the appropriate literature. These language forms are always directed to deeper levels of knowledge, not only to an intellectual understanding. The reason why you can use such language pattern with m.r. clients is very simple: passive linguistic competence is always higher than active performance. In other words, your client is always able to understand more, but this "more" needs not to be identical with your goals. In short, the utilization principle can be widely applied, and that on all levels of behaviors.

5. Trance (hypnosis)

Trance as a state is a common experience, trance induction a therapeutic method.

Erickson emphasizes that in a trance, people function on a special level of awareness; he called this state, characterized by hightened receptiveness and responsiveness, the unconscious mind. Research in this field (for example the hidden observer theory) – as in others also – is only done with normals. Usually researchers (not therapists) believe that m.r. persons are not hypnotizable.

This is only to justify methods of formal inductions, and that is merely because nobody tried it! In combination with the utilization principle one can use spontaneously occuring trance states; this is called the naturalistic approach. Nevertheless you have chances to elicit trance states in m.r. clients which don't rely on formal induction methods. One of the simplest methods is to make a person concentrate on topics she/he is mostly interested in (for example an important aspect of her/his personality) that's basic for indirect methods. Trance will also set one's mind on when she/he is totally engaged in a task (like a surgeon).
Usually I introduce a therapy session with the en-trance-question: "Do you know, why you are here actually?" This often produces immediate signs of trance.

Now, what is the therapeutic value of trance or being hypnosis? Trance as a therapeutic period puts the person into a position where she/he can break out her/his narrowed frames of thinking/reference and belief systems so she/he can experience other patterns of functioning internally. People communicate in different verbal styles about their inner experiences or their past. It appears that people find it helpful when they come to their own conclusions about the causes of their problems and discover their own solutions.

In my experience, catalepsy and positive hallucinations are trance phenomena m.r. clients indicate reliably. Catalepsy is a state to facilitate memory (kinesthetic memory) while positive hallucinations may deliver solutions.

Those arguments considered you can imagine how trance (hypnosis) can really be therapeutically helpful. As I mentioned earlier each piece of therapy serves as a field experiment, general conclusions concerning the population of m.r. clients would be unwarranted.

But when you reflect on the summarized advantages of Ericksonian psychotherapy (of which hypnotherapy is a part):

- individual (for each client a new theory)
- therapeutic activity (personal participation, ego functions)
- flexibility and adaptability
- multilevel communication
- a learning approach rather than a focus on pathology
- creation of magic and surprising realities
- experience instead of discussion
- encouraging minimal change (not "healing")
- altered states of consciousness
- humor rather than compassion
- change and building of self-concept
- influence-oriented therapeutic behavior (not a passive one)

It sounds encouraging, respectful and ethical. It would be an unnecessary restriction to separate and give up this population. Because Ericksonian therapy is highly individual and hypnotherapy is only a part of it, nearly every m.r. client should be considered as suitable for that kind of therapy.

References

Bateson G., 1979, Mind and nature. A necessary Unity. Frankfurt.

Boscolo L. et al, 1987, Milan Systemic Family Therapy. Conversations in Theory and Practice. New York.

Dolan Y., 1985, A path with a heart. Ericksonian utilization with resistant and chronic clients. New York.

Erickson M.H. 1958, Naturalistic techniques of hypnosis. Am.J. of Clin. Hypnosis 1, 3-8

Erickson M.H., 1964, Hypnotic techniques for resistant patients. Am. J. of Clin. Hypnosis, 1, 8-32

Erickson M.H., 1965, The use of symptoms as an integral part of therapy. Am. J. of Clin. Hypnosis 8, 57-65.
Erickson M.H., 1969, Historical note on the hand levitation and other ideomotor techniques. Am. J. of Clin. Hypnosis, 196-199.
Erickson M.H., Rossi E., 1979, Hypnotherapy: An exploratory casebook. New York.
Erickson M.H., Rossi E., 1981, Experiencing hypnosis: Therapeutic approaches to altered states. New York.
Erickson M.H., Rossi E., 1981, Hypnotic realities. New York Rossi S.
Gilligan St. G., 1987, Therapeutic trances New York.
Haley J., 1973, Uncommon therapy. The psychiatric techniques of M.H. Erickson. New York.
Hohn E., 1989, Hypnotherapeutic Principles in Psychotherapy of Mentaly Retarded Human Beings. Held on: 1st European Congress of Ericksonian Hypnosis and Psychotherapy, Heidelberg Sept. 20-24.
Hohn E. 1989, Zu dumm, um verrückt sein zu dürfen. In: Rotthaus W. (Hrsg): Psychotisches Verhalten Jugendlicher. Dortmund.
Keeney B.P., 1983, Aesthetics of Change. New York.
Lankton St. & Zeig J. Ericksonian monographs Vol I 1985, Vol II 1987, Vol. III 1988, Vol. IV 1988 and Vol. V 1989.
Miyata K., 1988, The Application of Ericksonian Approaches to Austistic Children. In: Lankton St, Zeig J. (Eds.): Treatment of special Populations with Ericksonian Approaches, Ericksonian Monographs Vol. III, New York.
Rossi, E.L. (Ed.), 1980, The collected papers of M.H. Erickson on hypnosis, Vol. I, II, III and IV, New York.
Sorrentino A.M., 1987, Handicap e reabilitazione. Una bussola sistemica nell'universo realizionale del bambino handicappato. Roma.
Stark J.A., 1988, Mental Retardation and Mental Health. Menolascino F.J. New York Abarelli M.H.
Zeig J., Lankton St., 1988, Developing Ericksonian Therapy, New York.

Došen, A., Van Gennep, A., Zwanikken, G.J. (Eds.) (1990). Treatment of Mental Illness and Behavioral Disorder in the Mentally Retarded. Proceedings of the International Congress, May 3rd & 4th, 1990, Amsterdam, the Netherlands. Leiden, the Netherlands: Logon Publications.

Chapter 17

Diagnosing and treating psychopathology in clients with a dual diagnosis: An integrative model

A. Pfadt

Nature of the problem

The mental health needs of mentally retarded clients who display severe forms of psychopathology are being increasingly recognized by clinicians and other service providers. This is evidenced by the international appeal of a conference on the Treatment of Mental Illness and Behavior Disorder in the Mentally Retarded, as well as in the burgeoning literature on such topics as diagnosing and treating psychiatric disorders in these challenging clients with a dual-diagnosis (e.g.; Menolascino & Stark, 1986).. However, there is still considerable disagreement among clinical practitioners and theoreticians about how to conceptualize and remediate the full range of psychopathology exhibited by these individuals. Even our terminology (use of different labels such as "psychopathology", "mental illness", or "behavioral disorder" by different investigators) reflects different judgments about the probable etiology and preferred modes of treating these conditions.

"Self-destructive" behavior as an examplar

To illustrate these differences, consider a phenomenon such as "self-destructive" behavior. As I have discussed previously (see Pfadt, 1988; 1989,a; 1989,b), the "facts" regarding this challenging condition very much depend on the theoretical perspective one adopts in trying to understand it. From a psychodynamic perspective, self-destructive behavior can be seen as a type of "psychopathology", reflecting intrapsychic conflicts and the failure of ego defense mechanisms to adequately protect the individual against overwhelming aggressive impulses. It may even be considered to be symptomatic of more severe psychiatric disturbance, since it is frequently observed in individuals with borderline personality disorders (Hurley & Sovner, 1988). For example,

Favazza (1988) estimated that 212 cases of self-mutilation may be expected per 100,000 individuals in the general population based on its association with a diagnosis of borderline personality disorder. However; from a radical behaviorist perspective, self-destructive behavior is conceptualized in terms of those publicly observable features that characterize its frequency, intensity, duration, etc. The clinician seeks to understand the relationship between antecedent circumstances and/or potentially reinforcing consequences that may trigger an outburst or account for its resistance to extinction by factors that would normally prevent is occurrence (e.g. pain or social disapproval). As such, it is identified as a "behavioral disorder" and is accounted for by the same processes (for instance; operant, and respondent, conditioning mechanisms described by Romanczyk, in press) that control the expression of any other response typography. The magnitude of the disagreements between these different "pre-paradigmatic" (see Kuhn, 1970) viewpoints can be appreciated by comparing the *focus* of each perspective, the *temporal orientation* each typically takes, the *treatment* procedures that follow from these theoretical assumptions, and the rules of evidence that are used to *evaluate* treatment outcomes. (See Table 1; in Pfadt, 1989,b).

It is pointless to attempt a resolution of these differences by an appeal to more "data", since what one sees is so deeply influenced by the underlying metaphysical assumptions that it is not even possible to agree on a common language to describe the phenomena in question. For example, when viewed from a psychodynamic perspective self-destructive behavior is often referred to as "self-mutilation" to emphasize that the target of the behavior is not the "physical" body but the "self." However, there is considerable disagreement among dynamically oriented clinicians about how to conceptualize this entity (see Greenberg & Mitchell, 1983), such as whether the self should be described in dynamic or static terms. In contrast, behaviorally-oriented clinicians typically use the term "self-injurious" behavior to emphasize that it is the publicly observable domain which is the area of interest (e.g., how much damage is caused and how is this damage inflicted). Here again, there are wide spread disagreements about how to slice up the behavioral stream (as seen in the contributions to the volume edited by Thompson & Zeiler, 1986), and interestingly an important topic is whether to adopt a dynamic or static model of the units of behavior (see Jacobs, et al. 1988). Admittedly, there are some hopeful signs that behaviorists and psychodynamically-oriented clinicians are beginning to listen to each other in a more respectful manner that at least makes some level of dialogue possible (see contributors to the volume edited by Arkowitz & Meser, 1984, for example). For the most part, however, clinicians in our field still act very much like the proverbial blind-men trying to comprehend an unfamiliar object like an elephant. Each is in contact with a limited part of the "big picture" and no integrative theory has yet emerged which would allow their descriptions of a "leg", "tail", "trunk" etc. to be fitted together correctly so that a recognizable figure could be constructed from their different descriptions.

Figure 1
A formal analytic model to be used as a conceptual grid for mapping psychological phenomena

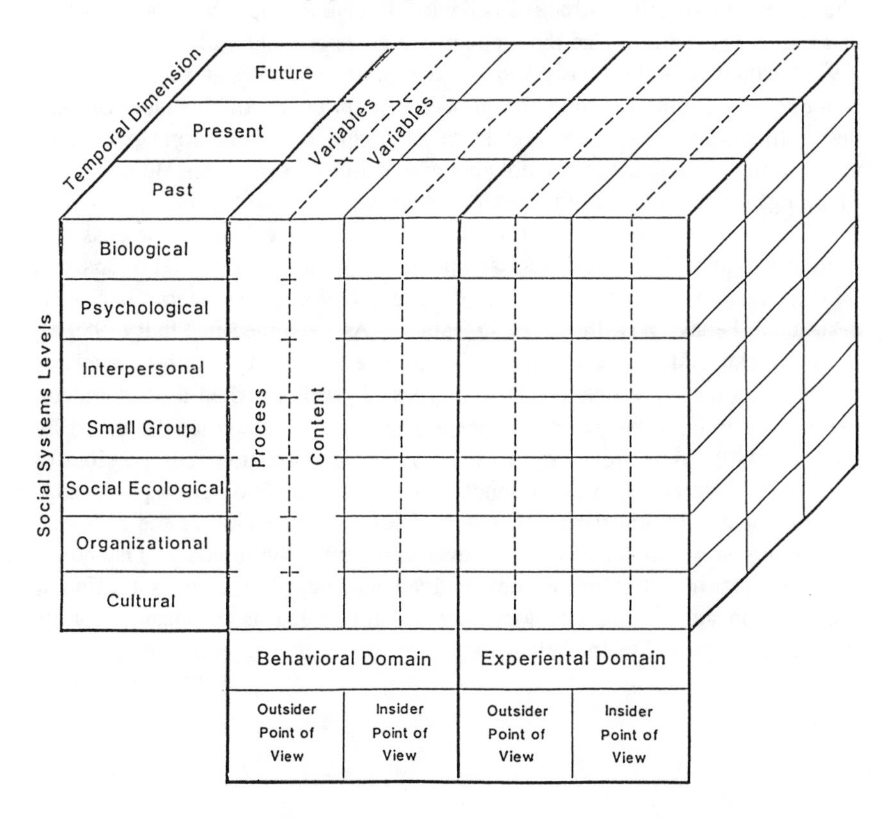

A proposed solution:A formal analytic model of psychopathology

Instead of attempting to resolve these disputes at a theoretical level of analysis, I have been attempting (see Pfadt, 1988; 1989,a; 1989,b; in press) to construct a formal analytic model of the nature of psychological phenomena which achieves an integrative perspective by spelling out the logical form that data can take. This model is represented in Figure 1 and can be thought of as a "conceptual grid" which serves as a map for exploring a phenomenon of interest. The parameters of this model represent psychological dimensions. Its three-dimensional structure contains 168 cells of potentially relevant information for describing the "life space" (Lewin, 1951) of an individual, a diagnostic category (e.g., Tourettes syndrome; see Pfadt, 1988), or a type of problem (e.g., self-destructive behavior) which is not restricted to a specific theoretical point of view. In fact, the power and potential contributions of the model come from the way in which it enables its user to transcend the limitations inherent in any particular viewpoint, especially one that attempts to tell us everything we need to know about a complex biopsychosocial phenomenon like self-destructive behavior. Recent articles by Favazza (1989) and Figueroa (1988) extend the range of variables originally discussed by Carr (1977) which must be considered in attempting to understand and treat this challenging condition. Using this model to explore all of the facts of self-destructive behavior can be thought of as "mapping a behavioral phenome" much in the same spirit as the collaborative effort known as the Human Gene Mapping project (Wahlstrom, 1990) is attempting to map the human genome.

The *social systems dimension* of the model (related to the process and content variables that are relevant at a particular social system level of analysis or organization) which can be used to explore a phenomenon like self-destructive behavior is illustrated in Table 1. As explained in Pfadt (1989,a), from a social systems perspective it is possible to identify different levels of organization that give rise to different types of "reality" when a phenomenon like self-destructive behavior is conceptualized using categories described by Taplin (1980). Moreover, within each level of organization it is possible to analyze the different types of influences contributed from biological, psychological, and socio-cultural variables which affect the expression of the problem. Depending on which social systems level of organization or analysis is chosen by a particular investigator, self-destructive behavior will be seen as a different phenomenon and different factors may be highlighted as responsible for its etiology or regarded as important for its treatment.

Table 1
Self-destructive Behavior Considered at Different Social Systems Levels of Organization and Analysis

	Level of Organization (Content)	Level of Analysis (Process)
Biological level	Motor discharge leading to tissue damage	Neurotransmitters Genetic mechanisms (as in Leach-Nyhan syndrome
Psychological level	Frequency or intensity of coordinated movement; Emotional experiences (pain, frustration)	Operant, respondent, or adjunctive conditioning paradigms; Id, ego, and super-ego, as mechanisms for producing intra-psychic conflict
Interpersonal level	Mutually co-ercive exchanges between agent and significant others; Intentional communications	Negative reinforcement trap; Internationalization of 'as-if' expectations
Social Ecological level	Relationship to self-restraint in a residential setting; Enmeshment within a family	Counter-habilitative contingencies operating at the group level; Escalating complementarity or symmetry (see Imber-Black, 1987)
Socio-cultural level	Classification of incidents according to official dogma ('Acting out,' 'self-injury,' 'self-mutilation,' 'stereotypy')	The politics of ideology and regulation

The behavioral/experiential domain of the model reflects the four logical possibilities of exploring either the behavioral (those publicly observable manifestations) or the *experiential* (the underlying thoughts, feelings, beliefs, attitudes, etc.) aspects of a problem from two different perspectives – the *point of view of an outside observer* or from the *internal frame of reference of the actor*. As discussed in Pfadt (1989,b; in press) these perspectives have traditionally been associated with the *radical behaviorist* viewpoint of BF Skinner, the *cognitive-behavioral* orientation of Albert Ellis, the *psychodynamic* formulations of Sigmund Freud, and the *client-centered, phenomenological* approach developed by Carl Rogers. This model acknowledges that these viewpoints may be incompatible in terms of their theoretical assumptions (and even helps to understand *why* they have been so resistant to attempts at unification). It facilitates an integrative perspective by allowing the user to creatively borrow from each tradition in order to understand a particular facet of the problem he/she may be attempting to solve. Elsewhere (Pfadt, 1989,a) I have shown how the model can accommodate both the radical behaviorist and phenomenological orientations to self-destructive behavior, so that the beneficial elements of both can be combined into a comprehensive approach to treatment.

The *temporal dimension* chosen by the investigator is also a critical factor in determining which variables are important to consider, since those historical factors responsible for the acquisition of a problem may not currently control its rate of expression. This issue is discussed in detail by Cohen et al (under review) which reviewed the distinctions between etiological and categorical diagnoses. Many controversies could be resolved (or at least better understood) if advocates for differing viewpoints were more clear about which temporal domain was being explained by the theory. For example, interpersonal factors [such as the emotional coldness of the so-called "refrigerator mother" (Bettelheim, 1967)] are no longer tenable as explanations for the etiology of autistic disorder (Rutter, 1988), but may be relevant in understanding the current expression of symptoms (although the mother may have been affected by the child as much as the other way around).

It is beyond the scope of this limited introductory statement to spell out the implications of this model for treatment planning. However, it should be readily apparent that use of such an integrative perspective is compatible with a comprehensive, multi-disciplinary approach that encourages each professional on the team to be respectful of the contributions that others could make as he/she attempts to contribute to an increased understanding of the challenging conditions displayed by individuals whom we characterize as dually-diagnosed. Information provided by neurological, psychiatric, and psychological evaluations could be mapped onto the parameters of the model using the "behavioral rounds" format described by Fahs (1988) so that a particular client's maladaptive dysfunctioning could be more fully appreciated. Hopefully we are approaching an era when simplistic solutions (use of *either* behavioral *or* psychopharmacological interventions) will no longer be advocated (or tolerated) for the complex problems of our clients. Like blind men exploring an elephant, each of us will gain a greater understanding of the whole by listening to the experiences of our colleagues who may be exploring a part with which we are not familiar.

References

Arkowitz, H., & Meser, S. (1984). *Psychoanalytic therapy and behavior therapy: Is integration possible.* NY: Plenum Press

Bettelheim, B. (1967). *The empty fortress.* NY: Free Press.

Carr, E. (1977). The motivation of self-injurious behavior: A review of some hypotheses. *Psychological Bulletin*, 84, 800-816.

Cohen, I., Sudhalter, V., Pfadt, A., Jenkins, E., Brown, W. & Vietze, P. (under review). Why are autism and the fragile X syndrome associated? Conceptual and methodological issues. *American Journal of Medical Genetics.*

Fahs, J. (1988) Multidisciplinary psychiatric consultation in mental retardation. *The NADD Newsletter*, 5 (2), 1-4.

Favazza, A. (1988). The plight of chronic self-mutilators. *Community Mental Health Journal*, 24, 22-30.

Figueroa, M. (1988). A dynamic taxonomy of self-destructive behavior. *Psychotherapy*, 25, 285-287.

Greenberg, J. & Mitchell, S. (1983). *Object relations in psychoanalytic theory.* Cambridge, MA: Harvard University Press.

Hurley, A., & Sovner, R. (1988). The clinical characteristics and management of borderline personality disorder in mentally retarded persons. *Psychiatric Aspects of Mental Retardation Reviews*, 7, 42-49.

Imber-Black, E. (1987). The mentally handicapped in context. *Family Systems Medicine* 5, 428-445.

Jacobs, W., Blackburn, J., Buttrick, M., Harpur, T., Kennedy, D., Mana, M., MacDonald, M., McPherson, L., Paul, D., & Pfaus, J. (1988). Observations. *Psychobiology*, 16, 3-19.

Kuhn, T. (1970). *The structure of scientific revolutions* (2nd Ed.) Chicago: University of Chicago Press.

Lewin, K. (1951). *Field theory in social science.* NY: Harper & Brothers.

Menolascino, F. & Stark, J. (1986). *Handbook of mental illness in the mentally retarded.* NY: Plenum

Pfadt, A. (1988, August). *Models of psychopathology* Paper presented at the 96th Annual Convention of the American Psychological Association, Atlanta, Georgia.

Pfadt, A. (1989,a). Evolving guidelines for the change agent: A systematic approach. In D. Schumann (Ed.) *Proceedings of the society for consumer psychology* (pp. 51-61). Washington, DC: American Psychological

Association.

Pfadt, A. (1989,b, August). *A formal analytic model of psychological phenomena: Its relevance to diagnosing and treating psychopathology in developmentally disabled persons.* Paper presented at the 97th Annual Convention of the American Psychological Association, New Orleans, Louisanna.

Pfadt, A. (in press) Group psychotherapy with mentally retarded adults: Issues related to design, implementation, and evaluation. *Research in Developmental Disabilities.*

Romanczyk, R. (in press). Aversive conditioning as a component of comprehensive treatment: The impact of etiological factors on clinical decision making. In S. Harris & J. Handleman (Eds.), *Life Threatening behavior: Aversive vs. non-aversive interventions.*

Rutter, M. (1988). Biological basis of autism. In F.Menolascino & J. Stark (Eds.). *Preventive and curative intervention in mental retardation* (p. 265-294). Baltimore: Paul H. Brookes.

Taplin, J. (1980). Implications of general systems theory for assessment and intervention. *Professional Psychology, 11*, 722-727.

Thompson, T., & Zeiler, M. (1986). *Analysis and integration of behavioral units.* Hillsdale, NJ: Erlbaum.

Wahlstrom, J. (1990). Gene map of mental retardation. *Journal of Mental Deficiency Research*, 34, 11-27.

Došen, A., Van Gennep, A., Zwanikken, G.J. (Eds.) (1990). Treatment of Mental Illness and Behavioral Disorder in the Mentally Retarded. Proceedings of the International Congress, May 3rd & 4th, 1990, Amsterdam, the Netherlands. Leiden, the Netherlands: Logon Publications.

Chapter 18

Systemic Family Therapy and Mental Retardation

K. Hennicke
C. Bradl

Introduction

In dealing with persons with mental retardation, German psychiatry is determined by a medical model assuming that an incurable defect or disease is defining all cognitive, affective and behavioral phenomena and consequently the whole personality system. These cognitive, affective and behavioral phenomena or symptoms are explained as the nature of mental retardation. This fundamental error determines theory and practice of psychiatry even today and is in principle continued by present psychology and special education; the critical consequence today is that we are missing an elaboration of modern psychopathology and appropriate treatment methods. The person with mental retardation is first an object of individual strategies focusing on the retardation, either in the way of psychiatric-medical treatment (e.g. psychopharmacology) or in the way of special therapies (e.g. holding).

During the last years a systemic approach was developed (introduced), understanding mental retardation as a handicap in the context of society and family, especially as social desintegration and separation, as "loss of cultural heritage" (Jantzen 1987). This is the most important finding, which was formulated as early as 1924 by Wygotsky (1975) with regard to blindness, long before introducing the systemic approach in psychotherapy and psychiatry.

In therapy and pedagogics the retarded person is now seen as a subject with his own history, being part of the surrounding social system by engaging actively in interaction and communication with other people; thereby the whole social system, the whole context will become the object of developmental training.

The two approaches are not mutually exclusive, but they are in an hierarchic relation. Selvini-Palazzoli says: "The quality of transactions in which the retarded child is involved (and in which it is interacting) determines its developmental work and the efficacy of rehabilitation work. The most ingenious pedagogic or rehabilitative program must fail when it is involved in a system of dysfunctional transactions" (in: Sorrentino 1988,14).

Theoretical concepts

With the introduction of the systemic paradigma in social psychiatry, new qualitative possibilities are emerging which are more adequate to both the problem and the actual therapeutic work with mentally retarded persons and their families.

We will verify this assumption referring to theoretical concepts (family stress concept and social network concept) and to our clinical experience based on systemic therapy.

Family as a social system

Defining the family as a social system comprehends its structure and functioning as a whole, which is a result of interaction, communication and affective relations between the members and subsystems following specific shared rules and patterns. Boundaries clearly define who is in and who is out of subsystem and family, as well as their functioning in a larger environment, e.g. the external context composed of the total of historic socio-economic and political conditions. The external context at least defines the meaning of the family.

Family stress theory

Family stress theory focuses on three variables:
stressor or the provoking event (A-factor), the meaning attached to the event by the family – individually and collectively (C-factor), family's resources (B-factor) and the degree of stress or crisis (X-factor); Reuben Hill's ABCX-model describes the basic theoretical categories of the process of family stress.

McCubbin et al (1983) have elaborated a cyclic process model of "Family Adjustment and Adaptation Response" to family crisis (FAAR-processes). The phase of family adjustment to stressful event is charaterized as resistance against substantial changes in life style and family structure. Avoidance, elimination and assimilation of the stressful demands are the most important coping strategies. Over time perhaps this reaction is no more adequate to meet the needs of the family members or the family as a whole. A family crisis emerges.

The following phase of family adaptation is called "Restructuring". Viable changes in family structures as a result of a process of shared definitions and of agreement on solutions and structural implementations are necessary to manage the demands and to maintain the family system. The family has successfully initiated a second order change, which now must be consolidated. The family unit is called upon to make additional changes in the family organisation and structure to support and complement the newly instituted patterns of behaviour.

It is very important that FAAR-processes can get stuck at one phase and may need to return to an earlier phase and work it through again. I mean that these processes really never end. McCubbin et al point to many factors which are very useful for family therapy.

Social network approach

The social network approach describes the function of social networks as a part of an external context in which individuals or families are involved. Coping with and managing acute and chronic strains on families depends especially on the availability of social support given by members of family or kinship, by informal networks (e.g. friends, neighborhood, mutual-help-groups) or normative or special institutions or help systems.

A general hypothesis

The outlined approaches outlined above can be summarized in a general hypothesis about families with mentally retarded members:

There are no differences between families with a mentally retarded member and other families; they show the same normative transitions and developmental needs in lifecycle. Nevertheless there are some additional conditions:

- basic organic structures and the nature of handicap
- prolonged and often lifelong dependence of the retarded member on the parents
- ambiguity of diagnoses and other assessments
- social segregation and stigmatization of the families
- confrontation with specific emotions such as shame, guilt, grief and – very important – their defence or denial
- lack of adequate social support systems.

Consequently, normative life events and transitions, in addition to the outlined severe chronic strains, compel the families to go through lifelong processes of adjustment and adaptation, far beyond what families without mentally retarded members have to manage. Without mobilization of additional psychical, physical, social and material resources, the family is unable to cope with these strains. In consequence, increased vulnerability (Herlth 1988) is not a natural consequence of birth of a handicapped child, but the result of multiple social strains, social labeling processes, discriminations and lack of services. Therefore increased vulnerability does not means weakness, insufficiency or pathology, but a continuous excessive demand on the family's capacity of functioning in a very high action level. In the same way, the often cited increased vulnerability of a person with mental retardation is not a natural result of an organic damage. Social strains and segregation, absence of the opportunity for aequivalent interaction and communication, demand a very high and perhaps impossible effort of adjustment and adaptation.

Clinical and therapeutical problems

Now I want to tell you about clinical and therapeutic problems in families with a mentally retarded member.

First of all these families mostly present expansive behavioral disorders of the retarded member: aggression, disruptive behavior, refusal, inappropriate sexual behavior and other disorders in all forms and intensities and in most different contexts. Very often, members of the family are suffering from physical and psychological symptoms of exhaustion.

In a structural view, the most important problems of these families are characterized as boundary-based problems:

1) The central position of the mentally retarded member: all interactive and communicative activities of family are focused upon him.

2) Symbiosis: when a retarded child is born, a symbiotic relationship may appear to be a useful response of the family system by coping with resulting demands and restoring family homeostasis. But it may be impossible that this structure remains long-term family functioning. In family development the necessary changes have to be made and managed; without these changes the family cannot meet its basic functions (i.e. autonomy, security, care, aid). The family consensus existing before is now soon falling. In a preventive perspective we have to identify early indications of changes in family members, which have to be taken up in family therapy and counseling. Symbiotic structures tend to divide the family in two parts with non-permeable boundary.

3) Triangulation: the parental and marriage system in families with a mentally retarded member are confronted with many demands with regard to parental roles (e.g. responsibility, care) as well as with regard to boundaries around the marriage system. Problems in this area arise easily and there seem to be no solution for them. Then triangulations take place frequently, i.e. a conflict is switched to another family member, in this case the retarded person taking the role of a scapegoat and/or becoming an object of overprotection being triangulated by both parents. Conflicts between parents appear to be quasi-real differences of opinions (e.g. about methods of education, necessarity of care, intensity of retardation, perspective for future life); they may dispute these matters excellently and without end with professionals, apparently in parental harmony and care. But a solution is not possible, especially if the professional therapist, social worker etc. is also involved in the family conflict without being

aware of it. In this case supervision-based conferences of all helpers could be successful efforts to clarify responsibilities.

4) Growing up and leaving home: the transition of puberty and leaving home of retarded juveniles frequently trigger off family crises. Strategies and coping patterns being successfully managed over many years suddenly become dysfunctional; repression or denial cannot fade out reality any more; behavioral disorders in the retarded person or exhaustion syndroms in other family members are piling up. This family development freqently results in acute institutionalization. This means a radical structural change, but in reality does not solve the basic family system problems and do not manage the trauma of sudden separation.

Important aspects of the systemic approach

We have summarized the most important aspects of the systemic approach as follows:

1) From symptom to social context: not only the defect or the symptom is significant, but the total of conditions in a manageable context in which the defect or the symptom arises, i.e. the social system (e.g. family) and her subsystems with its rules, transactions and communications. The complexity of conditions is not a simple cumulation of factors ("multi-factorial"), but its characteristic interdependency. A critical situation at the beginning of a therapy is this redefinition of the conditions for treatment.

2) From causal to circular thinking: instead of assuming simple causal relations there are complex circular relations; in the context of family systems the retardation or singular symptoms are causes and effects of certain behavioral phenomena at the same time.

3) Cooperation of available resources and help systems instead of continued specialization: increased specialization of programs and therapies for persons with mental retardation produce more segregation; we should aim rather at the utilization of available family resources and at the cooperation between normative systems (e.g. family) and professional help systems by having the same rights. This is a most important therapeutic act and contains – together with the clarification of responsibility of helpers, therapists and parents – the essence of the family therapy support system. There is no place for therapeutic omnipotence or professional dominance, but there must be an hierarchical relation betweem the systemic approach and other therapeutic or training activities or institutions.

Therapeutic practices

Consequently therapeutic practices can be outlined as follows:

1. Working with the family on the meaning of retardation/disease: dissolve the conceptions of the – mostly rigid – family model of retardation which frequently is an important condition constituting dysfunctional family structures, e.g. working towards more clarity on a very concrete level of communication with calmness in regard to dramatic symptoms and situations.

2. Working with the retarded member: introduction of the retarded member as an active subject operating with individual resources and responsibilities, managing his intra- and extra-family conditions or necessary developmental tasks by himself and in his own way.

3. Working with the parents-to-child-systems: clarify the responsibility being taken for the retarded member by both parents together, or allow more responsibility or more autonomy efforts from one parental person.

4. Working with the marriage system: develop or reinforce responsibility of married couples for themselves and for each other; support of the marriage system by esteeming identity of each spouse.

5. Managing the problems: make very concrete and realistic steps towards coping with present problems; mobilize internal and/or external resources; clarify responsibility and functioning of the various help systems intending a useful support for all family members; clarify short- or long-term plans for tfhe future of the retarded member (e.g. remaining at home, admission to an institution, transitional placement).

All five dimensions have to be taken in consideration at the same time, the focus changing in each case and the affective intensity related to present problems, family situation and therapy process. It must be done in a more optimistic atmosphere of coping after producing a very good, stable joining of all members of the family.

Conclusion

By introducing the systemic approach into treatment of people with mental retardation and behavioral disorders based on the family stress concept and the social network concept, we have pointed out strategies which exceed the medical model and offer new, more adequate approaches in diagnosis and especially in therapy. Mental retardation is seen as a possible human existence becoming a real retardation or handicap only in the context of family and society, i.e. by social desintegration and separation. The person with mental retardation is respected as a subject with his own history, jointly constituting his social context. Treatment, training and education are no longer related to symptoms or defects, but to the whole context which gives meaning to each situation and which defines the problems.

At present we are carrying out a larger empirical research project based on the theoretical concepts outlined above, on the findings about families with a mentally retarded member and on the extensive clinical experience in our psychiatric institution. Thereby we hope to make a modest contribution to "changing of paradigm".

References

Badura, B. (Hg.), 1981, Soziale Unterstützung und chronische Krankheit. Zum Stand sozialepidemiologischer Forschung. Suhrkamp, Frankfurt.

Balzer, B., Rolli, S., 1975, Sozialtherapie mit Eltern Behinderter. Beltz, Weinheim, Basel.

Bölling-Bechinger, H., 1988, Die Bedeutung des Trauerns für die Annahme der Behinderung eines Kindes. Praxis Kinderpsychologie Kinderpsychiatrie 37 175-179.

Boss, P., 1988, Family Stress Management. Sage-Publ., Newbury Park, London.

Bradl, Ch., 1987, Das Bild Geistigbehinderter in der Geschichte der Psychiatrie. In: Dreher, W. et al. (Hrsg.) a.a.O. S.125-153.

Bradl, Ch., Hennicke, K., Familien mit einem geistig behinderten Mitglied. Ein systemisch-sozialwissenschaftlicher Ansatz. Viersen 1990 (zur Veröffentlichung vorbereitet).

Brüderl, L. (Hg.), 1988, Theorien und Methoden der Bewältigungsforschung. Juventa, Weinheim, München.

Cierpka, M. (Hg.), 1988, Familiendiagnostik. Springer, Berlin usw.

Dornette, W., 1984a, Familien mit behinderten Kindern in der Familientherapie. In: Remschmidt, H. (Hg.): Psychotherapie mit Kindern, Jugendlichen und Familien. Bd.1, Stuttgart, 61-66.

Dreher, W. et. al. (Hg.), 1987, Geistigbehinderte zwischen Pädagogik und Psychiatrie. Psychiatrie-Verlag, Bonn.

Ferber, Ch.v., 1983, Soziale Netzwerke – ein neuer Name für eine alte Sache? Geistige Behinderung 22, 250-258.

Feuser, G., 1987, Zum Verhältnis von Geistigbehindertenpädagogik und Psychiatrie. In: Dreher et. al. a.a.O., 75-92.

Görres, S., 1983, Leben mit einem behinderten Kind. Piper, München lte Sache? Geistige Behinderung 22, 250-258.

Feuser, G., 1987, Zum Verhältnis von Geistigbehindertenpädagogik und Psychiatrie. In: Dreher et. al. a.a.O., 75-92.

Görres, S., 1987, Leben mit einem behinderten Kind. Piper, München.

Guski, E., 1989, Systemsicht und Familienorientierung am Beispiel der Frühförderung. Geistige Behinderung 28, 78-87.

Hennicke, K., 1987, Ist "die Psychiatrie" an allem schuld? Überlegungen zu einer alternativen Praxis in der Kinder- und Jugendpsychiatrie. In: Dreher et al. a.a.O., 154-165.

Hennicke, K., Bley, S., Beratung von Familien mit geistig behinderten Kindern – eine Aufgabe der Kinder- und Jugendpsychiatrie. Rhein. Ärzteblatt vom 10.10.1989, 762-764.

Herlth, A., 1988, Was macht Familien verletzlich? Bedingungen der Problemverarbeitung in familialen Systemen. In: Lüscher, K. et al. (Hg.): Die "postmoderne" Familie. Universitätsverlag, Konstanz, 312-326.

Jantzen, W., 1987, Allgemeine Behindertenpädagogik. Band 1: Sozialwissenschaftliche und psychologische Grundlagen. Beltz, Weinheim, Basel.

Jeltsch-Schudel, B., 1988, Bewältigungsformen von Familien mit geistig behinderten Söhnen und Töchtern. Marhold, Berlin.

Kluge, K.-J., 1982, Behinderte Kindern "erzeugen" behinderte Eltern? Elternstress und therapeutische Konsequenzen. Sozialpädiatrie 4, 97-99.

McCubbin, H.I. et al. (Eds.), 1983, Social Stress and the Family: Advances and Developments in Family Stress Theory and Research. Haworth Press, New York.

McCubbin, H.I., Figley, Ch.R. (Eds.) 1983, Stress and the Family. Vol.I/Vol.II. Brunner & Mazel, New York.

Minouchin, S., 1984, Familie und Familientherapie. Theorie und Praxis struktureller Familientherapie. Lambertus, Freiburg 6.

Schiller, B., 1987, Soziale Netzwerke und behinderte Menschen. Lang, Frankfurt/M.

Schlippe, A. von, 1986, Familientherapie im Überblick. Basiskonzepte, Formen, Anwendungsmöglichkeiten. Junfermann, Paderborn 5.

Schubert, M. Th., 1987, System Familie und Geistige Behinderung. Springer, Wien, New York.

Sorrentino, A.M., 1988, Behinderung und Rehabilitation. Ein systemischer Ansatz. Modernes Lernen, Dortmund.

Theunissen, G., 1989, Wege aus der Hospitalisierung. Asthetische Erziehung mit schwerstbehinderten Erwachsenen. Psychiatrie-Verlag, Bonn.

Wygotsky, L.S., 1975, Zur Psychologie und Pädagogik der kindlichen Defektivität. Die Sonderschule 20 H.2, S.65-72.

Došen, A., Van Gennep, A., Zwanikken, G.J. (Eds.) (1990). Treatment of Mental Illness and Behavioral Disorder in the Mentally Retarded. Proceedings of the International Congress, May 3rd & 4th, 1990, Amsterdam, the Netherlands. Leiden, the Netherlands: Logon Publications.

Chapter 19

Treatment of severe behaviour disorder in the mentally retarded from a systems approach

J. Griffioen
S. de Graaff
J.F. Gehrels

Introduction

This contribution gives an account of 'intensive team counseling' (further referred to as I.T.).

This special form of team counseling is directed at teams of residential care-staff members who are dealing with counseling and treatment of behaviourally disordered and/or mentally retarded persons (further referred to as 'residents').

The **type of problems** the residential care-staff has reported during the last few years varies, dependent on the level of the resident, from smearing, pica, aggression and automutilation to psychoses and depressions.

Features of Intensive Team Counseling

Counselling may take the form of **temporary assistance**. This form of help is given in two ways:

a. through 'informal' contacts between I.T. co-worker and residential staff when this co-worker happens to be in the ward to participate in the observation of different daily activities;

b. through regular discussions with the team at set times on the agenda, once a fortnight to once in a period of six weeks. The frequency is dependent on the seriousness of the situation and the phase of the counseling process.

It is a matter of **temporary help**. The I.T. co-worker counsels the team as long as necessary. As soon as the problems of the team have been solved, in other words when the team-members have reached a deeper understanding, or the problematic behaviour of the resident has become less or has become manageable to the care-staff, then I.T. can be stopped.

The number of sessions may vary from four to fifty. Generally speaking fifteen sessions seem to suffice over a period of one and a half to two years. In a few exceptional cases, follow-up sessions are held for another two or three years by way of prevention after the regular I.T. counseling has been stopped. These sessions take place once every three or six months.

An important feature of I.T. is its **two-sided approach**. Not only are the problems of the resident treated (by developing an accurate idea about his/her behaviour and its translation into interaction laid down in a plan of action), but also a lot of attention is paid to the attitudes and views of the care-staff. For example, they learn to accept that the resident is a person with a strongly marked character demanding a way of handling which is rather different from 'the care of naive, mental defectives'.

This approach must be continued to promote and support the stability of the resident. It is possible that this way of dealing with residents requires specific knowledge and skill wich must be maintained.

Underlying principles

In the institute where the form of counseling described here has been developed, we are of the **opinion** that the mentally retarded person should be able to find full expression of his potential. That's why counseling is always in every aspect 'as normal as possible, as different as necessary'. In concrete terms of care-policy, this means among other things that in the living accommodation a good living-climate is created which is not intentionally therapeutic. This certainly doesn't exclude that a fitting living-accomodation may have therapeutic effects on a resident (cf. 'Eerste graadsstrategie' by Kok, 1985, van Leeuwen 1988). For this reason behaviourally disordered persons usually don't live in one group together, but integrated in ordinary wards.

With regard to the choice of methods of treatment, aversive therapy is emphatically rejected. This methodology clashes with the ethical principles as laid down in the philosophy of care-statement.

The principle of I.T. is one of system-theory, which means that the **interaction of the resident with his surroundings** (care-staff, daily programme, living conditions) is central. This does not at all exclude examinations of intra-psychical and biological functioning. Physical and psychical/cognitive data – and these are often limitations – have to be accepted and considered as established facts. Sometimes they must be emphasized to understand interactions better.

The interaction on the level of the group (residents among each other, care-staff among each other and care-staff and residents together) is also included in the assessment of the problems involved. Sometimes problems which were considered as the individual problems of a resident can be solved by measures on this level.

As the care-staff determine the care, interaction and daily life of the residents, the advice given should fit in with their knowledge, experience and working conditions. **Concrete pedagogical advice** how to deal with residents is a second principle of I.T.

The two principles together lead to a theory of an orthopedagogical oriented practice. In the definition and the approach of the problems involved, this is clearly expressed. No mention is made of behaviourally disordered persons or of problematic behaviour, but of a **problematic situation in interaction and education. (P.O.S**: Van Acker, 1989: van Leeuwen, 1989; Rispens, 1989, 1990; de Ruyter, 1989; Steutel, 1989, ter Horst, 1980) or of interaction with difficult people with the purpose to restore and to be beneficial to ordinary life (ter Horst, 1977).

Procedure

The procedure of I.T. was set up in accordance with the regulative cycle of Van Strien (Van Strien, 1989; Stevens, 1982): definition of the problem; collection of data and development of an accurate idea; diagnosis: imperative; planning: advice with regard to agreement on dealing with and treatment of residents; intervention: counseling of the care-staff in the implementation of advice given; evaluation and development of new ideas, adjusted advice, etc.

For the benefit of delegation, much value is attached to written reports of the information relating to the resident and the discussion with all concerned. It is well-known that written files accompany residents much longer than oral care-staff. If only for that reason, oral report is insufficient.

Stages in the I.T. approach

Intake

During a staff meeting in the ward about a particular resident it is decided to call in the help of Intensive Team Counselling. The I.T. co-worker is contacted. A short report of problems involved is given and an appointment is made for further consultation. Among other things, discussions involve the circumstances and possibilities of the team, the experience of the problem and the way in which the team has been dealing with the problems of the resident in the last few weeks or months.

The staff-advisers (pedagogue and physician) and the staff of the ward are kept well-informed by the I.T. co-worker.

Collection of information

The research activities of the co-worker start with the collection of detailed information. This is the stage in which historical and actual anamnesis are put side by side by means of the medical and psychological/pedagogical file. Reports are consulted, also those of third parties such as working-department, logo-, physio-, ergotherapy, creative activation and school. Moreover, the living conditions and the way the problematic situation has been dealt with are considered. With regard to every aspect of the resident's life, questions are asked as Ter Horst (1977) does.

So the activities in this stage are:

- getting acquainted with the team
- discussion of the problem with the team
- co-operation in the ward and association with the resident
- writing of the anamnesis (medical/psychological/pedagogical)
- study of day-reports.
- drawing up of list of questions and the processing of the information obtained.
- contracts with other staff members (e.g. physio- and ergotherapist).

Definition of the problem

On the ground of data collected it is possible to form an accurate idea of the situation. Then hypotheses are formulated and compared with available information and subsequently rejected or accepted. In this stage of analysis and synthesis the I.T.co-worker needs knowledge and skill as well as the necessary 'Fingerspitzengefühl' to be able to wind up by formulating the call for assistance, the imperative (Baartman, 1983) of the resident.

If necessary, hypotheses in connection with information found are also judged on the ground of a study of relevant literature. The therapeutic consequences of these hypotheses are also studied to find out if they can be translated into practical advice usable to the care-staff. These advices should not conflict with the realisation of a living climate for the other residents.

Although the information collected, the definition of the problem and the imperative are put down in writing to form a coherent story, they are in many cases discussed with the team at an earlier stage. This opens the possibility of checking them with the observation of the care-staff and of supplying them, as those directly concerned, with useful information and of giving them insight which may stimulate them to suggest alternatives.

To bring about that the care-staff will form an accurate idea, it is advisable to give general background information in the form of a simple article from a professional paper or from a book.

The literature chosen should also describe what this problem means for the day-to-day treatment of the resident.

Besides forming accurate ideas, the purpose of the information is that the care-staff in their concrete daily activities can comply better with what is desirable for the resident in his circumstances.

Formulation of instructions and advice

In most cases, the team already gets the first suggestions and advice during the first discussions. To begin with, this is often a matter of variations of surroundings, such as the changing of table-arrangements or bedtime, different leisure activities, adjustments of duty-roster and the like.

If on the basis of information found the way of dealing with a resident has to undergo marked changes, both the reason and the new treatment of the resident are discussed in detail with the team. Dependent on the situation, this is done with the help of a plan of action previously put down in writing, or the team can use the reports of the discussions in which the advice is recorded.

Advice can pertain to three catagories: vital aspects (health, weight, food, medication, exercise), functional aspects and social aspects.

Advice regarding vital aspects are often arrived at in cooperation with the physician. Among these are adjustments in medication.

Advice with a functional aspect have to do with duty-roster, furniture, day-programme, composition of the group and the like.

The social aspects in the advice pertain to the way of dealing with the resident in a narrow sense, e.g. the way of communicating with the resident, the handling of rules, the contacts maintained with the resident and the like.

Implementation

The implementation of advice and instructions finds an emphatic follow-up in the discussions with the team. The guide is the definition of the problem, to which the implementation is compared all the time.

The I.T. co-worker is regularly present in the ward to watch the implementation by the care-staff and if necessary to set examples. Team discussions may refer to these examples.

All discussions with the team are put down in a report by the I.T. co-worker. If necessary, day reports are adjusted or standardized to follow the developments as closely as possible.

In regular discussions between care-staff and staff advisers it is considered which aspects impede and stimulate the implementation of the plan of action: medication, the composition of group or team, the regulation of activities and similar things.

Evaluation

Finally, by means of regular discussion with the care-staff it is possible to evaluate and correct the problem definition and give further advice.

In conclusion, a final report is written and discussed.

This final report contains the plan of action developed earlier, supplemented with the results of the new treatment and the conditons to maintain this situation.

After six months, a follow-up discussion is held, in which the major points are worked through and the results are compared again.

In this stage, the approach, conditions and pitfalls are handed over to ward-staff and care-staff.

Conclusion

After about eight years of experience with this form of counseling, we can state that the ratio of success is high. Contributing to this result may be the following aspects:

- a thorough research of the documents relative to the case
- detailed observations
- good translation of theoretical advice into practical procedure
- intensive counseling of the team
- specialized knowledge and skill of the I.T. co-worker.

By the intensive approach of both team and I.T. co-worker, the first, admittedly sometimes small, results may be obtained in a relatively short time. This stimulates the motivation and strengthens the wish to bring about a change in the problematic situation, and it also stimulates everyone concerned to carry on.

References

Acker, van, J. 1989, 'Apartheidspolitiek in orthopedagogenland' in: *Tijdschrift voor Orthopedagogiek,* p. 523-526.

Baartman, H. 1983, *Psychotische Kinderen,* Lisse.

Brink, van den, C. 1977, *Tussen twee verhalen,* interne nota 's Heeren Loo-Lozenoord, Ermelo.

Horst, ter, W. 1977, *Het herstel van het gewone leven,* Groningen.

Horst, ter, W. 1980, *Algemene Orthopedagogiek,* Groningen.

Kok, J.F.W. 1985, *Specifiek Opvoeden,* Amersfoort/Leuven.

Strien, van, P.J. 1984, 'Naar de verwetenschappelijking van de praktijk', in: *Tijdschrift voor Orthopedagogiek,* p. 162-180.

Stevens, L.M. 1982, 'Diagnostiek bij Leerproblemen', in: Baarda, D.B. en Zwaan, E.J. (red.), *Alternatieven in de psychodiagnostiek,* Nijmegen.

Leeuwen, van, J.J.C. 1988, 'Het opvoedingsbegrip van J.F.W. Kok' in: *Tijdschrift voor Orthopedagogiek,* p. 378-387.

Leeuwen, van, J.J.C. 1989, 'Rispens' problematische opvoedingstheorie' in: *Tijdschrift voor Orthopedagogiek,* p. 509-513.

Rispens, J. 1989, 'Over het problematische van het begrip Problematische Opvoedings Situatie' in: *Tijdschrift voor Orthopedagogiek,* p 411-427.

Rispens, J. 1990, 'Traditie en vernieuwing. Over het object van de orthopedagogiek' in: *Tijdschrift voor Orthopedagogiek,* p. 36-51.

Ruyter, de, P.A. 1989, 'Is de terugkeer van Rispens een vooruitgang' in: *Tijdschrift voor Orthopedagogiek,* p. 514-522.

Steutel, J.W. 1989, 'Over het object van de orthopedagogiek' in: *Tijdschrift voor Orthopedagogiek,* p. 527-540.

Došen, A., Van Gennep, A., Zwanikken, G.J. (Eds.) (1990). Treatment of Mental Illness and Behavioral Disorder in the Mentally Retarded. Proceedings of the International Congress, May 3rd & 4th, 1990, Amsterdam, the Netherlands. Leiden, the Netherlands: Logon Publications.

Chapter 20

Family Based Intervention: A Model for In-Home Treatment of Individuals with Dual Diagnosis

K.R. Mirick

As the identification of the population with dual diagnosis continues, professionals in mental retardation and mental health attempt to deal with the problems posed by service delivery, diagnosis and treatment. In the 1980s the model for care shifted from the large state institution to the community allowing many mental health problems to be noticed by the general public (Reiss, in press).

In Virginia, institutions serving individuals with mental retardation are separated from hospitals treating patients with mental illness. Community based mental retardation programs may not accept individuals with challenging behaviors due to the disruption they cause, amount of supervision required and the lack of staff training available. Private psychiatrists are reluctant to diagnose mental illness in individuals with mental retardation and more often label the problem a behavioral disorder. Historically, assessment tools have been insufficient and mental health disorders have been overshadowed by the presence of mental retardation (Reiss, in press).

With separation in specialties, limited funding and inadequate diagnostic assessment, individuals with dual diagnosis or a behavioral disorder are likely to remain in the family of origin without treatment or be placed in institutions that are willing to take them. Services for children are even more limited or nonexistent. If individuals with dual diagnosis or challenging behaviors are to be maintained in the family of origin, traditional mental health practices of treatment in a clinical setting on a weekly basis may not be enough to assist the family. Watson (1974) pointed out that in-home training reduces important stimulus control problems inherent in other clinical intervention methods. Allin (1988) concluded that training of parents in the natural environment allowed them to impact on a wide range of behaviors that would threaten family unity, client independence and community resources. After a review of the literature on family involvement in intervention with children having severe handicaps,

Snell (1984) determined that successful involvement of family members may be viewed as preventative and have life long effects.

Family Based Intervention

The Family Consultant Program offers an alternative to traditional models of treatment. Comprehensive assessments in the natural environments, parent training in Positive Programming (LaVigna, Willis & Donnellan, 1989) and individualized treatment plans are provided in the home on a weekly basis and in day placements as needed.

The regional program serves Southeastern Virginia which includes 1.5 million people and 3,426 square miles (8,873 square km). Funding of the $143,000 budget is a joint effort of the State of Virginia, Community Alternatives Inc, and Virginia Beach Community Services Board. The population targeted includes those individuals with mental retardation and a behavioral disorder living in a family home. Since July 1989, 15% of the population previously labeled behavioral disorder (N = 74) is dually diagnosed to include major depression, bi-polar disorder, oppositional disorder, personality disorder, conduct disorder, and psychosis. An additional 12% of the individuals in treatment have been identified by the program as needing mental health services but not receiving them.

Six years ago (1983), when the Family Consultant Program began, the goal was to reduce admissions to the state institutions by providing the alternative of in-home treatment. Statistics reported from 1983-1986 on a service population of over 250 indicated that 86% remained in the home. Of the present random sample of 31 families completing treatment in the last year, 28 (90%) have remained in the home.

Referral

Requests for services are made through the case management systems of the eight Community Services Boards in Southeastern Virginia. Case managers link the family with a variety of community support services to assist in maintaining the individual in the home. The Family Consultant Program is seen as short term intensive treatment. Contact and coordination with the case management system also insures follow up for the family after treatment is completed. Staff limitations result in a waiting list of approximately 30 families. Priority for service selection is established by the case managers when a case opening is available. Each of the three consultants handles a caseload of 10 families so that a total of 30 can be served at one time.

Criteria for Referral

Applicants to the program must: (1) Reside with a natural or surrogate family in a home setting located in Southeastern Virginia; (2) Have a diagnosis of mental retardation; (3) Have severe abnormal behavioral patterns that may include aggression toward self, others and or the environment. There is no age restriction or discrimination. The majority of the population served each year are children.

Pre-Treatment

This phase of the program requires four to six weeks and is critical to the development of appropriate treatment goals. The consultant performs a comprehensive assessment by spending one to two hours per week in the home environment and one to two hours in the school or vocational setting per individual. Several components are included in this phase.

Rating Scales

The American Association on Mental Retardation Adaptive Behavior Scale (Nihira, Foster, Shellhaas, & LeLand, 1974) or The Vineland Adaptive Behavior Scale(Sparrow, Balla & Cicchetti, 1984) are used to determine the functioning level of the individual referred.

The Maladaptive Behavior Check List, designed for the program, is scored during an interview with the parent to assist in identifying and defining behaviors that are disruptive. The rating is based on the parent's perception of the frequency of behaviors prior to beginning actual baseline data collection. This measure is also taken at the end of treatment to determine if the parent's perception of the level of behaviors has improved. The Home Visit Observation Scale is a subjective rating, designed for the program, to measure the parent's positive parenting skills and attitudes. Consultants complete the first scoring after at least 5 hours of observation of the parent and child in the natural environment and identify those areas that are important for training. This rating scale is repeated at three and six months into treatment to determine the family's increased ability to sustain positive parenting skills and attitudes.

Observation

Determinations based on observation are made by the consultant in the following areas: functional use of the behavior in natural environments, communication deficiencies, reward menus, environmental factors or rewards that may be maintaining the behaviors, onset and changes in behavior patterns, impaired social skills, medical or mental health issues affecting the behavior patterns, the parent's expectations of the individual, the functioning of the family unit and the commitment of the family to behavioral change.

Training

The primary care providers begin training during the pre-treatment period in the general principles of positive reward, ignoring inappropriate behaviors, and Gentle Teaching (McGee, Menolascino, Hobbs, & Menousek, 1987). Whenever possible, both parents are involved in training to increase consistency in implementation, responsibility for care and positive attitudes. Parents are not expected to be behavior therapists or to learn the language of Behavior Modification only to understand how attention and reward affect behaviors. Training for each family is individualized. Several methods are available to include weekly sessions in the home, modeling, video taped feedback, video tapes of techniques, and reading materials based on the family's educational level. Each family is assigned one or two chapters a week to read and review at the next visit. Baker, Heifetz, & Murphy (1980) discussed that a combination of manuals, professional guidance and training, as the occasion arises, may have long range benefits. The Family Consultant Program offers training and treatment in the natural environment where the behaviors routinely occur.

Baseline Data

Parents are taught data collection during pre-treatment. The consultant determines, through observation and independent recording, if the baseline is correct and assists with additional training to insure accuracy. If a parent is unable to keep accurate data, consultant data is used and emphasis is placed on conducting the treatment plans.

Rapport

Consultants dress in a casual manner to help the family be more comfortable with their presence in the home. Techniques are presented in a non-threatening way and existing practices are not criticized. Rationale for change is given and examples of positive results with other families. Training sessions and methods are adjusted to the routine of the family. A level of trust is built between the family, the individual in treatment and the consultant.

Training Plan

The goals for the Individual Training Plan (ITP) are designed jointly with the family, consultant and referring case manager. Based on the results of the assessment and baseline data, goals are prioritized and criteria for success are established. A contractual agreement with the family is signed by all participating to indicate consensus.

Treatment

Procedures to address goals on the ITP are written out for each family using simple instructions in step by step format. Weekly visits are continued to provide more specific training, insure treatment procedures are correctly followed, collect parent data, monitor progress and make adjustments as needed. Reliability checks on data collection are periodically made by the consultant. Treatment methods are also discussed and taught to teachers or vocational staff if the behavior is seen in other settings to establish consistency within the family and across natural environments. All treatment plans are based on positive programming and do not include aversive procedures or punishment techniques. If behaviors are dangerous or self injurious, Gentle Teaching Techniques (McGee, 1987) are incorporated into the model and substituted for existing aversive or punishment practices. Building of appropriate behaviors through praise, teaching alternative methods of communication, addressing skill deficiency, increasing attention span, and providing appropriate and more stimulating activities are an integral part of treatment. This phase continues for three to six months per individual and concludes with the expectation that the family is trained sufficiently to handle behaviors as they occur using positive techniques.

Results

Positive changes in the attitude and practices of the parent are indicated in the Home Visit Observation Scale (HVOS). The scale includes 47 statements identifying positive and negative parenting skills. Consultants score on a 1 to 5 scale from 'not at all' to 'very much'. The Parent's score is compared to the total possible score and a percentage is computed. Those families who were successful (n = 21) showed 50% or more on the first scoring of the HVOS and 20% or more increase in positive parenting skills after treatment. These scores correspond with 50% or higher goal achievement. Six families in this group achieved over 90% scores on the HVOS and 100% goal attainment. The Maladaptive Behavior Checklist categorizes 55 behaviors into self-stimulation, aggression, sexual, social and self injurious patterns. Frequencies ranging from over 5 times a day (4 points) to 1 time a week (1 point) are rated for each behavior based on the parent's perception. Total number of points is recorded prior to treatment and at the completion of treatment. Successful families (n = 21) achieved a 50%-100% reduction in maladaptive behaviors. Those families without progress in treatment (n = 10) scored 50% or less on the first scoring of the HVOS, 20% or less increase in parenting skills, and 0% goals achieved. Evaluation of those families identified three problem areas, (1) mental health issues not acknowledged in one parent, (2) mental health issues not treated in the individual receiving service, and (3) abusive patterns of discipline that were resistive to change. When treatment was not possible in the home the consultant recommended to the case manager that the individual be offered alternative community based placement and treatment resumed. As a result of these recommendations one man moved into a community apartment, two children were institutionalized and seven children remained in the home without treatment.

Follow-Up

Follow-up after completion of treatment is provided upon request of a parent or referring case manager. Most concerns can be addressed by phone, but if the behavior is serious a home visit is conducted to determine if readmission to the program is necessary. Determination of the long term effects of training for the successful families in the sample (n = 21), who could be contacted (n = 12), included a telephone survey by the consultant. For this group the average number of months since completing treatment was seven. Only one family reported that the child had been admitted for a psychiatric evaluation. All other families reported that all targeted behaviors were under control, no new behaviors had developed, procedures were effective and the child was still in the home.

Future Study

The primary responsibility of the Family Consultant Program is to provide service; however, with a flexible orientation to empirical investigative procedures, a review of the behavioral techniques used with the 500 families served since 1983 could provide valuable information. In 1983 and 1984 one consultant used aversive techniques in the home setting. Long term effects of aversive vs non-aversive methods could be investigated. In the past six months two of the individuals treated with aversive procedures in 1983 required institutionalization.

Summary

Unfortunately, Family Based In-Home Intervention is often eliminated due to time restraints and budget concerns. However, this alternative model may be more successful on a long term basis than more traditional models. Positive by-products of treatment include: increased positive attitudes of family members, further assimilation of the individual into the family unit, increased adaptive behavior, enhanced parental confidence, and appropriate day placements in educational and vocational programs. In-Home Intervention also offers assessment of the strengths, weaknesses, and needs of a family; and assistance in identifying service gaps. Presently, alternative family placements in the community, additional support services from mental health and training for educational and vocational staff in positive programming are needed.

This alternative model for treatment of individuals with mental retardation and mental illness or a behavioral disorder deserves further consideration, study and implementation to insure that treatment and training is provided in the least restrictive environment with the greatest probability of long term effects.

References

Allin, R. B., Jr. (1988). Intensive home-based treatment interventions with mentally retarded/emotionally disturbed individuals and their families. In J. A. Stark, F. J. Menolascino, M. H. Albarelli, & V. C. Gray (Eds.), Mental Retardation and Mental Health Classification, Diagnosis, Treatment, Services (pp. 265–280). New York: Springer-Verlag.

Baker, B. L., Heifetz, L. J., & Murphy, D. M. (1980). Behavioral training for parents of mentally retarded children: One year follow-up. American Journal of Mental Deficiency, 87, 31–38.

LaVigna, G. W., Willis, T. J., & Donnellan, A. M. (1989). The role of positive programming in behavioral treatment. In E. Cipani & M. J. Begab (Eds.), The Treatment of Severe Behavior Disorders, Monographs of the American Association on Mental Retardation, 12, 59–83.

McGee, J. J., Menolascino, F. J., Hobbs, D. C., & Menousek, P. E. (1987). Gentle Teaching, A Non Aversive Approach for Helping Persons with Mental Retardation. New York: Human Services Press, Inc.

Nihira, K., Foster, R., Shellhaas, M., & LeLand, H. (1974). American Association on Mental Retardation Adaptive Behavior Scale. Washington, D. C.: AAMR.

Reiss, S., (in press). Assessment of psychopathology in persons with mental retardation. In J. L. Matson & R. P. Barrett (Eds.), Psychopathology and Mental Retardation (2nd edition). New York: Grune Stratton.

Snell, M. E., & Beckman-Brindley, S. (1984). Family involvement in intervention with children having severe handicaps. Journal of the Association for Persons with Severe Handicaps, 9, 213–230.

Sparrow, S. S., Balla, D. A., & Cicchetti, D. V. (1984). Vineland Adaptive Behavior Scales. Circle Pines, Minn: American Guidance Service.

Watson, L. S., & Bassinger, J. F., (1974). Parent training technology: A potential service delivery system. Mental Retardation, 12, 3–10.

Došen, A., Van Gennep, A., Zwanikken, G.J. (Eds.) (1990). Treatment of Mental Illness and Behavioral Disorder in the Mentally Retarded. Proceedings of the International Congress, May 3rd & 4th, 1990, Amsterdam, the Netherlands. Leiden, the Netherlands: Logon Publications.

Chapter 21

Cognitive re-education of mentally retarded persons as instrument for their social integration: an Italian experience

L. Moderato

The social integration of mentally retarded persons is a long and difficult process, because of the numerous problems which have to be faced. The first class of problems undoubtedly consists of the social and human implications connected with this integration. Nonetheless, this will not be the topic of this paper, whose aim instead is to deal with the problems connected with handicap from the point of view of re-education. Re-education plays a very important role because it can be the element unleashing the whole process of social integration. In fact, as well as being a key factor in the growth and development of the individual, social integration must also be a process of active knowledge of and interaction with the surrounding environment. This implies that the subject must possess those instruments which allow the interaction to occur. Obviously, in order to achieve this, it is particularly important that the mentally retarded persons possess a range of social as well as cognitive behaviours. These two factors are correlated and complementary; consequently, progress at a cognitive level is the basis for a similar progress at a social level, which in its turn will be determining the strengthening and the application of more cognitive acquisitions. In other words, the person possessing a higher number of cognitive skills has more chances to interact correctly and adaptively with the surrounding environment, profiting from all the learning occasions offered by the environment itself.

Having said this, I think a general, brief specification is necessary in order to clarify our conception of psychological development which is based on the most recent theories of Behaviour Analysis by S.W. Bijou, D.M. Baer, P. Moderato, S. Perini and others.

The psychological development of any person can be described as the progressive change of the interactions between the behaviour of individuals and the events in their environment.

This progressive modification is the result of numerous factors and events occurring all through one's life, from one's birth to one's death. Among these we could briefly mention, for instance, the reflex and innate behaviours typical mainly of the first stages of life, the psycho-physical maturation of the organism, the behaviours and the abilities which are gradually learned in the various situations, the consequent elaboration of new and old knowledge, the adjustment and adaptation of abilities to new demands coming from the environment, and so forth.

It may be useful to highlight that in this interactive context the behaviour and the responses produced by the organism are only a part of the whole developmental process, because these responses are on the one hand determined by classes of stimuli preceding the behaviour itself, and on the other hand they can be subject to variations according to the consequences and the effects on the environment. The individual, then, plays a fundamental role in the progressive elaboration of these events through the emission of diversified responses to the various environmental situations. These responses, though belonging to the same category, gradually acquire more adaptive capacities through their continuous change. Besides, the sets of responses have no limits in number; they are determined by the characteristics of the species, the biological maturity, the history of the continuous interactions of the individual with the environment where he/she lives from his/her birth onwards.

Each person, then, even the handicapped, continuously modifies the environment with the aim of improving his/her general and particular living conditions. In this way the environment is able to determine changes in the behaviour, and these changes in their turn modify the environment. These modifications, together with other more biological and "natural" ones, produce new behavioural responses that consequently further modify the environment. The result of this process is the development of psychologically unique individuals.

Going back to the topic of this paper, what has been said up to now shows the fundamental importance of re-education applied to handicapped persons. Re-education can affect the psychological development through the teaching of cognitive and motor skills that can become the instruments to interact correctly and adaptively with the surrounding world, thus increasing the potentialities of social integration of the person. As a matter of fact handicap can be described in terms of disabilities, that is to say of the presence or absence of cognitive, motor and social skills. It is clear that a person possessing a high number of cognitive skills has more chances to integrate himself in the community because he/she interacts correctly and adaptively with the surrounding environment, profiting from all the learning occasions that this environment offers. That is why the aim of re-education is to provide the person with a number of abilities as high as possible in order to reduce at the same time the state of handicap.

For example, when a child is in a group, he/she will have serious difficulties in socializing if he/she cannot even play with children of his/her own age. The skills required by any play can be ascribed to the cognitive, the motor or the social spheres, because, in order to be able to play, a child must be able to perform certain operations (recognise the colours, associate them correctly, classify objects, run, comply with the rules, wait for his/her turn and so on).

Even in the family the person who is able to dress, wash and eat on his/her own can have a better level of educational interactions with his/her parents and brothers and sisters thus profiting in the best way from all the stimulations given to him/her, with a consequent increase in the level of integration in the community.

In the case of persons with learning and social-behaviour problems it is necessary to apply programmes of rehabilitation with scientific rigour. These programmes must include the control of antecedent stimuli present in the environment, the evaluation of the behaviour responses of the person, the control of the consequences which the response itself has on the surrounding environment – on the physical as well as more generally on the social and "cultural" environment. In such a context a stage of primary importance in these re-educational activities is the choice of the most appropriate "setting" for the realisation of the educational interaction. The "setting" can be defined as that factor which is able to affect an interactional sequence changing the force and the characteristics of the functions of the stimuli and of the responses involved in that interaction. A noisy and badly lit training room, for example, decreases the abilities of concentration even though correct methods are applied.

In addition to the choice of the setting which is most appropriate to facilitate the acquisition of abilities, concepts and ideas, another fundamental element is the correct management of the consequences caused on the environment by the behaviour of a person. It has been largely acknowledged that the force of an operant behaviour largely depends on its past effects on the environment. If behaviours (of any kind: cognitive, social, motor etc.) are reinforced by the stimuli-consequences, then it is clear how important it is to produce in the re-educational praxis stimuli-factors facilitating an increase in both the frequency and the force of the response. That is why these stimuli act as reinforcers. The control of reinforcers can thus increase the probability that the behaviour reappear in similar conditions, until it then becomes part of the handicapped person's behaviour, that is to say it can be generalised to different situations.

The analysis and the choice of the most appropriate strategies of reinforcement must clearly be an important element in the whole process of re-education and rehabilitation.

A re-educational praxis following these criteria may require, in the case of seriously mentally retarded persons, the application of the programmes of re-education to single individuals, because this makes it possible to overcome the obstacles represented by the different times and modalities of learning of each individual. I would like to stress the fact that these re-educational activities must not further exclude the individual from society, in fact they must be considered as an instrument to stimulate the social and intellectual rehabilitation of the handicapped person. All this is possible only if this stage of teaching at an individual level is included in an educational scheme of wide range with a rigorous definition of the goals (conceived as skills to acquire) and an equally rigorous system checking on the level of the achievements. This educational scheme can also include particular moments of the day dedicated to the study in depth and the tackling of those difficulties whose overcoming allows the individual a greater freedom of action and more independence in the world of the so-called normals.

An example of how the re-educational activity can be organized in a public rehabilitation centre in accordance with what has been said before can be represented by our experience at the Social-Educational Centre of the Local Social-Sanitary Unit (U.S.S.L.) number 68, in Lombardy, Italy.

This re-education centre is attended by seriously mentally retarded persons, even adults, with serious difficulties in the cognitive, social and motor spheres. Because of the extreme seriousness of the cases treated, the programmes of rehabilitation are prepared individually. They take into consideration the kind and stage of the pathology and they have three main aims: first, the achievement of personal self-care (eating alone correctly, dressing alone, washing oneself, use of the toilet etc.); second, the learning of basic and more complex cognitive skills; third, the acquisition of motor abilities and manual dexterity, gradually more refined and advantageous for the performance of particular operations. Moreover, special attention is given to the achievement of increasingly more appropriate forms of social behaviour.

These goals are attained in two different stages. The first stage consists of learning trainings at an individual level (one teacher, one pupil) aimed at the attainment of specific rehabilitation objectives concerning the cognitive and motor spheres and self-sufficiency. The result achieved at this first stage are experimentally collected and quantified in order to check continually on the level of rehabilitation.

The second stage consists of "support" activities conceived with regard to the objectives attained or to be attained at the first stage (individual training), assuring in this way a generalization of the skills acquired. These activities are organized in groups with the other people treated in the Centre. This means that the rehabilitation praxis is organized in such a way that, within one single group work different operations can be identified: they have a different level of difficulty and they can be performed by people with different skills.

With an organization of this kind the "learning training" becomes functional and it attaches importance to the working "support" activities, in fact it allows their realization, whereas the working "support" activities are functional and attach importance to the trainings because they create the reason for the participation in the training itself.

After the pupils have received a certain degree of personal and social self-sufficiency and some cognitive and motor skills, they are introduced in the working world, or they attend either professional schools for normal pupils or professional apprenticeships in local factories.

I think this is really the final aim of the rehabilitation of handicapped persons: creating a link with every-day life and building up that intelligence which is nothing more than the correct use of one's own skills in different situations.

This way of proceeding involves not only the technical staff dealing directly with the problem of handicap, but also the whole community which thus plays an "educating" role. The community is part of the educational scheme which is seen as a complex and varied continuum where each component (family, school, job, leisure etc.) can have its own specific role thanks mainly to the presence of a rigorous and operational definition of the goals as well as of the methods necessary for their achievement.

References

Baronchelli L., Moderato L., (1984). L'apprendimento della seriazione in soggetti handicappati gravi adulti. In R. Larcan, P. Moderato, S. Perini (Eds.) Nuove prospettive nella scienza del comportamento: normalita' e patologia dell'apprendimento. Messina: Carboneditore.

Bijou, S.W. & Baer D.M., (1978). Behaviour Analysis of child development. Prentice Hall, Inc. Englewood Cliffs New York.

Bijou, S.W. & Dunitz-Johnson E., (1981) Interbehavioral analysis of developmental retardation. The Psychological Record, 31, 305–329.

Moderato, L., Moderato P., Pergolizzi F., (1982). Handicap psicofisico o handicap sociale? Rivista Sperimentale di Freniatria. 5.

Moderato L., Paltrinieri M.E., (1984). Il recupero di soggetti handicappati adulti: utopia o realta'? E.T. Educational Technology, vol.1, 3–4.

Moderato L., Paltrinieri M.E., (1989). Lavoro e handicap. Unicopli. Milano.

Skinner B.F., (1953). Science and Human Behavior, New York: McMillan.

Došen, A., Van Gennep, A., Zwanikken, G.J. (Eds.) (1990). Treatment of Mental Illness and Behavioral Disorder in the Mentally Retarded. Proceedings of the International Congress, May 3rd & 4th, 1990, Amsterdam, the Netherlands. Leiden, the Netherlands: Logon Publications.

Chapter 22

An educational approach to behavioural disorders

G.H. van Gemert

Introduction

This paper grew from working as an external consultant in a very problematic situation around a moderately mentally handicapped resident of an institute for the care of mentally retarded people. After years of discussion with the institute the parents were at their wit's end. Every time they required a different approach of their daughter from the institute, they were told that the current approach was the best achievable. Eventually, they sent photographs to the press of their daughter living in what they called an inhuman situation: solitary, often naked, aggressive and being met with a minimum of decorum. The resulting publicity worked as a catalyst to bring about fundamental changes in the resident's environment and the way people interacted with her.

Now, about a year later, things are going much better. Our client is living at the same place as before, but in a situation that has been changing continually, both physically and socially. The institute and the government invested in personnel to develop a new approach. The resident visits the day activity centre five days a week, without problems. The parents claim that their daughter is far better approachable than before. The staff of the institute conclude that all kinds of adaptive skills appear. So, is this paper meant to be the presentation of a success story?

Not really. Sure, things are going well at an individual level. But before we will be satisfied, the approach will have to be continued without too much extra investment of personnel compared with regular situations. For this, it is not only necessary to give good instructions to the daily caregivers. Firstly, the resident herself should be and feel responsible for the quality of her life as much as possible. Secondly, the organization must be prepared to support the approach. In other words, our approach must be integrated into the organisation and culture of the institute, which is far more than only tolerate or encapsulate it.

Most existing approaches to behavioral disorders were not very helpful in the case we are discussing today. In our view, this is fairly typical. In our analysis of the reasons for this, we will address several topics. First, we will discuss the central concept of 'behavioural disorders' with mentally retarded people. After that we will discuss the most important approaches to behavioural disorders. Last we will describe our own approach.

Behavioural disorders with mentally retarded people

'Mentally retarded people' differ widely in the ways they express themselves and in the amount and quality of special care they need (Van Gennep 1983; Grossman 1983; Touwen 1988). Nevertheless, they share certain characteristics, of which a deficit in verbal communication is very important for today's topic. Mentally retarded people with behavioural disorders are likely to be found in residential settings without very much access to community resources. Actually, aggression and destruction will be the differentiating characteristics between people living in a residential setting and others (Campbell et al. 1982). In an often-used pragmatic description of 'severe behavioural disorders' (Hoeing 1982) these characteristics play a prominent role.

At the level of description, a number of problem behaviour inventories and observation scales giving reliable outcomes is available (e.g. Nihira et al. 1969; Kraijer & Kema 1982; Rawlings 1985; Intagliata et al. 1986; Silverstein et al. 1987). These instruments include aggressiveness, destruction, running away, stubbornness etc. In short: all behaviours violating a cultural rule or norm are supposed to be relevant (Denkowski & Denkowski 1985; Kral 1985; Mace et al. 1986). Problem behaviour may vary with age and gender. Duker et al. (1986) found more problem behaviour with males, and a decrease of problem behaviour with age greater than 35 years. James (1986), however, does not find such a decrease, which may depend on differences in the care system they were reviewing.

At first glance, it seems appropriate to describe the behaviour of mentally retarded people on a concrete, observable level. The advantage of this is the reliability with which data on the *frequency* of problem behaviour can be gathered (e.g. Buss 1966; Coons 1984; Kraijer 1988). In individual cases, however, frequency measures miss important aspects of the 'real thing':

- the main complaint of daily caregivers about residents with behavioural disorders is their unpredictability (Van Gemert 1986). Changing from being nice to being unmanageable can be a matter of seconds (Rienks 1986). As a result, the resident is a constant *threat* to the people in his environment, requesting a large emotional investment from the personnel.
- the resident's behaviour may vary enormously between situations, depending on the people who are attending, the physical and social

structure of the situation etc.

This might explain why the evidence about the external and internal validity of standardized instruments concerning maladaptive behaviour is, to put it mildly, not very decisive (Eyman & Call 1977; Van Gemert 1981; Scanlon et al. 1982).

This brings us to the concept of 'behavioural disorder' as such. In our view, this is a *social category* (Rosch 1978; Cantor et al. 1980). Caregivers use the term, summarizing their stressful experiences with the resident. The way this social category is used can be mapped (Van Gemert 1985). As a consequence, a successful approach should start with intersubjectivity on the meaning of so-called 'problem behaviour'. Only then a complete description of the problems, useful as a first step to solving them, is possible.

Different approaches of behavioural disorders

In theory and practice, a relatively small number of approaches to behavioural disorders with mentally handicapped people can be found. By 'approach' we mean a more or less consistent whole of professional activities aimed at improvement of the problematic situation. An approach is a stepwise process (or cycle, see Van Strien 1986) by which practical measures are designed (defining the problem, making a diagnosis, choosing goals, setting up plans, implementing the plan and evaluating it). We will discuss different approaches, giving attention to four aspects:

- **Level of approach**
  Any approach will influence several levels of the care system in which the resident lives. One of those levels is focused upon. To simplify matters, we will distinguish between three system levels: (sub)individual, relational and group level (Mataheru et al. 1990).
- **Perspective**
  This aspect concerns the long term, normative frame of reference, important for the direction in which essential choices are made during interpretation and planning.
- **Interpretation of behaviour**
  All approaches want to reduce the frequency of certain behaviours and to raise the frequency of desirable behaviour. There are differences, however, in the way behaviour is perceived.
- **Intervention design**
  This aspect concerns the infrastructure needed or organized by the approach, plus the concrete means that are used by those who perform the intervention.

We will discuss four approaches labeling them as psychodynamic, behaviour modification, categoral and educational, respectively. A lot of information about approaches may be found in the bibliographies by Day et al. (1988) and Wiegman (1989). The description is summarized in figure 1.

Figure 1
Characteristics of approaches

	Psychodynamic	Behaviour modification	Categoral	Education
Level of approach	(sub)individual	individual	group	relation
Perspective	deficit, impairment	trainable, normalization	permanent protection	recovery of normal life respect
Interpretation behaviour	symptom	lack of adaptive behaviour	confirmation	signal for communication
Intervention design	1-to-1 specialism	1-to-1 mediation structuring	no therapeutic goal structuring	interaction by daily care-takers

The psychodynamic approach

This heterogeneous group of approaches have in common that their central concepts are of an (intra)individual character, derived from disciplines like neurology, psychiatry and clinical psychology. As a result, the level of approach is individual or subindividual in both diagnosis and intervention. Differential diagnosis and explanation are far more elaborated within these approaches than intervention.

Generally, prognosis is pessimistic, given the stability of personality. A deficit model (Van Gennep 1983) is central to the approach. Sometimes intervention is aimed at recovery (Došen 1983), but more often only stabilization and control are thought possible.

Behaviour is seen as a symptom of a certain impairment, disability or handicap (see ICIDH 1980). A frequently used explanation concerns an immature personality (Menolascino 1969; Došen 1981), perhaps as a result of educational neglection (Janssen et al. 1984; Goeman 1986), or periods of risk during development (Kral 1985). Others see affective and psychiatric disorders as a cause of the behavioural disorder (Gielen 1986; Kraijer 1987; James 1986; Menolascino 1988). A third explanation is the existence of an information processing disorder, for instance Pervasive Developmental Disorder (DSM-III). Inadequate reactions to stimuli (rigidity or a lack of structure) are caused by this impairment, requiring from caregivers a flexible and well-balanced interactive style.

Intervention mostly takes the form of one-to-one therapy by highly specialized professional personnel. This may be a specific form of therapeutical interaction (Menolascino 1988). The implication is that categoral institutes are an efficient means to offer the right infrastructure for intervention (Bijl 1986; Willemse 1986). Medication is another important therapeutical means (Van Essen & Romein 1983), but this is not adequate for any long term application (Noorda 1988; Van Loon & De Boer 1989).

Behaviour modification

Behaviour modification, and operant conditioning in particular, has a long history of application in mental retardation (Ullman & Krasner 1965; Kanfer & Phillips 1970; McLean et al. 1972; Duker 1986). Its level of approach is the individual's behaviour.

Its main perspective is that the individual is trainable. Behavioural disorders are seen as a lack of adaptive behaviour (e.g. Greca et al. 1982). Unintentional reinforcement may be an important factor giving continuity to problem behaviour (Rojahn 1984; Schloss 1982; Burke et al. 1985). Intervention is highly structured. Often, daily caregivers are instructed as intermediaries between therapist and resident (Tharp & Wetzel 1969). This requires a strictly scheduled organization.

The value of behaviour modification as a means for training is undisputed. However, the unpredictability of the resident's behaviour casts doubt on its applicability in general. Very often, the resident is quite competent with respect to desirable behaviour. We do not have to train him, we should organize circumstances in such a way that the desirable behaviour increases. Token systems and other environment-shaping techniques, with their rigid infrastructure (Denkowski & Denkowski 1985; Theunissen 1986; Seys 1987), do not teach the resident self-efficacy. On the contrary, the resident may be made more dependent on other people than before, which will express itself as a lack of generalization and transfer of the learned skills (Campione et al. 1982; Kramer et al. 1988).

Categoral approach

In many Dutch institutes a 'special' group, department or house exists for mentally retarded people with behavioural disorders. Very often, the 'special environment' and the resulting individualization of care is installed without being very clear about the therapeutical concepts to give meaning to this care.

Residents on these 'groups' have in common that they were expelled from other groups because of their disruptive behaviour (e.g. Algra 1986). In fact, residents are placed in such a group because of their former behaviour rather than a positive prognosis or perspective.

The perspective is pessimistic. Even if there is an improvement in the resident's behaviour, it will be very difficult to continue the approach in other settings. The relapse rate after remission is high (Fidura et al. 1987). The structuring of the living environment is aimed at control and prevention of undesirable behaviour. The main idea is that the resident is not able to cope with the complexity of the real world, so he has to be protected by a well-regulated and simplified environment. There will be a fine-meshed network of 'do's and don'ts', functioning as rules for the caregivers, giving them, like the resident, very little room for individual choice and variation.

In a situation like this, showing 'symptoms' will get survival value for the resident (Altman 1975). At the same time, when the resident breaks through the strict control, it is seen as a confirmation of the need of the approach. As a next step, it is quite probable that the environment will be even more 'simplified', directive and rigid, resulting in a negative cycle consisting of problem behaviour, deterioration of the living environment, decline of decorum and increasing stress for all participants. The intentionality of the situation demands a lot of energy from the daily caregivers, up to the point of breakdown and loss of creativity.

Educational approach

Education may be described as living together of a child and adults who, based on their views, prepare the child for an independent life of its own within a certain community' (Nakken 1987). Education requires a relation between child and adult charactarized by spontaneity and a lack of explicit intentionality (Rispens & Bosman 1985). Education, however, is also intentional. Adults choose a meaningful perspective, a more or less vague long-term goal that functions as a guiding principle for interaction. Without a meaningful perspective, there is nothing for the child to live for, and there are no clear norms for behaviour. Given that mentally handicapped people are dependent on others, care should resemble education to enhance their independence as much as possible.

The main level of approach is the relation between resident and daily caregiver. The starting point is that the resident, the daily caregivers and all other participants are together responsible for the problem behaviour and its improvement. This will result in a multi-level approach of the problem situation with optimal interaction as its primary focus.

The perspective in an educational approach disorder is 'recovery of normal life'. This differs from normalization (Wolfensberger 1971) inasmuch the approach is aimed at creating living conditions which are as normal as possible. This requires equivalence and symmetry in the relation between resident and other people. Respect is a key word. Responsibility is another. Both terms are two-sided: each participant needs room for choice and initiative, but may be tackled about the things he does or does not do. Respecting limits and norms is as important as self-efficacy.

Behaviour is seen as having always social and comunicative qualities. Someone who can disrupt a situation 'at will', in so doing exerts power and communicates with other people. Maybe he is only using strange-looking ways of communication (Velthausz 1986). 'Hallucinations' may carry the message "I will not speak to you", whatever the validity of a psychiatric interpretation. This is in accord with an attribution view on problem behaviour (Ferguson & Rule 1983). Even with mentally retarded people, problem behaviour and especially aggression is not an impulsive act (Berkowitz 1989), only to be regulated by certain cognitive mechanisms (Zilman 1983). It is the result of a process of communication in which both partners' attributions, norms and values play a crucial role.

Practical implications: the project approach

The relation with the resident is structured by an individual intervention plan, derived from the educational perspective. An individual intervention plan is reached by a three-step-process: (a) problem definition and diagnosis (b) perspective and goal setting and (c) implementation and evaluation (Nakken 1988). Throughout the process, observation, mostly using video, is an important means for gathering data, not only about the resident's behaviour, but also, and more important, about the behaviour of the caregivers. In phase (a), recordings are made of a broad spectrum of daily life situations. By discussing the video recordings, individually and in the group, caregivers are confronted with their style of interaction. Later on, recordings are made of specific situations, aimed at verification of diagnostical hypotheses. In phase (b), video may be used to investigate the resident's competence with respect to proposed goals. In phase (c), specific situations, chosen beforehand, are recorded for modeling, coaching and evaluation of interaction styles that have been agreed upon. It is important not to present solutions before phase (a) is really finished. A quick response to the demand for 'guidelines' will endanger the creativity of the caregivers.

The implementation of an educational approach may be seen as a organizational project, guided by a team consisting of one or more external consultants (Egan 1985). A consultant gives advice, models intervention and guides the change process, without taking over the responsibility of the caregivers. The consultants are assisted by a case manager with an independent position with respect to the institute. Ongoing coaching and evaluation being the engine of the process, it is important that data be gathered about concrete interactions in an independent way by the case manager.

At the residents' level, the daily program must contain enough tasks and challenges to elicit meaningful behaviour. This can be done by arranging a 'hidden diary' (a list of things that minimally should be done each day). It is hidden for the resident because it lacks prearranged times and places, which are to be chosen by resident and caregivers together. Improvisation in the way items of the diary are executed is encouraged. The optimal style of interaction is characterized by a continuing dialog with equal chances at turn-taking (Coulthard 1977) and initiative. At the other hand the relation is 'frozen' (by withdrawal from interaction) or blocked in case of unacceptable behaviour of the client or escalation in that direction. Meaningful conversation is about concrete topics, preferably the here and now, and often evaluative: it should become clear which behaviour is desirable or not. However, there is no moralism, i.e. the violation of a norm is not a conversation as such ('Why'-questions about resident's behaviour are not allowed).

A new approach will always start in a situation structured by a different, 'old' one. Caregivers need a working situation with the same characteristics as the relation with the resident. This may be easier said than done. In fact, a prominent part of the approach may consist of the confrontation with the institute's culture, of which the former approach was a part. To manage such an environment, caregivers' views concerning the intervention plan must be made explicit and be discussed in relation to their style of interaction with the resident. The best way to reach consensus is to create intervision sessions at regular intervals, assisted by observational data. The plan should be supported by consensus among the daily caregivers in the first place and other participants in the second. At another organizational level, agreements with other participants in the organization must exist to prevent negative interference from higher levels of organization. Very often, this will require a change of institutional culture.

As regards content, many elements from other approaches may be integrated in each phase of the planning progress, as long as they do not interfere with the principles of education. This is especially true for those approaches which take a different level of approach. For instance, it is quite possible and sometimes necessary to use medication, or behaviour modification to reach certain goals. The educational approach offers a frame of reference for other approaches. Their use will depend on their capacity to generate solutions for the problems for which the resident needs assistence.

References

Algra, H. (1986), Een plek voor iedereen (?). Bijna tien jaar categorale woonvoorziening voor zwakzinnige mensen met moeilijk hanteerbaar gedrag op Noorderhaven. In: G.H. van Gemert & A. Dirks (red.) Gedragsgestoordheid – de stand van zaken. Utrecht: NGBZ.

Altman, I. (1975), The environment and social behavior. Monterey: Brooks/Cole.

Berkowitz, L. (1989), The frustration-aggression hypothesis: an examination and reformulation. Psychological Bulletin, 106, 59-63.

Bijl, K. (1986), Problematiek en perspectief betreffende gedragsgestoorde, hoger functionerende zwakzinnigen in Noord-Holland. In: G.H. van Gemert & A. Dirks (red.) Gedragsgestoordheid – de stand van zaken. Utrecht: NGBZ.

Burke, M.M., Burke, D. , Forehand, R. (1985), Interpersonal Antecendents of Self-Injurious Behavior in Retarded Children. Education and training of the mentally retarded: the journal of the division on mental retardation, Vol. 20, afl.3.

Campbell, V., Smith, R., Wool, R. (1982), Adaptive Behavior Scale Differences in Scores of Mentally Retarded Individuals Referred for Institutionalization and Those Never Referred. American Journal of Mental Deficiency, Vol. 86, No. 4, pp 425-428.

Campione, J.C., Brown, A.L., Ferrara, R.A. (1982), Mental retardation and intelligence. In: Sternberg, R.J. (Ed.) Handbook of human intelligence. Cambridge: Cambridge University Press.

Cantor, N., Smith, E.E., deSales French, R., Mezzich, J. (1980), Psychiatric diagnosis as prototype categorization. Journal of Abnormal Psychology, 89, 181-193.

Coons, W.H., Haley, G.A., Maharaj, N.R. (1984), Behavioural assessment of disturbed, institutionalized retardates. Canadian Journal of Psychiatry, Vol. 29, april.

Coulthard, M. (1977), An introduction to discourse analysis. London: Longman.

Day, K., Hamilton, J., Smith, P. (1988), Behaviour Problems in Mental Handicap: an annotated Bibliography 1970-1985. London: Royal College of Psychiatrists.

Denkowski, G.C., Denkowski, K.M. Community-based residential treatment of the mentally retarded adolescent offender. Phase 1, Reduction of aggressive behavior. Journal of community Psychology, Vol. 13.

Došen, A. (1981), Kontaktgestoordheid bij zwakzinnige kinderen. Klinische ervaringen. Behandelingsmethoden bij psychisch gestoorde zwakzinnige kinderen. Publicatie no. 29 van het NGBZ. Utrecht.

Došen, A. (1983), Psychische stoornissen bij zwakzinnige kinderen. Lisse: Swets & Zeitlinger.

Duker, P. (1986), Probleemgedrag bij zwakzinnigen: analyse en behandeling. In: Handboek voor Gedragstherapie. Deventer: Van Loghum Slaterus.
Duker, P.C., Druenen, C.van, Jol, K., Oud, H. Universiteit van Nijmegen. (1986), Determinants of Maladaptive Behavior of Institutionalized Mentally Retarded Individuals. American Journal of Mental Deficiency, Vol. 91. No. 1, 51-56.
Egan, G. (1985), Change agent skills in helping and human service settings. Montery: Brooks/Cole.
Essen, Ch. van, Romein, Th. (1983), Onderzoek naar het gebruik van medicamenten in de intramurale zwakzinnigenzorg. Oisterwijk: De Hondsberg.
Eyman, R.K., Borthwick, S.A., Miller, C. (1981), Trends in maladaptive behavior of mentally retarded persons placed in community and institutional settings. American Journal of Mental Deficiency, Vol. 85, No. 5, 473-477.
Ferguson, T.J., Rule, B.G. (1983), An attributional perspective on anger and aggression. In Geen, R.G., Donnerstein, E. (Eds.) Aggression: theoretical and empirical reviews, Vol I. Theoretical and methodological issues. New York: Academic Press.
Fidura, J.G., Lindsey, E.R., Walker, G.R. (1987), A special behavior unit for treatment of behavior problems of persons who are mentally retarded. Mental Retardation, Vol. 25, No. 2, 107-111.
Gedragsproblemen bij zwakzinnigen. Gek in de z .... Dat gaat me boven de pet. Verslag van studiedag. Amsterdam.
Gemert, G.H. van (1985), 'Gedragsgestoordheid' bij zwakzinnigen. Lisse: Swets & Zeitlinger.
Gemert, G.H. van (1986), Handelingsverlegenheid jegens gedragsgestoorden. In: G.H. van Gemert & A. Dirks (red.) Gedragsgestoordheid – de stand van zaken. Utrecht: NGBZ.
Gemert, G.H. van (1981), het vaststellen van gedragsgestoordheid bij zwakzinnigen. tijdschrift voor Zwakzinnigheid, Autisme en andere ontwikkelingsstoornissen, 18, 34-50.
Gennep, A.Th.G. van (1983), Zwakzinnigheid en zwakzinnigenzorg. In: A.Th.G. van Gennep, (Red.) Inleiding tot de orthopedagogiek. Meppel: Boom.
Gielen, J.J.M. (1986), Gedrag en zingeving. In: G.H. van Gemert, & A. Dirks (red.) Gedragsgestoordheid – de gang van zaken. Utrecht: NGBZ.
Goeman, H. W. (1986), Psychiatrische stoornissen bij gedragsmoeilijke zwakzinnigen. In: G.H. van Gemert & A. Dirks (red.) Gedragsgestoordheid – de stand van zaken. Utrecht: NGBZ.
Greca, A.M. La, Stone, W.L., Bell, C.R. (1982), Assessing the Problematic Interpersonal skills of Mentally Retarded Individuals in an Vocational Setting. Applied Research in Mental Retardation, Vol. 3, pp 37-53.

Grossman, H.J. (Ed.) (1983), Classification in mental retardation. Washington DC: American association on Mental Deficiency.
Intagliata, J., Rinck, C., Calkins, C. (1986), Staff response to maladaptive behavior in public and community residential facilities. Mental Retardation, Vol. 24, No. 2, 93-98.
James, D.H. (1986), Psychiatric and behavioral disorders amongst older severely mentally handicapped inpatients. Journal of Mental Deficiency Research, 30, 341-345.
Janssen, C.G.C., Akker, C. van den, Jacobs, W. (1984), Thuisverblijvende zwakbegaafde jong-volwassenen met emotionele of gedragsproblemen. Een verkennend onderzoek naar vragen om hulp. Tijdschrift voor orthopedagogiek, XXIII, 337-351.
Kanfer, F.H., Phillips, J.S. (1970), Learning foundations of behavior therapy. New York: John Wiley and Sons.
Kraijer, D.W. (1988), Psychosociale diagnostiek. In: G.H. van Gemert, W.K. Noorda (Red.) Leerboek Zwakzinnigenzorg, 2e druk. Assen: Van Gorcum.
Kraijer, D.W., Kema, G.N. (1982), Sociale Redzaamheidsschaal voor Zwakzinnigen. Lisse: Swets & Zeitlinger.
Kral, G. (1985), Aggressives Verhalten bei geistig Behinderten. 'Heilpädagogische Forschung' Bd. XII, H.2, pag. 175-188.
Kramer, J.J., Piersel, W.C., Glover, J.A. (1988), Cognitive and social development of mildly retarded children. In: Wang, M.C., Reynolds, M.C., Walberg, H.J. (Eds.) Handbook of special education. Vol.2: Mildly handicapped conditions. London: Pergamon.
Loon, H. van, Boer, J.E. de (1989), Pharmacotherapie, een bescheiden plaats op het therapeutische palet. In: Verheij, F., Loon, H. van (Red.) Intensieve residentiële behandeling van kinderen. Assen: Van Gorcum.
Mace, F.C., Page, T.J., Ivancic, M.TS., O'Brien, S. (1986), Analysis of Environmental Determinants of Aggression and Disruption in Mentally Retarded Children. Applied Research in Mental Retardation, Vol. 7, 203-221.
Mataheru, J.M., Wiegman, R.D. Gemert, G.H. van (1990), Over signalering en interpretatie van gedragsstoornissen bij geestelijk gehandicapten. Nederlands Tijdschrift voor Opvoeding, Vorming en Onderwijs, 6, 2, p. 62-75.
McLean, J.E., Yoder, D.E., Schiefelbush, R.L. (Eds.) (1972), Language intervention with the retarded. Baltimore: University Park Press.
Menolascino, F.J. (1969), Emotional Disturbances in Mentally Retarded Children. American Journal of Psychiatry, 126: 2, august.
Menolascino, F.J. (1988), Syndromes of depression in persons with severe mental retardation. In: Depression in the mentally retarded. Proceedings of the International Symposium, Ede. Leiden: PAOS.
Nakken, H. (1987), Op (welke) weg met de orthopedagogiek (?). Tijdschrift voor Orthopedagogiek, 156-168, Oratie Rijksuniversiteit Groningen.

Nakken, H. (1988), Het opstellen van handelingsplannen. In: G.H. van Gemert, W.K. Noorda (Red.) Leerboek Zwakzinnigenzorg, 2e druk. Assen: Van Gorcum.

Nihira, K., Foster, R., Shellhaas, M., Leland, H. (1969), Adaptive behavior scales. Washington DC: American Association on Mental Deficiency.

Noorda, W.K. (1988), Het gebruik van psychofarmaca in de zwakzinnigenzorg. In: G.H. van Gemert, W.K. Noorda (Red.) Leerboek Zwakzinnigenzorg, 2e druk. Assen: Van Gorcum.

Rienks, S. (1986), Begeleidingsaspecten bij gedragsgestoordheid. In: G.H. van Gemert & A. Dirks (red.) Gedragsgestoordheid – de stand van zaken. Utrecht: NGBZ.

Rispens, J., Bosman, R.E. (1985), Op weg naar een orthopedagogische handelingstheorie I. Tijdschrift voor Orthopedagogiek, 3, 111-132.

Rojahn, J. (1984), Self-Injurious Behavior in Institutionalized Severely/Profoundly Retarded Adults – Prevalence Data and Staff Agreement. Journal of Behavioral Assessment, Vol.6, No.1.

Rosch, E. (1978), Principles of categorization. In: Rosch, e., Lloyd, B.B. (Eds.) Cognition and categorization. Hillsdale: Lawrence Erlbaum Ass.

Scanlon, C.A., Arick, J.R., Krug, D.A. (1982), A matched sample investigation of nonadaptive behavior of severely handicapped adults across four living situations. American Journal of Mental Deficiency, 86, 526-532.

Schloss, P.J. (1982), Verbal interaction patterns of depressed and non-depressed institutionalized mentally retarded adults. Applied Research in Mental Retardation, Vol. 3, pp 1-12.

Seys, D.M. (1987), Kwaliteit van zorg: zorg voor kwaliteit. Dissertation Katholieke Universiteit Nijmegen.

Silverstein, B.J., Olvera, D.R., Schalock, R. (1987), Allocating direct-care resources for treatment of maladaptive behavior: the staff intensity scale. Mental Retardation, Vol 25, no. 2, 91-100.

Strien, P.J. van (1986), Praktijk als onderzoek. Assen: van Gorcum.

Tharp, R.G., Wetzel, R.J. (1969), Behavior modification in the natural environment. New York: Academic Press.

Theunissen, I. (1986), De behandeling van gedragsgestoorde, licht geestelijk gehandicapten. In: G.H. van Gemert & A. Dirks (red.) Gedragsgestoordheid – de stand van zaken. Utrecht: NGBZ.

Touwen, B.C.L. (1988), De ontwikkeling van het zenuwstelsel en zwakzinnigheid. In: G.H. van Gemert, W.K. Noorda (Red.) Leerboek Zwakzinnigenzorg, 2e druk. Assen: Van Gorcum.

Ullman, L.P., Krasner, L. (1965), Case studies in behavior modification. New York: Holt, Rinehart & Winston.

Velthausz, F. (1986), Communicatief gedrag bij diepzwakzinnigen. Dissertation Rijksuniveristeit Utrecht.

Wiegman, R.D. (1989), Bibliografie t.b.v. het onderzoek Vroegtijdige onderkenning van Gedragsstoornissen bij Geestelijk Gehandicapten. Groningen: Vakgroep Orthopedagogiek Rijksuniversiteit.
Willemse, A.J.N.M. (1986), De opvang van gedragsgestoorde bewoners als beleidsprobleem. In: G.H. van Gemert & A. Dirks (red.) Gedragsgestoordheid - de stand van zaken. Utrecht: NGBZ
Wolfensberger, W. (1971), Will there always be an institution? I: the impact of epidemiological trends. Mental Retardation, 9, 14-20.

Došen, A., Van Gennep, A., Zwanikken, G.J. (Eds.) (1990). Treatment of Mental Illness and Behavioral Disorder in the Mentally Retarded. Proceedings of the International Congress, May 3rd & 4th, 1990, Amsterdam, the Netherlands. Leiden, the Netherlands: Logon Publications.

Chapter 23

Treatment of persons with a mental handicap: trends in orthopedagogy

A. van Gennep

Introduction

The prevalence of behaviour problems in the general population is about 3 to 6 percent. Estimates of behaviour problems in the mentally retarded population range from 30 to 50 percent.

In my own research in the Netherlands I found in group homes 15% mild and 15% severe behaviour problems; in institutions I found about 15% mild and about 50% severe behaviour problems (including about 10% very severe problems).

In the seventies there was a mass departure from the medical model in Northwestern Europe and North America.

The view of mental disorder at the time was in terms of "either – or," for instance:

- the cause is either organic or psychological;
- the disorder is either endogen or exogen;
- the person with disorders is either ill or sane;
- the treatment is either causal or symptomatic.

But human behaviour, including disordered human behaviour, is often caused by more factors; a mental disorder often has organic ánd psychological causal factors; in mental disorder there often is a transaction of endogen ánd exogen factors; in mental life there is no clear boundary between illness and health.

The special education, habilitation and behaviour analysis literature reveals, according to Travis Thompson (1987), three families of behaviour problems.

1. A first family of problems is caused by neuropathological conditions: certain genetic, chromosomal and pre-, peri- and postnatal defects cause mental retardation that is commonly associated with behavioural and emotional

problems. Collectively, these problems include people with mental retardation, whose emotional and behavioural problems are among the most difficult to treat using current methods. The majority of people with behaviour problems remain in large institutions because of extremely violent behaviour, severe self-injury, or bizarre, repetitive behaviours that are unacceptable in most community settings. Many of these currently untreatable problems have specific biological etiologies and regulating conditions that can either be prevented or treated neurochemically.

2. In a second family of behaviour problems there also is a relation between behaviour disorders and brain damage. These problems include stereotyped movements, self-injury, unprovoked rage reactions, severe property destruction and extreme non-compliance. These problems are minimally and only transiently responsive to environmental intervention.

3. Most behaviour problems of people with mental retardation, including many with identifiable brain damage, reflect an interaction of impaired cognitive-intellectual functioning with their experience and current circumstances. These problems include those characteristic of personality disorder, adjustment reaction, anxiety and minor depressive disorders. Typical problems such as aggression, hyperkinesis, social withdrawal and noncompliance are often secondary to failure to learn to cope socially, vocationally or academically. The vast majority of behavioural problems of people with mental retardation *are in and of themselves the problem* and are not symptoms of anything else. These behavioural problems can be prevented or cured by arranging experiences and rearranging current environments to permit people with mental retardation to cope more effectively with their surroundings. For most retarded children, prevention and early intervention are synonymous with effective training of parents and early education teaching personnel.

So, there are behaviour problems with specific biological etiologies that are currently untreatable by environmental intervention; there are problems, also related to brain damage, that are only minimally and transiently responsive to environmental intervention; but most behaviour problems reflect an interaction of brain damage with experience and environment: they are in and of themselves the problem and can be cured by arranging experiences and rearranging current environments.

Those experiences and environments are the focus of orthopedagogical treatment.

Orthopedagogy is concerned with the study of rearing or bringing up (amongst others) persons with a mental handicap. Rearing (and bringing up) are defined as the stimulation of development. So, according to orthopedagogy, development occurs within the context of rearing (or bringing up).

1. Organic-natural development, that is the actualization of innate potentials. Growth and maturation are important processes. Actualization occurs

partly with help of the rearing persons: we call this the pedagogical climate.

2. Socio-cultural development, that is the socialization of the developing person. Learning is an important process. Socialization occurs with help of the rearing persons: we call this the pedagogical actions.

3. Self-development, that is the personalization of the developing person. Personalization occurs in relation with other persons, typically the rearing persons: we call this the pedagogical relation.

So, rearing (or bringing up) is essential for development. Parts of the rearing process are the pedagogical climate, the pedagogical actions and the pedagogical relation. The rearing process ends when the developing person becomes independent. Because persons with a mental handicap will never become independent, they will always need pedagogical help: we call this help orthopedagogical care.

Behaviour problems of people with a mental handicap in orthopedagogical perspective

Problems in the development of persons with a mental handicap are viewed, in an orthopedagogical perspective, as partial weaknesses in the development. The result of these weaknesses is that a person with a mental handicap, from birth on, perceives and experiences his environment differently. This results in a disturbed relation with that environment. The interaction of the primary partial weakness and the secundary relation disturbance results in a restricted development and increased partial developmental weaknesses. Partial weaknesses and relation disturbances intertwine and that's why an orthopedagogue has a treatment task.

The secundary disturbance with the environment becomes manifest in behaviour problems.

Behaviour problems are defined in orthopedagogy as a variety of excessive, chronic, deviant behaviours which violate the perceiver's expectations of appropriateness and which the perceivers wishes to see stopped.

This definition includes four elements.

1. The perceiver: who regards the behaviour as a problem?
2. The disturber: who is perceived to be the focus of the problem?
3. The problem behaviour: how is the problem described?
4. The problematic situation: in what situation does the problem behaviour occur?

An orthopedagogical classification of problem behaviour in mental retardation includes four patterns:

1. conduct disorder: for instance aggression/destruction or self-injury,
2. emotional disorder: for instance anxious/withdrawn behaviour, depressive behaviour or autism,
3. immaturity: for instance hyperactivity or attention deficit disorder,
4. other behaviour problems, for instance stereotyped behaviour, rumination or unaccepted sexual behaviour.

Theories of behaviour problems in an orthopedagogical perspective

Behaviour problems may be caused by organic, psychological and/or social factors. Scientific theories emphasize one of these causal factors and mostly relate this factor to a certain treatment strategy. Relevant theories are: biological theories, psychodynamic theories, learning theories and ecological theories.

1. Biological theories maintain that organic impairments must be viewed as the most important causal factors influencing behaviour problems. The associated treatment is drug therapy.

2. Psychodynamic theories emphasize intrapersonal conflicts as a reflection of interpersonal conflict-relations. Behaviour problems are viewed as symptoms of these underlying conflicts. Associate treatments are psychoanalytic, client-centered and other psychodynamic therapies.

3. Learning theories view behaviour as learned; they do not exclude organic causal factors. The learning theorist views the manifested behaviour as the problem that must be dealt with; this behaviour is not seen as a symptom of a deeper problem. Learning theories promote behaviour modification as treatment strategy.

4. Ecological theories (or environmental theories) maintain that the environment is the causal factor of behaviour problems: these problems result from inadequate interactions between the person with a mental handicap and the environment (family, siblings, teachers, cultural subgroups and so forth). Treatment consists of modifying elements in the ecology including the person with mental handicap, so that more constructive interactions between this person and the environment takes place.

Orthopedagogical theories emphasize factors that are also but unilaterally emphasized in the theories mentioned above.

- Orthopedagogy also emphasizes environment (like ecological theories), because organic-natural development always occurs in interaction with a growth-stimulating environment.
- Orthopedagogy also emphasizes learning in social behavior acquisition (like learning theories) because socialization is viewed as a result of the teaching activity of rearing persons.

– Orthopedagogy also emphasizes conflict relations (like psychodynamic theories), because personalization is viewed as a result of (positive) relations with rearing persons.

The difference of orthopedagogical theories with the other theories is that orthopedagogical theories do not emphasize either growth or learning or relation: these three elements are interrelated in orthopedagogical theories on development. In the associated treatment strategy these three elements will be interrelated in a specific but not eclectic way.

Treatment of behaviour problems in orthopedagogical perspective

A certain causal factor can lead to different disabilities and a certain disability can be the result of different causal factors. So, there is no direct relation between causal factors and disabilities.

That's why it is not easy to plan a treatment. Between behaviour problem and treatment there is a gap that can be bridged by interpreting the behaviour problem as a request for help. This interpretation must be seen as a hypothesis and the treatment as a test of the hypothesis.

The interpretation, the hypothesis, is based on data that are collected by anamnesis, observation and diagnosis. These data can be used as arguments for an interpretation, only if there is an interpretation framework that can give meaning to the data. The theories mentioned above give such a framework.

A behaviour problem must be interpreted in an orthopedagogical perspective.

The Dutch orthopedagogue Kok defines a behaviour problem as a request for specific orthopedagogical help: that is a specific overaccentuation in the pedagogical process. According to Kok, we can distinguish three overaccentuations in the orthopedagogical help: in the affective relation, in the cognitive aspect or in the motivational aspect.

The Dutch orthopedagogue Baartman distinguishes three types of behaviour problems as requests for help: inadequate following of rules, following invalid rules and not accepting rules.

So, different orthopedagogical theories result in different interpretations of behaviour problems: Kok emphasizes the developmental processes of growth and maturation; Baartman emphasizes the developmental process of learning; both emphasize relation.

As stated above, I emphasize growth ánd learning ánd relations in a changing interaction.

Orthopedagogical treatment focuses on the real-life situation; specific therapies are supportive to the treatment in the real-life situation. For example,

Kok distinguishes a hierarchy in treatment: a first grade and a second grade strategy.

The real life strategy

The primary orthopedagogical strategy has three aspects: climate creation, situation handling and relation. In my view all three aspects play a role in concrete treatment strategies; depending on the request for help one of them has the main accent and the other two an additional accent. Love is not enough. Human development is not only a process of personalization in relation with others. Development and orthopedagogical treatment also need a growth-stimulating climate and a learning situation.

The climate in the real life situation must stimulate growth, that is there must be a well-functioning environmental system, so that the mentally retarded person with behaviour problems can develop positively. For behaviour including problematic behaviour is situation-specific; different environments have a different effect on development and behaviour. So behaviour can be influenced and problematic behaviour can be modified by modifying the environment.

Some aspects of such a modifying treatment or therapeutic climate are: atmosphere, organization, space and time.

- The atmosphere sets the basic note for life in a group or an institution. The atmosphere is experienced in attitudes of the direct care staff, and can be characterized by the opposition of a cosy, affirmative and stimulating attitude versus a strict, blaming and restrictive attitude.
- The organization in the environment refers to the autonomy of the direct care staff, the degree of hierarchic specialization in the direct care staff, the shift system and the turnover of the direct care staff.
- The space is structured by the geography of the house (private rooms, living room, kitchen) and the furnishing of the space (furniture, curtains, mirrors and so forth).
- The time is structured by the life rhythm: sleeping, getting up, eating, learning, working, recreating as a daily rhythm; work days and weekend as weekly rhythm; ordinary days and holidays as yearly rhythm.

The activity of the rearing person also influences behaviour including problematic behaviour of the person with a mental handicap. This activity can be characterized from a cognitive point of view by the opposition of structuring versus varying, from a motivational point of view by the opposition of accepting versus regulating.

1. a) Structuring refers to making (more) clear the structure of the situation so that the handicapped persons living in that structure can develop in and by this structure. Structuring of the situation is important in the case of immaturity, for instance hyperactivity or attention deficit disorder.

b) Varying refers to international change of the situation so that variation, flexibility and breaking of 'sameness' occurs. Varying is important in the case of formalistic behaviour, for instance autism.

2. a) Accepting refers either to accepting 'a handicapped person as he is' or to accepting 'the problem behaviour of the handicapped person'. This is not the same thing: one can accept the handicapped person with his problem behaviour or one can accept the handicapped person but not his problem behaviour. This last situation occurs mostly. Sometimes however the problem behavior developed because a handicapped person was not accepted as a person because of his handicap, for instance in the case of anxious/withdrawn behaviour. Persons with this behaviour must have the psychological space to become a person and that means that in the beginning of the treatment period the limits must be enlarged.

b) regulating refers to the learning to accept and/or to follow valid rules by the mentally handicapped persons with behaviour problems. This is important in the case of conduct disorders, for instance aggression, destruction or self-injury. In a behaviour modification strategy, several methods are developed to discourage problem behaviour and to encourage other behaviour by reward and punishment. The original mechanistic, harsh behaviour modification is changed by (amongst others) McGee, in 'gentle teaching'. Reward teaching is the primary focus of gentle teaching. This must be done by techniques like ignoring, interrupting and redirecting problem behaviour. Gentle teaching is a pedagogy of liberation, according to McGee.

The relation can be directed at two different problems, who ask for a different approach.

1. Sometimes the behaviour problem asks for a more frequent and intensive relation, for instance anxious/withdrawn behaviour or self-injury. A non-directive approach is indicated. In the beginning the handicapped person with behaviour problems must be allowed to express negative emotions. The rearing person must have a good insight in the nature of these negative emotions and react in a positive way to these negative emotions. Then the handicapped person experiences acceptation. On this basis a positive relation between the rearing person and the handicapped person may develop.

2. Sometimes the behaviour problem expresses that there is no (more) need for a relation, for instance in handicapped persons with autistic behaviour or handicapped persons with conduct disorders. The rearing person must offer a relation and set limits at the same time; the handicapped person with behaviour problems must accept these limits because of the related person. Yet

these relations must be simple and functional: otherwise the incapability to make contact would be emphasized and existing resistance would increase.

The supportive strategies

Supportive strategies are therapies and training programs which support the real-life situation strategy. Important orthopedagogical strategies are, amongst others, aesthetic education, play therapy, music therapy and motor therapy.

- In aesthetic education (Theunissen) the person experiences the plasticity of the world and the variation of possibilities for expression in interaction with matter.
- In play therapy (Hellendoorn) the person may express psychological problems in images, if verbal expression is difficult.
- Music therapy tries, with music as medium, to motivate, to activate and to vitalize the mentally handicapped person with behaviour problems, in order to lay the foundations for further development.
- Motor therapy does the same, but uses body movement as medium.

These supportive strategies must develop from the total treatment plan and the results must be integrated in the real life situation.

References

Baartman, H. (1986) Diagnostiek, interpretatie en handelen, in: Levering, B. en Weelden, J. van, *Over het bijzondere van de orthopedagogiek*, Groningen: Wolters-Noordhoff.

Craft, M., Bicknell, J. and Hollins, S. (eds) (1985) *Mental Handicap: a multidisciplinary approach*, Eastbourne: Baillière Tindall.

Dreher, W., Hofmann, Th., and Bradl, Chr. (eds) (1987) *Geistigbehinderte zwischen Pädagogik und Psychiatrie*, Bonn: Psychiatrie-Verlag.

Fidura, J.G., Lindsey, E.R. and Walker, G.R. (1987) A Special Behavior Unit for Treatment of Behavior of Persons who Are Mentally Retarded, *Mental Retardation*, vol.25, no. 2, 107–111.

Gennep, A. van (1989) *De kwaliteit van het bestaan van de zwaksten in de samenleving*, Amsterdam: Boom.

Kirk, S.A., Gallagher, J.J. (Canadian Edition by C. Day) (1985) *Educating Exceptional Children*, Eastbourne: Nelson Canada.

Kok, J.F.W. (1988) *Specifiek opvoeden: orthopedagogische theorie en praktijk*, Leuven/Amersfoort: Acco.

Myers, B.A. (1987) Conduct Disorders of Adolescents With Development Disabilities, *Mental Retardation*, vol.25, no. 6, 335–340.

Oliver, C. Murphy, G.H., and Corbett, J.A. (1987) Self-injurious behaviour in people with mental handicap: a total population study, *Journal of Mental Deficiency Research*, 31, 147–162.

Stark, J.A. Menolascino, F.J., Albarelli, M.H. Gray, V.C. (eds) (1988) *Mental Retardation and Mental Health: Classification, Diagnosis, Treatment, Services*, New York: Springer-Verlag.

Thompson, T. (1988) Prevention and Early Treatment of Behavior Disorders of Children and Youth with Retardation and Autism, in: J.A. Stark et al. (eds), *Mental Retardation and Mental Health*, New York: Springer Verlag.

Došen, A., Van Gennep, A., Zwanikken, G.J. (Eds.) (1990). Treatment of Mental Illness and Behavioral Disorder in the Mentally Retarded. Proceedings of the International Congress, May 3rd & 4th, 1990, Amsterdam, the Netherlands. Leiden, the Netherlands: Logon Publications.

Chapter 24

Self-injurious behavior in the mentally retarded and treatment by opiate antagonists

H. Kars
W.M.A. Verhoeven

Introduction

Since the late seventies, research is performed on the relationship between biochemical disturbances in the central nervous system (CNS) and aggressive or self-injurious behavior. This kind of research is based upon two different hypotheses; the first dealing with disturbances in central serotonergic transmission and the second with abnormalities in endogenous opioid systems.

The research line implicating disturbances in serotonin (5-hydroxy-tryptamine; 5HT) transmission was originally started by the observations of Brown and coworkers who reported a strong and significant inverse relationship between an independently scored measure of life history of aggressive/impulsive behavior in patients with personality disorders and levels of the 5-HT metabolite 5-hydroxy-indoleacetic acid (5-HIAA) in cerebrospinal fluid (CSF) (Brown et al., 1979). Subsequently, several studies were performed, reporting significant decreases in the concentration of CSF 5-HIAA in patients with several kinds of violent behavior (Brown et al., 1982; Linnoila et al., 1983). In addition, Virkkunen et al. (1987) reported significantly lower concentrations of CSF 5-HIAA in arsonists, while Lidberg et al. (1985) did similar observations in subjects with criminal homocide.

In patients with self-injurious behavior (SIB), Greenberg and Coleman (1976) investigated the plasma 5-HT levels. They reported a relation between patterns of behavior problems, including SIB, and depressed plasma 5-HT levels. In these patients with low plasma 5-HT levels, elevation of 5-HT levels into the normal range by administration of a variety of psycho-active agents, appeared to be associated with improvement of behavioral disturbances.

These findings, and those of other investigators, suggest that disturbances in 5-HT metabolism, as reflected by lowered CSF 5-HIAA concentrations and plasma 5-HT levels, are implicated in the pathogenesis of aggressive behavior and related disturbances, irrespective of the psychiatric diagnosis (for a review and references see: Tuinier, 1989).

The research line implicating disturbances in endogenous opioid systems is based on the hypothesis that an enhanced activity of endogenous opioid neuropeptide systems may underline SIB. Support for this hypothesis can be obtained from the results of animal experiments, indicating that opioid-agonistic agents may induce self-mutilation effects (Herman et al., 1980) and from human studies in children with SIB, reporting increased concentrations of endorphin-like material in CSF (Gillberg et al., 1985), and enhanced levels of plasma beta-endorphin (Sandmann, 1988). In consequence of these observations, a limited number of clinical studies has been performed using the opiate antagonists naloxone or naltrexone in the treatment of SIB-subjects. Some studies reported an inhibitory effect of opiate antagonists on SIB (e.g. Herman et al., 1987), while others failed to found such effects (e.g. Beckwith et al., 1986).

Method

In the present study we investigated the effects of treatment with naltrexone on the frequency of SIB in 6 male subjects with profound mental retardation (Kars et al., 1990). Subjects were treated with naltrexone in a dose of 50 mg orally once daily or placebo, during 3 weeks following a double-blind placebo-controlled cross-over design. The experimental period was preceded by a 2-week baseline period, while in between the two cross-over periodes of 3 weeks, a one week wash-out period was included. Individual scoring instruments were designed to quantitate the frequency of SIB. Assessments were performed twice daily over a fixed period of time by well-trained ward personal. In addition, the duration of restraint time was measured.

Results

Analysis of the data revealed a statistically significant decrease in the frequency of SIB in the third week of treatment with naltrexone in 2 subjects (nrs. 1 and 2; table 1). In both subjects the improvement was clinically relevant, in that the reduction of SIB-frequency was reported also by the nursing staff. In one subject (nr. 6; table 1) a statistically significant reduction of the frequency of SIB was found in the second week of active treatment, that however was not reported by the nursing staff as being of any clinically relevance. In the other subjects, no effect of naltrexone on SIB-frequency was found. In none of the subjects naltrexone influenced the duration of restraint

Table 1

				P				N		
nr. 1	23.4±3.0	31.7±6.4	34.4±8.5	24.4±6.5	23.9±4.6	26.7±3.7	26.1±4.3	14.6±3.5	8.9±2.4**	18.3±4.1	16.1±5.1
				N				P		
nr. 2	4.9±1.0	5.6±0.8	3.3±0.6	2.4±0.4	2.0±0.5***	2.9±0.3*	2.9±0.6	3.9±0.9	5.6±0.7	6.3±1.3	4.6±0.7
				P				N		
nr. 3	10.8±1.9	19.7±6.2	17.5±3.6	30.0±1.3	32.0±6.9	27.6±7.2	17.8±7.3	37.0±9.8	22.5±5.2	21.5±6.4	22.2±7.4
				N				P		
nr. 5	37.3±5.9	20.1±5.1	34.1±6.3	20.0±5.7	25.9±6.1	24.7±6.8	21.6±2.8	17.1±5.2	21.1±5.6	15.2±4.7	20.1±5.1
				N				P		
nr. 6	15.0±4.6	5.4±1.7	18.6±5.2	4.9±2.0*	2.3±0.9	4.4±2.2	10.1±3.1	15.7±5.4	1.7±1.7	0.0±0.0	7.4±2.8
				P				N		
nr. 4	3.1±0.3	3.6±0.4	4.1±0.7	4.0±0.4	3.7±0.5	4.7±0.5	3.3±0.6	4.3±0.5	2.6±0.6	2.3±0.8	3.8±0.5
				N				P		
nr. 5	41.4±5.5	22.6±5.5	26.7±4.1	19.3±3.2	22.4±3.5	35.7±7.2	22.9±4.7	31.7±6.0	42.1±8.4	42.0±11.0	31.0±9.1
				N				P		
nr. 6	18.1±4.5	2.9±1.8	12.1±4.6	5.7±3.8*	5.4±3.0	7.7±4.2	14.0±4.3	22.2±6.6	1.7±1.7	2.9±2.9	10.4±3.9

LEGEND TO TABLE 1
Mean frequency ± SEM of 5 SIB subjects (upper part) or mean restrain score
± SEM of 3 SIB-subjects (lower part) during treatment with placebo (P) or 50 mg naltrexone (N) once daily orally, following a double-blind cross-over design.
* Indicates significant treatment effects of naltrexone as compared to the corresponding period of placebo treatment
(* $p \leq 0.05$; ** $p \leq 0.02$; *** $p \leq 0.01$).

time, albeit in one (nr. 6; table 1) a nearly significant reduction was found in the second week of active treatment.

Discussion

Our results, indicating a decreasing effect of naltrexone on SIB-frequency, are in agreement with those of other investigators, reporting an inhibitory effect of opiate antagonists on SIB (for references see: Kars et al., 1990).

The effectiveness of opiate antagonists in reducing the frequency of SIB may be the result of the antagonizing effects of these compounds on endogenous opioids like beta-endorphin, that may be responsible for maintaining a relatively tonic level of pain insensitivity in subjects with SIB. The effect of opiate antagonists may however also be related to the elemination of the reinforcing properties of endorphins.

Conclusion

Thus, two hypotheses are at present investigated regarding the pathogenesis of aggressive and related behavioral disturbances including self-injurious behavior. The results obtained sofar indicate that serotonergic as well as peptidergic abnormalities may be involved. Future studies in SIB-subjects should therefore be focused on the putative relationship between these two hypotheses, in order to investigate whether functional disturbances in serotonergic and endogenous opioid systems are involved in the pathophysiology of these disorders. Moreover, well-designed clinical studies in SIB-subjects are warranted with either naltrexone treatment over a longer period of time or specific serotonergic compounds, to elucidate the potential therapeutic effect of such treatment strategies.

References

Beckwith, B.E., Couk, D.I., Schumacher, K., 1986, Failure of naloxone to reduce self-injurious behavior in two developmentally disabled females. Appl. Res. Ment. Retardat 7: 183-188.

Brown, G.L., Goodwin, F.K., Ballenger, J.C., et al., 1979, Agression in humans correlates with cerebrospinal fluid amine metabolites. Psychiatry Research 1: 131-139.

Brown, G.L., Ebert, M.H, Goyer P.F., et al., 1982, Agression, Suicide, and Serotonin: Relationships to CSF Amine Metabolites. Am J. Psychiatry 139: 741-746.

Gillberg, C., Terenius, L., Lunnerholm, G., 1985, Endorphin activity in childhood psychosis. Arch Gen Psychiatry 42: 780-783.

Greenberg, A.S., Coleman, M., 1976, Depressed 5-Hydroxyindole Levels Associated With Hyperactive and Agressive Behavior. Arch Gen Psychiatry 33: 331-336.

Herman, B.H., Leslie, F., Goldstein A., 1980, Behavioral effects and in vivo degradation of intraventricularly administrered dynorphin-(1-13) and D-Ala2dynorphin-(1-11) in rats. Life Sci 27: 883-892.

Herman, B.H., Hammock, M.K., Arthur-Smith, A. et al., 1987, Naltrexone decreases self-injurious behavior. Ann Neurol 22:550-552.

Kars, H., Broekema, W., Glaudemans-van Gelderen, I., et al., 1990, Naltrexone attenuates self-injurious behavior in mentally retarded subjects. Biol. Psychiatry, in press.

Lidberg, L., Tuck, J.R., Asberg, M., et al., 1985, Homicide, suicide and CSF 5-HIAA. Acta psychiatr. scand. 71: 230-236.

Linnoila, M., Virkkunen, M., Scheinin, M., et al., 1983, Low cerebrospinal fluid 5-hydroxyindoleacetic acid concentration differentiates impulsive from nonimpulsive violent behaviour. Life Sci. 33: 2609-2614.

Sandman, C.A., 1988, ß-Endorphin disregulation in autistic and self-injurious behavior: a neurodevelopmental hypothesis. Synapse 2: 193-199.

Tuinier, S., 1989, De psychiater en de wilde man; een veldstudie over de relatie psychiatrisch syndroom en criminaliteit. Thesis, Free University Amsterdam, pp 124-147.

Virkkunen, M., Nuutila, A., Goodwin, K., et al., 1987, Cerebrospinal Fluid Monoamine Metabolite Levels in Male Arsonists. Arch Gen Psychiatry 44: 241-247.

Došen, A., Van Gennep, A., Zwanikken, G.J. (Eds.) (1990). Treatment of Mental Illness and Behavioral Disorder in the Mentally Retarded. Proceedings of the International Congress, May 3rd & 4th, 1990, Amsterdam, the Netherlands. Leiden, the Netherlands: Logon Publications.

Chapter 25

Treatment of autistic disorders in the mentally retarded with the adrenocorticotrophic hormone (4-9) analog ORG 2766

J.K. Buitelaar

Introduction

Infantile autism is a pervasive developmental disorder of childhood which necessitates often institutional care or long lasting coaching of parents, family and children.

Considerable co-morbidity exists between autistic disorders and mental retardation. At least 70 % of the autistic patients suffer from profound to mild mental retardation. Nevertheless, autistic disorders have been found to differ sharply from non-autistic mental retardation, among others by the age of onset of the development of epileptic fits, medical correlates, sex distribution, patterns of cognitive disabilities and discrimination of socioemotional cues (Rutter & Schöpler, 1987). Correct differential diagnosis for both conditions bears implications for prognosis and treatment planning.

The gains of routine psychopharmacological interventions in autism (e.g. neuroleptics) are quite modest.

Hence we have studied the behavioral effects of the neuropeptide Org 2766 in autistic children in two controlled clinical trials (Buitelaar et al., 1990 a,b,c). Org 2766 is a modified adrenocorticotropic hormone (ACTH)-fragment. ACTH 4-9 which has no substantial steroidogenic activity, and is active on oral administration (Pigache and Rigter, 1981). As conceptual background of these studies served that autism is marked by information processing deficits and neuropeptides from the ACTH-"family" influence the processing of information and improve learning, memory, social behavior and adaptation (de Wied and Jolles, 1982). Brain opioid systems seem to be implicated in autism (Panksepp and Sahley, 1987). Org 2766 has been shown to ameliorate mood and increase sociability in elderly people with mild cognitive impairments and in mentally retarded adults (Sandman et al., 1980).

Methods

In the first trial, 14 outpatient children participated. Diagnosis was by DSM-III criteria (12 infantile autism, 2 atypical pervasive developmental disorder). Mean age was 8 years, mean IQ was 68 with 8 subjects with IQ lower than 70, mean social quotient was 51. In the second trial, 20 children participated (11 were the same as in the first trial). Diagnosis by DSM-III-R criteria (all autistic disorder). Mean age was 8.3 year, mean IQ was 67 with 10 subjects with IQ lower than 70.

A placebo controlled double blind cross-over design was employed. Active treatment was by 20 mg Org 2766 /child/day during 4 weeks in the first trial and 40 mg Org 2766 /child/day during 8 weeks in the second trial.

Outcome variables were an ethologically analysed playroom observation (van Hooff, 1982) and behavior checklist ratings obtained from parents and teachers. Analysis of the playroom data included frequency measures of behavior elements, detailed examination of the interaction of child and experimenter by way of information-theoretical measures (Steinberg, 1977) and description of the temporal contingency and functional similarity aspects of the organization of behavior (Buitelaar et al., 1990 b,c). Checklist ratings were the Aberrant Behavior Checklist (Aman et al., 1985), and the Clinical Global Impressions MIMH.

Results

No physical side effects were observed in both trials. In the second trial one subject dropped out because of intermittent gastrointestinal problems. It appeared that he had received only placebo so far.

In the first trial no significant drug effects were found on the behavioral checklist ratings. In the playroom treatment with Org 2766 was associated with significant increases of locomotion, changing toys and talk behaviors and with a significant decrease of stereotyped behaviors (Table 1)

Table 1

	B	P	Org(2)	Org(4)
change toys (fr)				(a,b,c,*)
mean	1.4	2.1	1.9	3.0
s.d.	2.3	4.3	2.4	2.8
talk (fr)				(a*)
mean	26.5	28.0	31.8	34.3
s.d.	21.5	26.0	24.6	26.6
stereotypic b.(sec)		(d**)		(b*)
mean	103.9	161.2	142.9	70.6
s.d.	159.1	202.6	240.8	147.2
locomote (sec)				(a*)
mean	14.4	23.6	21.0	32.0
s.d.	20.9	35.1	21.6	22.9

B = baseline autistic children, group mean and s.d.(N=14)
P = placebo
Org(2)= after 2 weeks Org 2766
Org(4)= after 4 weeks Org 2766
a: Org(4 w.) compared to baseline
b: Org(4 w.) compared to placebo
c: Org(4 w.) compared to Org(2 w.)
d: placebo compared to baseline
* $p < .05$ (Wilcoxon, two-tailed)
** $p < .01$

The parents considered 11 children (out of 14) as improved on the basis of the treatment preference scale. The behavioral changes of the responders were typed as "more attentive, witty, shows more interest in what is happening around". The investigators rated 8 children as individual responder. These children could be identified in the playroom measures by a high baseline level stereotyped behaviors and a low baseline level talk behavior. The significant decreases of stereotypy could be attributed to this subgroup.

In the analysis of the organization of behavior a slight but significant increase of the transmission-efficiency (TE) inter-child value was found after Org 2766 (Table 2).

The TE value is a measure for the predictability of the behavior of an individual. The higher the TE inter-child value, the more predictable the behavior of the child is from the behavior of the experimenter, and the higher the TE intra-child value, the more predictable the behavior of the child is from its other behavior in the same time period of 5 seconds.

Table 2
Transmission-efficiency (TE) values for the placebo and org 2766 condition. TE values are based upon individual matrices (n=14)

	placebo	*Org 2766*	Wilcoxon
TE-"intra child"	30.3 ± 2.4	31.2 ± 4.2	ns.
TE-"inter child"	9.0 ± 2.2	11.5 ± 5.0	p < .05
TE-"inter exp."	17.1 ± 5.1	18.5 ± 6.1	ns.
TE-"intra-exp."	40.9 ± 10.2	45.7 ± 14.6	ns.

An increase in TE-inter child value after Org 2766 treatment may be interpreted as an increased interaction of the child with the experimenter. Subsequent analysis of the structure of behavior suggested that this increased interaction could be attributed for a large part to an improved coordination of the child and the experimenter's gaze and smile behaviors (Buitelaar et al., 1990 b).

In this first study drug effects became apparent only after 4 weeks Org 2766 treatment (Table 1). For this reason we did a second study with a double dose Org 2766 and a longer treatment period.

On the behavior checklist ratings we did obtain significant drug effects this time. Org 2766 was most outspoken on the social withdrawal subscale of the Aberrant Behavior Checklist which was completed by the parents.

In the playroom observation a significant increase was found of the frequency of play behaviors as well as of the interactive quality of the play behaviors. Furthermore we were able to replicate the increase of the TE inter-child after Org 2766 treatment (Org 2766 value twice as high as placebo and baseline values, Buitelaar et al., 1990 c).

In both studies individual responders were identified in the IQ range lower than 70.

Conclusion

Org 2766 seems to be an interesting activating compound for autistic children with severe mental retardation as well as with subnormal IQ's and merits further study on the behavioral, but also neurophysiological, neuropsychological and biochemical level. Especially the absence of untoward or side effects makes Org 2766 suitable for administration in retarded subjects.

The social behavior modulating effects of Org 2766 in animal models could be demonstrated to be Naltrexone reversible, which indicates that Org 2766 exerts this effect via endogeneous opioid systems (Niesink & van Ree, 1983). Hence we suppose that the behavioral effects induced by Org 2766 in these autistic children may be mediated by opioid systems also, and that these effects are due to a slow release of endogeneous opioids.

References

Aman, M.G., N.N. Singh, A.W. Stewart, C.J. Field, (1985), The Aberrant Behavior Checklist: a behavior rating scale for the assessment of treatment effects. *American Journal of Mental Deficiency*, 89 (5), 485-491.

Buitelaar, J.K. (1989). Is the pro-opiomelanocortin system implicated in the neuroregulation of autism ? Paper presented at the *Conference on the Experimentel Biology of the Autistic Syndromes*, March 29-31. Durham, U.K.

Buitelaar, J.K., H. van Engeland, J.M. van Ree & D. de Wied, (1990 a). Behavioral effects of the adrenocorticotrophic hormone (4-9) analog Org 2766 in 14 outpatient autistic children. *Journal of Autism and Developmental Disorders* (in press).

Buitelaar, J.K., H. van Engeland, C.H. de Kogel, H. de Vries, J.A.R.A.M. van Hooff, J.M. van Ree (1990 b). The adrenocorticotrophic hormone (4-9) analog Org 2766 in autistic children: effects on the organization of behavior. (submitted).

Buitelaar, J.K., H. van Engeland, C.H. de Kogel, H. de Vries, J.A.R.A.M. van Hooff, J.M. van Ree (1990 c). The adrenocorticotrophic hormone (4-9) analog Org 2766 benefits autistic children: report of a second controlled clinical trial (submitted).

Hooff, J.A.R.A.M., van (1982). Categories and sequences of behavior: methods of description and analysis. In: *Handbook of methods in nonverbal behavior research*, Eds. K.R. Scherer, P. Ekman, 362-438. Cambridge University Press.

Niesink, R.J.M., J.M. van Ree, (1983), Normalizing effect of an adrenocorticotropic hormone (4-9) analog Org 2766 on disturbed social behavior in rats. *Science*, 221,960-962.

Panksepp, J., T.L. Sahley, (1987). Possible brain opioid involvement in disrupted social intent and language development of autism. In: *Neurobiological Issues in Autism*, Eds. E. Schöpler, G.B. Mesibov, 357-374. New York, Plenum Press.

Pigache, R.M., H. Rigter, (1981), Effects of peptides related to ACTH on mood and vigilance in man. *Frontiers in Hormone Research*, 8, 193-207.

Rutter, M. & E. Schöpler, (1987). Autism and pervasive developmental disorders: concepts and diagnostic issues. *Journal of Autism and Developmental Disorders*, 17 (2), 159-186.

Sandman, C.A., B.B. Walker, C.A. Lawton, (1980), An analog of α-MSH/ACTH 4-9 enhances interpersonal and environmental awareness in mentally retarded adults. *Peptides*, 1, 109-114.

Steinberg, J.B. (1977). Information theory as an ethological tool. In: *Quantitative Methods in the Study of Animal Behavior*, B.A. Hazlett (Ed.), 47-74. New York, Academic Press.

Wied, D. de, J. Jolles, (1982), Neuropeptides derived from the pro-opiocortin: behavioral, physiological, and neurochemical effects. *Physiological Reviews*, 62 (3), 976-1059.

Došen, A., Van Gennep, A., Zwanikken, G.J. (Eds.) (1990). Treatment of Mental Illness and Behavioral Disorder in the Mentally Retarded. Proceedings of the International Congress, May 3rd & 4th, 1990, Amsterdam, the Netherlands. Leiden, the Netherlands: Logon Publications.

Chapter 26

Pharmacotherapy and art therapy in the management of challenging behaviour

S.R. Sadik

Challenging behaviour is common in people with a mental handicap (Reid, 1978; Corbett, 1979). Reiss (1985) in a review of recent studies estimates that between 15 tot 20% of adults with developmental disabilities also have emotional and behavioural disorders. While challenging behaviour could result from institutionalisation (Spitz, 1949) it is cited to be one of the reasons for admission to institutions (Primrose, 1971) as well as preventing discharge into the community (Eyman and Call, 1977). In terms of severity of the mental handicap, it is accepted that people with a mild mental handicap have the same range of emotional and behavioural disorders like the non-handicapped population. However, it is common practice to infer "behaviour problems" from isolated signs or symptoms of "mental illness" (Menolascino, 1989).

Regarding treatment, the use of pharmacotherapy in the management of challenging behaviour is widespread (Craft and Schiff, 1980). It is often noted, however, that there is the contradictory practice of the excessive use of pharmacological agents versus the singular use of the principles of applied behaviour analysis (Menolascino, 1989). The last two decades have seen the invaluable contribution of a variety of psychotherapeutic approached. Art therapy has been increasingly applied to the development, rehabilitation and management of people with a mental handicap (Marinow, 1967; Wilson, 1977; Kunkle-Miller, 1978). There is now a growing professional consensus regarding the helpful combined role of these treatment approaches and acknowledgment of the need for a more balanced, holistic and humanising approach.

Case Report

Mr. D.T. is a 51 year old male with mild mental handicap (full scale IQ of 64) who comes from a family marked by considerable violence. His father had previous history of imprisonment and his mother suffered from chronic mental illness. The patient has one sister, who is described as mildly mentally handicapped and one brother who previously received a junior prison sentence.

At the age of eight, the patient was moved to a residential school for the "educationally subnormal" until he was sixteen. After he left school he was never employed for more than a few days.

Mr. D.T. has been behaviourally disturbed since mid childhood. At the age of ten years he was charged with larceny and placed on three years' probation. A further two years' probation followed a similar offence at the age of sixteen. Subsequently he was admitted to a big mental handicap institution and was later transferred to another. His behaviour during his stay was marked by absconding and violence. On one occasion while he was out of hospital in 1961 he committed rape, following which he was admitted to a special hospital under a restriction order (discharge could only be authorised by the Home Secretary). During his twenty-four year stay in the special hospital, his challenging behaviour persisted.

Mr. D.T. was transferred to the local mental handicap institution in July 1985 following a period of six weeks assessment in a local interim secure unit.

Between July 1985 and July 1988 the patient continued to present a management problem. Various therapies employed singularly have failed to show any significant improvement in his behaviour. In July 1988, a multidisciplinary rehabilitation programme was initiated. It consisted of counselling by nursing staff, art therapy, vocational training and psychiatric assessment. The psychiatric diagnosis of Personality Disorder (ICD9 301.7) was made in an associable individual with limited conversation, hostile and suspicious but without abnormal beliefs or experiences.

EEG revealed no focal abnormality or paroxysmal abnormality. CT brain scan showed normal attenuation of the cerebral substance. The ventricles and sulci appeared normal. There was no evidence of space occupying lesion or other abnormality.

Multidisciplinary meetings have demonstrated a fluctuating improvement in the patient's behaviour initially, but three months later the frequency and severity of his challenging behaviour became very difficult to contain. This culminated in the patient killing his own pet rabbit with a knife, as well as threatening other residents and staff. Staff and management felt that the patient became extremely dangerous and could no longer continue to care for him.

Although clinical observation still excluded psychotic features, the patient's art work provided a medium for communication. Based on individual and group activities it revealed aggression, loss of sense of reality and persecutory experience. This was later confirmed by a blind independent art therapy assessment (see below). In view of his dangerous behaviour, a trial of zuclopenthixol decanoate was instituted to enhance the rehabilitation process. This was introduced intramuscularly 200 mg weekly. Within two weeks the patient became cooperative, communicative and amenable. Zuclopenthixol was reduced to 200 mg every two weeks six months later.

The patient's improvement was maintained over the following year. He achieved regular escorted visits initially and later was allowed unescorted outings outside the hospital. He started to participate actively in a variety of vocational activities and has since been on two holidays without any report of untoward incidents. The patient became cheerful, confident, his suspicious attitude disappeared and he was gaining partial insight into his past behaviour. During art therapy sessions, the patient was reported to be relaxed, contributing to the group discussion, was able to talk about his previous traumatic experience and developed an affectionate relationship towards a female resident.

In view of the patient's improvement, the multidisciplinary team have been contemplating discharging him to a group home in the community.

Figure 1 shows the frequency of problem behaviours from July 1985 to date.

Independent Art Therapy Assessment

This was arranged to verify the improvement noticed clinically. Two groups of six paintings before and after zuclopenthixol was given were randomly selected and blindly assessed by an independent Senior Art Therapist. The themes that emerged from the assessment were:

Violence, perversion and detachment in a male person.

Paintings portrayed feelings of fear, anger and strong sense of loss of reality. The first group of paintings appeared threatening with strong persecutory and hallucinatory qualities. They show lack of awareness of reality, ambiguity, psychotic experience and destructiveness.

The second group of paintings still showed lack of reality and inner space, but with less overt aggression. No report was made of any persecutory or hallucinatory features.

Figure 1
Frequency of problem behaviours July 1985 – April 1990

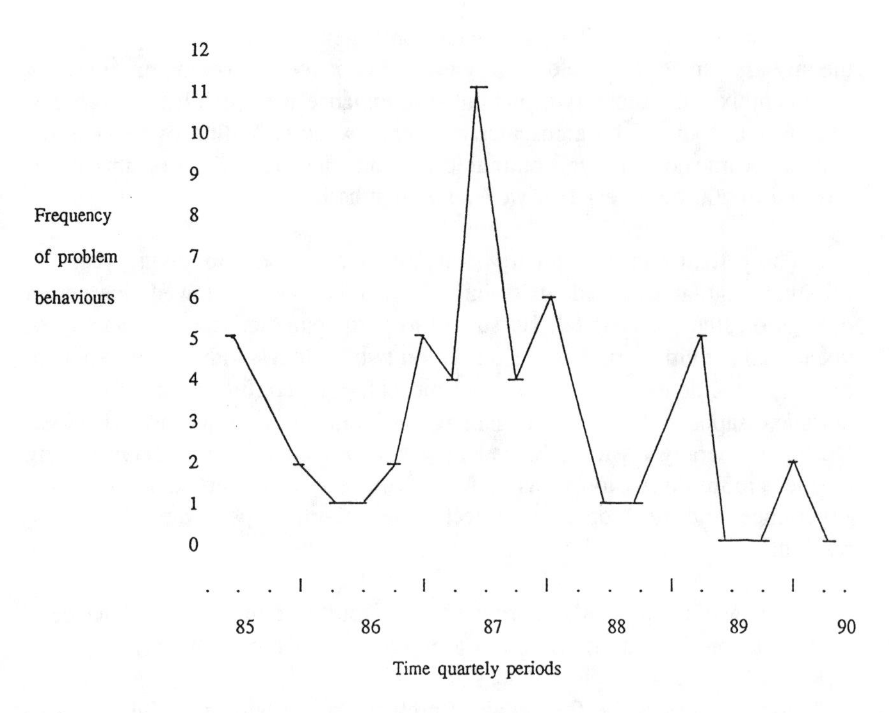

Figure 2 is a sample of the first group and figure 3 is a sample of the second group.

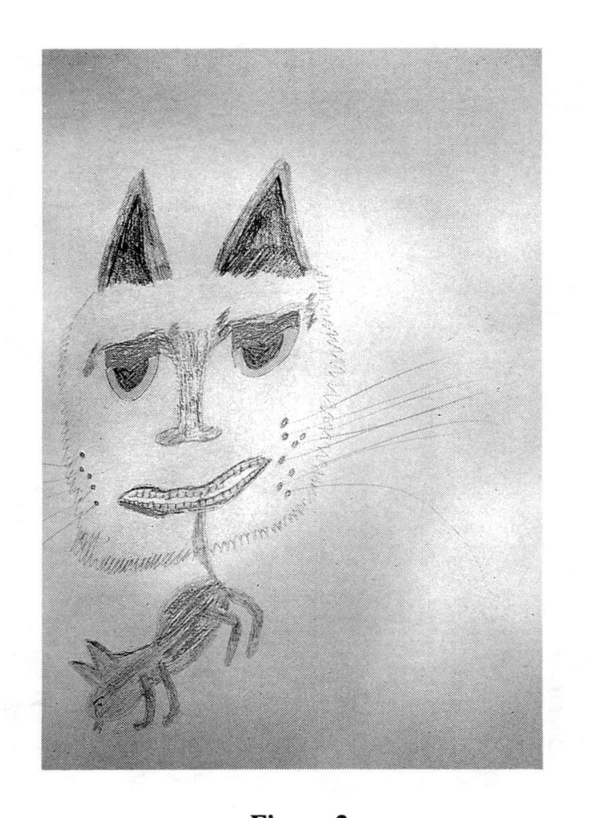

Figure 2
Drawing dated 05.06.88

Figure 3
Drawing dated 09.11.89

Discussion

This case has demonstrated the merits of multidisciplinary assessment and clinical management of challenging behaviour in people with a mental handicap. In particular the combined role of Art Therapy and Pharmacotherapy has been invaluable. Although the exact diagnosis remains uncertain, the response they generated appears to support the suggestion that there are qualitative differences of psychiatric and emotional disorders in people with a mental handicap, some of which may represent unique syndromes (Menolascino and Eggar, 1978; Webster 1970). Large population studies are required to establish the place of Art Therapy as a diagnostic tool.

Professionals in the mental handicap field need to be aware of the greater variation in the presentation of psychiatric illness in people with a mental handicap compared to the general population. An acceptance of the contribution of a wide variety of therapeutic approached, close collaboration and a constructively critical attitude need to be adopted to be able to respond to the challenge. As demonstrated, the extended application of Art Therapy and well controlled and monitored pharmacotherapy could be very rewarding.

Acknowledgements

I am grateful to Vera Vasahelyi, Senior Art Therapist, for her independent art therapy assessment, thanks to Dr. Nick Bouras for his advice, and to Mrs. Marilyn Balkwill for her dedicated secretarial support.

References

Corbett, J.A. (1979), Psychiatric Morbidity and Mental Retardation. In Psychiatric Illness and Mental Handicap. James, F.E. and Snaith, R.P. (Eds). Gaskell Press, London.

Craft, M.J. & Schiff, A.A. (1980), Psychiatric Disturbance in Mentally Handicapped Patients. British J Psych, 137, 250–255.

Eyman, R.K. & Call, T. (1977), Maladaptive Behaviour and Community Placement in Mentally Handicapped Patients. American Journal of Mental Deficiency, 82, 137–144.

Kunkle-Miller, C. (1978), Art Therapy with Mentally Retarded Adults. Art Psychotherapy 5, 123–133.

Marinow, A. (1967), Art Therapy as a Method of Rehabilitation. Psychotherapy and Psychosomatics, 15 (1), 43.

Menolascino, F.J. (1989), Mental Illness in the Mentally Retarded: Current State of the Art in the United States. Seminar 85: Mental Retardation, World Psychiatric Association, Athens, October 1989.

Menolascino, F.J. & Eggar, M.L. (1978), Medical Dimensions of Mental Retardation. Lincoln: University of Nebraska Press.

Primrose, D.A. (1979), A Survey of 502 Successive Admissions to a Subnormality Hospital from 1 January to 31 December 1970. British Journal of Mental Subnormality 17, 25–28.

Reid, A.H. (1976), Psychiatric Disturbance in the Mentally Handicapped. Proceedings of the Royal Society of Medicine 69, 509–12.

Reiss, S. (1985), The Mentally Retarded Emotionally Disturbed Adult. In Children with Emotional Disorders and Developmental Disabilities. Sigman, G. (Ed). Grune and Stratton, NY.

Spitz, R. (1949), The Role of Ecological Factors in Emotional Development. Child Development 20, 145–146.

Webster, T.G. (1970), Unique Aspects of Emotional Development in Mentally Retarded Children. In F.J. Menolascino (Ed). Psychiatric Approaches to Mental Retardation (pp. 3–54). New York: Basic Books.

Wilson, L. (1977), Art Therapy with the Mentally Retarded. Am J of Art Therapy, 16, 87–97.

Došen, A., Van Gennep, A., Zwanikken, G.J. (Eds.) (1990). Treatment of Mental Illness and Behavioral Disorder in the Mentally Retarded. Proceedings of the International Congress, May 3rd & 4th, 1990, Amsterdam, the Netherlands. Leiden, the Netherlands: Logon Publications.

Chapter 27

Psychotropic Drug Use in Mentally Retarded Adults – Prevalence and Risk Factors

W. Meins

Prevalence

Psychotropic drug treatment is probably the most frequently used method of therapy for chronic and more severe behavior problems of mentally retarded persons. Studies on psychotropic drug prevalence – most of them performed in the U.S.A. – have recently been summarized by Aman and Singh (1988). Accordingly, 30–50% of institutionalized and 26–36% of mentally retarded adults attended to otherwise are administered psychotropics regularly. During the past few years, however, there has been a pleasant tendency towards a more cautious prescription of psychotropics (Poindexter 1989). Corresponding results obtained in New Zealand, for example, point to national peculiarities (Aman et al., 1985). Accordingly, it seemed to be useful to determine for the first time the proportion of those mentally retarded persons regularly taking psychotropics and/or anticonvulsives in the F.R.G.

The study sample consisted of a total of 1154 mentally retarded adults in the city of Hamburg. The distribution with respect to age, sex and habitation is shown in table 1. Those mentally retarded persons living in group homes of different sizes (2–66 inhabitants), distributed throughout the city area, as well as varying intensity of care are regarded as "non-institutionalized". The "institutionalized" group consists only of adult inhabitants (> 18 years) living in a large institution (for details see: Meins 1988 and 1989a).

Table 1
Sample Characteristics and Drug Usage

Sample characteristics	No. of persons surveyed	% receiving drugs		
		Psychotropic	Neuroleptic	Anticonvulsant
Age (Years)				
I 19-40	422	25	22	30
II 41-59	503	22	18	16
III ≥ 60	229	16	11	6
Chi^2 (df=2)		6.67*	13.89***	62.45***
Sex				
Male	664	25	22	21
Female	490	17	14	17
Chi^2 (df+1)		9.39**	16.74***	NS
Sample				
Institutionalized	765	26	22	23
Non-Institutionalized	389	13	11	12
Chi^2 (df=1)		26.88***	23.13***	20.70***
Total	1154	22	18	19

NS p >.05
* p <.05
** p <.01
*** p <.001

Furthermore, the essential results are shown in table 1. Correspondingly, at least one psychotropic drug is taken by 22% of the persons of the entire sample. There is a distinct correlation to sex, setting and an inverse correlation to age for psychotropic drugs on the whole and for neuroleptics: the number of psychotropics taken in the youngest age group is approximately double as high as in the group of persons older than 60 years. Two thirds of all psychotropic drugs prescribed are neuroleptics. The other psychotropic drug groups not listed in table 1 together amount to a prevalence rate of 9%, barely half of it being tranquilizers. The share of mentally retarded adults simultaneously treated with several psychotropic drugs is 43%. Nearly every fifth person receives anticonvulsives, the prevalence of which is clearly related to setting and age (table 1). Finally, it should be mentioned that 24% of the mentally retarded adults treated with anticonvulsives are additionally administered psychotropic drugs.

For both groups – the institutionalized and the non-institutionalized – both psychotropic drug prevalence and anticonvulsive prevalence is markedly lower than most prevalence rates previously published. This is definitely also true for rates specific to age, provided that a comparison is possible (Intagliata and

Rinck 1985). The psychotropic drug prevalence for the non-institutionalized group corresponds to the rate determined in a comparable sample in New Zealand (Aman et al. 1985). Both studies may indicate a more cautious approach to prescription of psychotropic drugs, compared to the U.S.

The sample examined seems to show an essential peculiarity in view of the fact that, with advancing years, there is a most considerable decrease in psychotropic drug prevalence and, above all, anticonvulsive prevalence. Although the results of the studies on psychotropic drug prevalence of mentally retarded old persons are contradictory by all means (Aman 1990), there appears to be a tendency of a positive correlation between age and psychotropic drug prevalence (e.g. Buck and Sprague 1989; Intagliata and Rinck 1985). On the contrary, a higher incidence of epilepsy in mentally retarded old persons – as well as a less marked decrease in anticonvulsive prevalence – is similarly documented, as well as the well-known correlation to the degree of mental retardation (Corbett 1981; Lund 1985). In the sample examined, however, the prevalence rate of psychotropic drugs and especially anticonvulsives decreases in advancing years in such an extreme way that a considerable underrepresentation of severely mentally retarded persons additionally suffering from psychological disturbance has to be expected in age group III. This may probably be a direct consequence of the atrocities committed during the Nazi era, which quite a few inhabitants of the institution studied had fallen victim to.

Risk factors

In the following, the factors to which the prescription of psychotropic drugs is related are analyzed in detail. As is known, aggressive behavior represents the feature which is most consistently associated with psychotropic drug treatment of institutionalized mentally retarded persons (Intagliata and Rinck 1985; Stone et al. 1989). In the present study we tried to find the answer to the question why some of those mentally retarded adults with maladaptive behavior are administered psychotropic drugs and some are not.

A total of 692 of the institutionalized mentally retarded persons mentioned above – corresponding to 90% – were screened for the incidence of aggressive behavior problems. The case definition was based on whether aggressive behavior against persons or objects had been observed during the past four weeks. This applied to 16% (n = 109). These 109 persons were then examined more closely (for details see: Meins 1989b), concerning:

- demographic characteristics; adaptive behavior by means of the "Adaptive Behavior Scale" (Nihira et al. 1975); the degree of mental retardation (four-grade rating scale reaching from mild to profound);
- type, frequency and severity of aggressive behavior, the latter measured on a four-grade scale according to the staff reactions, reaching from "no reaction" up to "ask for help" (also see Hill and Bruininks 1984);
- and, finally, psychotropic drug treatment.

As shown in table 2, every second of those persons with aggressive behavior is under psychotropic drug treatment.

In case of absent aggressive behavior, this rate only amounts to 24%. The significantly more frequent psychotropic drug treatment of the group showing aggressive behavior applies equally to men and women as well as to the two age groups.

A step-by-step discriminant analysis was made in order to find out about the variables distinguishing persons with aggressive behavior being under psychotropic drug treatment from those with aggressive behavior not being under psychotropic drug treatment. 15 independent variables were included altogether. Significant distinction between both groups could be made by only five variables, together accounting for 29% of the variance (table 3). The higher the absolute value of the so-called standardized discriminant coefficient of a variable is, the higher its accounting value is; therefore, age is the most significant and the staffresident ratio is the least significant feature. Correspondingly, a psychotropic drug treatment of the mentally retarded persons with aggressive behavior studied is all the more probable,

- the younger they are,
- the more motor skills they have
- the fewer self-help skills they have,
- the rarer a trigger of aggressive behavior can be perceived by the staff
- and the better the staff:resident ratio of the corresponding ward is.

Table 2
Relationship between Aggressive Behavior, Psychotropic Drug Use, and Demographic Characteristics

	Aggressive Behavior				
	Yes (n=109)		No (n=583)		
	Psychotropic Drug Use (%)				
Demographic Characteristics	yes	no	yes	no	Chi^2
Age (Years)					
19-40	66	34	18	82	47.97***
> 40	29	71	16	84	4.94*
Sex					
Male	56	44	29	71	16.84***
Female	42	58	16	84	15.71***
Total	50	50	24	76	30.79***

* p <.05
*** p <.001

The characteristics "younger", "better motor skills" and "no trigger perceivable" can be assumed to be associated with an increase of – actual or alleged – threat. In addition, "minor self-help skills" and "no trigger perceivable" often certainly complicate pedagogic-psychological interventions, so that a psychotropic drug treatment is preferred. Even though a higher staff number does not necessarily lead to improved care (Landesman-Dwyer 1981), it has to be taken into account that exactly those persons who are the most difficult to look after and who require great expenditure of care, live in groups looked after by a high staff number. The group climate which, in any case, is already heavily burdened should rather necessitate to protect the other inhabitants, the staff or the person affected himself from the possible effects of maladaptive behavior.

Table 3
Discriminant Analysis: Variables Predicting Psychotropic Drug Use

Variables	Standardized Discriminant Coefficient
Age	0.620
Motor Skills	– 0.484
Stimulus	0.471
Self–Help Skills	0.377
Staff:Resident Ratio	– 0.317

It is surprising that obviously neither frequency nor severity of aggressive behavior is associated with psychotropic drug treatment. With certain reservations it has to be considered that the severity of maladaptive behavior defined by four possible ways of staff reactions in the present study represents a too inaccurate method of measurement. The fact that psychotropic drug treatment is not related to the frequency of maladaptive behavior corresponds with the results of a different study recently published (Chadsey-Rusch and Sprague 1989). In this study both the continuation and termination of neuroleptic drug treatment did not prove to be related to the frequency of individual behavior problems either. It is rather assumed by the author "... that staff perceptions of maladaptive behavior, in combination with favorable attitudes toward drug treatment influenced the decision ..." (p. 614). In consideration of the result submitted here it might be added that what matters is the question of finding out about further personal and institutional characteristics for the incidence of maladaptive behavior more than the isolated perception of maladaptive behavior.

I have attempted to elucidate at least part of what is associated with the decision in favor of a psychotropic drug treatment. A number of aspects, such as e.g. the staff attitude towards such a treatment, were not taken into account. However, we should not believe that all the criteria relevant for decisions can be clarified completely. Irrational or at least very subjective ideas most frequently play a part in reaching a decision in favor of or against a psychotropic drug treatment.

References

Aman M.G. (1990) Considerations in the use of psychotropic drugs in elderly mentally retarded persons. J. Ment. Defic. Res. 34, 1–10.

Aman M.G., Field C.J. and Bridgman G.D. (1985) City-wide survey of drug patterns among non-institutionalized mentally retarded persons. Appl. Res. Ment. Retard. 6, 159–171.

Aman, M.G. and Singh N.N. (1988) Patterns of drug use: Methodological considerations, measurement techniques, and future trends. In Psychopharmacology of the Developmental Disabilities, M.g. Aman and N.N. Singh (eds), pp. 1–28. Springer Verlag, Berlin.

Buck J.A. and Sprague R.L. (1989) Psychotropic medication of mentally retarded residents in community long-term care facilities. Am. J. Ment. Retard. 93, 618–623.

Chadsey-Rusch J. and Sprague R.L. (1989) Maladaptive behaviors associated with neuroleptic drug maintenance. Am. J. Ment. retard. 93, 607–617.

Corbett, J. (1981) Epilepsy and mental retardation. In Epilepsy and Psychiatry, E.H. Reynolds and M.R. Trimble (eds). pp. 138–146. Churchill Livingstone, Edinburgh.

Hill B.K. and Bruininks R.H. (1984) Maladaptive behavior of mentally retarded individuals in residential facilities. Am. J. Ment. Defic. 88, 380–387.

Intagliata H., and Rinck C. (1985) Psychoactive drug use in public and community residential facilities for mentally retarded persons. Psychopharmacol. Bull. 21, 268–284.

Landesman-Dwyer S. (1981) Living in the community. Am. J. Ment. Defic. 86, 223–234.

Lund J. (1985) Epilepsy and psychiatric disorder in the mentally retarded. Acta psychiatr. scand. 72, 557–562.

Meins W. (1988) Behandlung mit Antiepileptika – Eine Erhebung bei geistig behinderten Erwachsenen. Rehabilitation 28, 10–14.

Meins W. (1989a) Psychopharmakogebrauch bei geistig behinderten Erwachsenen. Psychiat. Prax. 15, 218–222.

Meins W. (1989b) Aggressives Verhalten bei geistig behinderten Personen: Prävalenz und Zusammenhang mit sozialer Unterstützung. Heilpäd. Forsch. 15, 98–103.

Nihira K., Foster R., Shellhaas M. and Leland H. (1975) AAMD Adaptive Behavior Scale. AAMD, Washington D.C.

Poindexter A.R. (1989) Psychotropic drug patterns in a large ICF/MR Facility: A ten-year experience. Am. J. Ment. Retard. 93, 624–626.

Stone R.K., Alvarez W.F., Ellman G., Hom A.C. and White, J.F. (1989) Prevalence and prediction of psychotropic drug use in California developmental centers. Am. J. Ment. Retard. 93, 627–632.

Došen, A., Van Gennep, A., Zwanikken, G.J. (Eds.) (1990). Treatment of Mental Illness and Behavioral Disorder in the Mentally Retarded. Proceedings of the International Congress, May 3rd & 4th, 1990, Amsterdam, the Netherlands. Leiden, the Netherlands: Logon Publications.

Chapter 28

Behaviour treatment and behaviour therapy within the limits of the dutch care for the mentally retarded

G. van Osch

1. Frame of reference

The distinction between behaviour treatment and behaviour therapy runs parallel to the items "mini" and "maxi" in the title. In behaviour treatment (mini) the area of intervention is large. However, the measures taken are less radical than in the behaviour therapeutic intervention (maxi). To clarify this reference, the following framework is given (fig.1. Van Osch, 1986 en 1988):

Figure 1

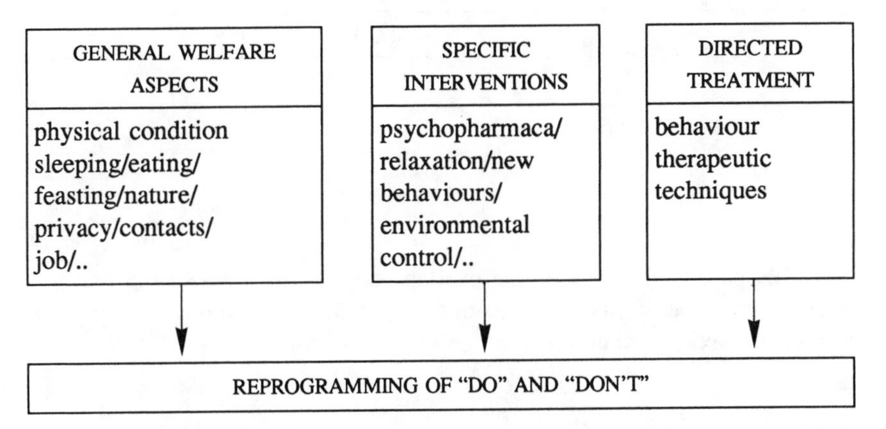

Not every complaint needs a complete therapeutic process. That would be a superfluous spending of time and money. Sometimes it is sufficient to improve some sources of everyday pleasure which gives more perspective to a *harmonious and happy* life. Perhaps the reprogramming delivers new opportunities for systematic amelioration of the general welfare. Only when we do not, or not sufficiently, succeed, we have to decide to apply specific and more radical interventions, e.g., psychopharmaca, relaxation or differential reinforcement of other behaviour. Sometimes even this investment is not satisfactory. Then a therapeutic approach can be effective and efficient. After these considerations it may be clear that a treatment can only be succesful if our measures lead to a reprogramming of "do" and "don't", and by doing so to a better life.

2. (S)GLGG

The Dutch Ministry of Health, Welfare and Culture, has described the mentally retarded with conduct disorders as "(S)GLGG": very(S) disturbing(G) persons with a mild(L) mental(G) handicap(G). The range of successively higher grades of disturbing behaviour (LGG, GLGG and SGLGG) is asking for an intensifying of the care (fig.2.).

Figure 2

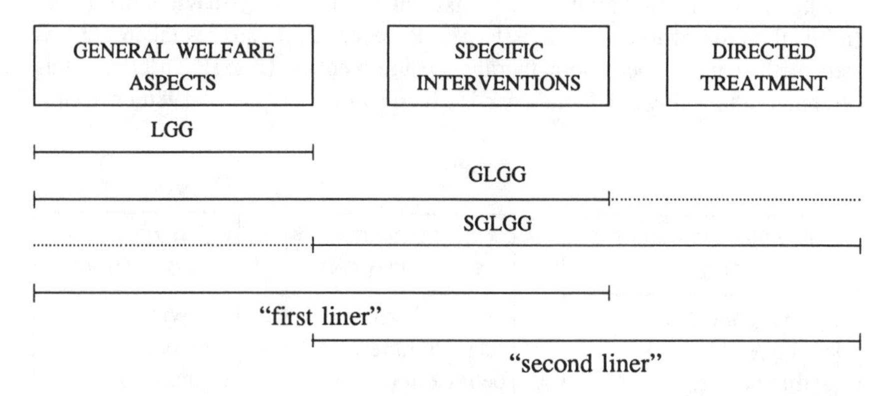

This paper will focus on the overlap between the areas of the first and second line (echelon), i.e. the area of the specific interventions, a mixture of mini- and maxi-interventions.

3. Specific interventions

3.1. Specific environmental control

The aim of our interventions in mental illness and conduct disorders is the reprogramming of "do" and "don't". What does this "do" and "don't" imply? The following figure gives an overview (fig.3.).

Figure 3

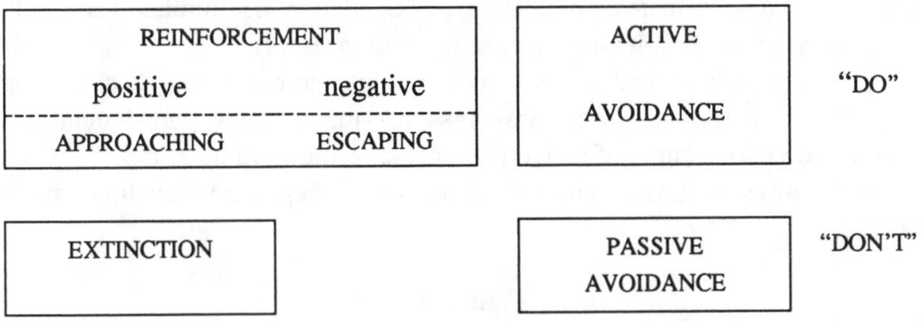

<table>
<tr><td colspan="2">REINFORCEMENT
positive   negative</td><td>ACTIVE
AVOIDANCE</td><td>"DO"</td></tr>
<tr><td>APPROACHING</td><td>ESCAPING</td><td></td><td></td></tr>
<tr><td colspan="2">EXTINCTION</td><td>PASSIVE
AVOIDANCE</td><td>"DON'T"</td></tr>
</table>

The terminology is taken from Bakker (1987). Approach means to evoke positively experienced stimuli, resulting in positive reinforcement of the behaviour. Escape is the elimination of negatively experienced stimuli, resulting in negative reinforcement of this escaping behaviour. Both are modes of reinforcement and therefore, they are grouped together.

Active avoidance is a combination of the two ways of reinforcement i.e. taking measures to assure as few negative stimuli as possible – it's really a way of doing. In other, more technical words, it is the answer to the question: which gives me a guarantee against bad luck and troubles and make me certain of efficient aproaches and escapes?

Apart from these three "do's" there are two forms of "don't". Extinction is a process of gradual reduction of responses due to the omission of reinforcement. Passive avoidance means: being confronted with negative stimuli which cannot be escaped. In other words: punishment.

All these processes are very important in our daily life. The two ways of avoidance are protecting us. Approach means an enrichment of our life. Escape gives us liberty. And extinction is a way of saving energy. In these terms, mental health means that the different processes maintain their impact in all situations. In this way we obtain the utmost of our investments in life.

Mental illness arises when one process and especially active avoidance prevails upon another or exists at the cost of another. Why especially "active avoidance"? Research confirms that this rather complex process (of guarantee) can easily degenerate to a fatal vicious circle of increasing avoidance. In this pathological process passive avoidance plays a prominent role: negative stimuli, experienced by the individual as being arbitrary or response-independent, reinforce the vicious circle.

What does the life of any moderately or mildly mentally handicapped look like? In any case, he is less able to discriminate between profitable approach and avoidance. Furthermore, failing more often than non-handicapped people, the handicapped gets more punishment. Passive avoidance is a way of learning as well, however, a rather dangerous one. By "negative attention getting" learning goes in the direction of antisocial/psychopathic or psychotic behaviour. What will prevail, the former or the latter, depends on the question: does the child learn to discriminate or not. The psychopath can discriminate very well, in contrast with the psychotic (fig.4. at the bottom right).

A second pathological process goes through the centre (fig.4. at the top right). We have already seen how response-independent punishment can augment the vicious circle of active avoidance, resulting in neuroticism. When the whole process gets a chronic character, a psychotic development is probable.

Figure 4

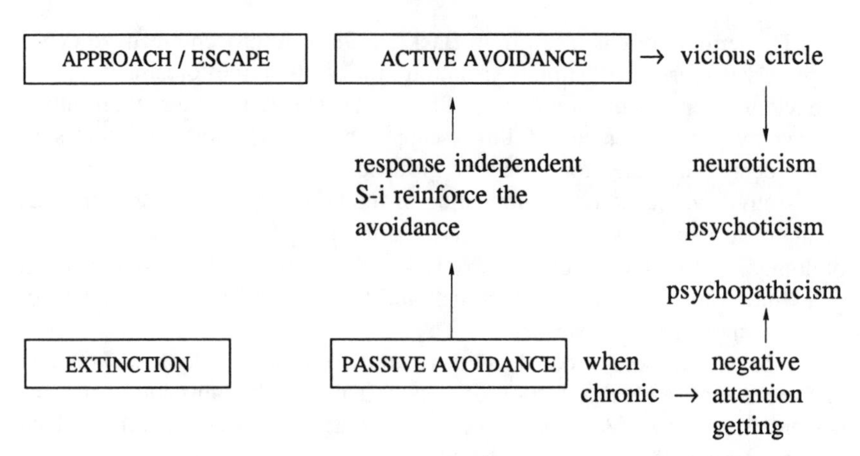

How can we stop or slow down this kind of process? Environmental control is the first way (fig.5.).

Figure 5

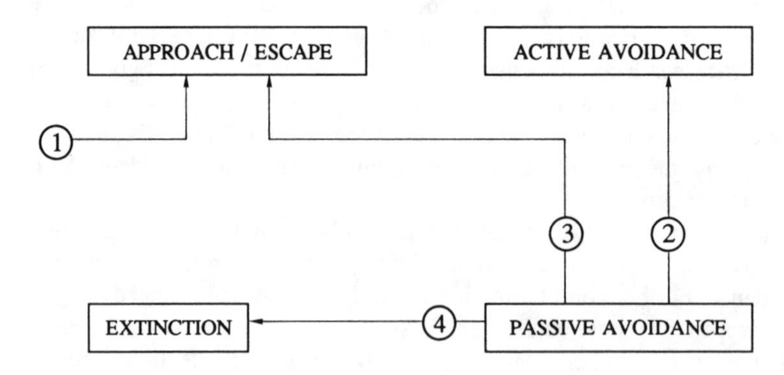

(1) Let the handicapped person experience the pleasure of approach. However, at his own level. Many handicapped people suffer from being overcharged all their lives. By organizing a lot of regression for these overcharged people they may recover their breath: to (re)discover the primitive feelings of pleasure, delight and rest, giving a rest, with respect and appraisal. Another way to promote approach is to organize social training. And again: adapted to their own level of functioning. Most of the training programs have failed because they have been too difficult for our target group.

(2) The most direct and essential measure is to make punishment response-dependent and, of course, to stop response-independent punishment. In this way the throttling vicious circle is widening a little. Although logical and clear, it may be very difficult to implement this in an institution. As with all techniques on contingency management, the implementation demands a very cohesive staff with an open mind to ethical questions. One of the most effective ways of contingency management is the reward and penalty-system. This system however, is very vulnerable in the hands of an inexperienced team.

(3) Making the passive avoidance response-dependent results in another positive effect. If punishment is response-dependent as well as escapable, the learning of new discrimination furnishes the active avoidance with fresh stimulus material. And so the resistance against pathological avoidance is growing.

(4) Any kind of self-destructive behaviour requires a resolute termination of it. How can we do this without producing the negative side-effects of active avoidance? Perhaps the solution of this question attributes more to the alleviation of our problems than the modes of environmental control just mentioned. Quite in general, it can be stated that in these cases of force majeure the positive effects of punishment increase when the process of extinction is cooperating simultaneously. Thus, we ought to prevent our measures to have any reinforcing value. The technique of "time out" fulfils this requirement. The individual should realize: "my behaviour is giving me no advantages; this moment is the absolute zero-point and – how paradoxically ! – it gives me an enriching experience". Needless to say that this measure demands an open-mindedness and ethical warrants.

3.2. Specific facilities

The necessarily facilities are roughly mentioned in the former paragraphs. We can range them as follows:

(1) *Relaxation.* Fore this we do need much time and space. We have to distinguish:

free relaxation: two times a day the individuals enjoy quiet music while in a relaxed position in the group and on a voluntary basis.

obliged relaxation: to stay in bed or hydro, individually and in an agreeable manner. The staff is involved on a more or less continuous schedule.

required relaxation: using physical restrain by the staff, the individual is urged to give up his agitation.

(2) *Separation*. As a rule, separation is used as a form of time out (see above). It is applied briefly, laconic and without a fuss afterwards. Sometimes separation is a way of social deprivation: the purpose is to load up the social stimuli. However, the risks of this technique make it a part of the maxi-interventions (see figure 1.).

(3) *Observation and registration*. Reporting honestly and reliably is indispensable in a group that exhibits so many events. It constitutes one of the most relevant and important aspects of implementing the adequate attitude for treatment in the institution. In our ward we are using a five points scale from "++" to "––" for each individual, linked with five behavioural features (see appendix). The schedules can be easily elaborated by Chi-squared-test and can be visualized in graphics. Feedback to the staff is an important aspect of implementation.

(4) *Psychopharmaca*. With the use of psychopharmaca an attempt can be made to show the behaviour treatment measures to full advantage.

(5) *Social competency training*. It can be given in a curriculum or can be merged in the daily program. The advantage of the curriculum is its contribution to the indispensable enrichment of the environment. A disadvantage is its large investment in personnel, time and space.

(6) *Ethics*. As stated previously, some interventions are threatening the life environment as a whole, especially when ethical aspects are neglected by the staff. There should be guarantees for ethically justified treatment. Establishing an independent ethical committee for an institution or an entire region could be such a guarantee.

(7) *Implementation*. A solid team of educators – as we have – is a conditio sine qua non. Pre-investment in creating a sufficiently powerful position and role in the management of the ward, teaching of personnel, permanent education of the staff, etcetera, is always profitable: the costs will regain themselves. Nevertheless the costs can be very high, in particular concerning the time and perhaps stress!

3.3. Specific methods: mini interventions

In the preceding paragraphs several mini-interventions are mentioned. With mini-interventions the chance of enduring succes is emphasized – in terms of generalization in time, place and person – rather than the extent of the changed behaviour (Ager, 1987). In other words, small but constant gain is more pursued than a big but uncertain success. Therefore maintaining "natural contingencies" (Baer & Wolf, 1967) is purpose number one. The treatment will be adapted to it and not vice versa. In this way the desirable behaviour will be incorporated in the daily routines. In concrete terms this means:

- create situations beforehand which control adequate behaviour. Only intervene when necessary. A well-considered programme proved effective in daily practise belongs to it. Forming an open and critical team is such a situation. Facilities as a time out and a relaxation-room are necessary to maintain the results of interventions. Things like these are mentioned before; now the rationale, the idea behind it may become clear.
- organize a reward and penalty-system in such a way that it can be perished automatically in course of time; that's to say, to be dissolved in natural contingencies.
- in almost all the cases DRO (differential reinforcement of other behaviour) has to be preferred over the other techniques, because DRO makes use of already existing behaviour and is thus saving energy for establishing new behaviour.
- finally, and we are back now to our starting point: a mentally retarded person doesn't really refuse his cooperation but he is lacking discriminating potential. Continuous feedback in the right direction and preferably in small steps performs wonders, for instance by monitoring. Another advantage is the enriching effect on the environment.

4. Maxi-interventions or behaviour therapy

Only when the specific measures mentioned above are implemented in an institution, therapeutic intervention can be done in a justified way. In institutions without competent behavioural therapists one can take refuge in "supermediation", i.e. supervision by a professional and specialised second liner. Three processes always form part of the therapeutic treatment: the development of a functional *analysis* based on contingency data, the design of a *treatment* according to this and the *evaluation* by carefully selected instruments. The heart of the whole process is the functional analysis: enlarging a fragment of the holistic "N=1"-theory in such a way that some details can be modified with a mobilizing effect on one's life.

References

Ager, A. (1987). Minimal intervention: a strategy for generalized behaviour change with mentally handicapped individuals. Behav. Psychother., 15, 16-30.

Baer, D.M. and Wolf, M.M. (1967). The entry into natural communities of reinforcement. In: Control of Human Behaviour, vol. 2. R. Ulrich, T. Stachnik and J. Mabry (Eds.). Glenview, Ill: Scott Foresman.

Bakker-de Pree, B. (1987). Constructionele gedragstherapie, Nijmegen: Dekker-Van de Vegt.
Osch, G. van (1986). Dwangmatigheid bij zwakzinnigen; enige casuïstiek, RUIT, nr. 46 (12), 12-25.
Osch, G. van (1988). Gedragstherapie. In: Leerboek Zwakzinnigenzorg, G.H. van Gemert, W.K. Noorda (Eds.). Van Gorcum, Assen-Maastricht.

Appendix

Example observation schedule

N.N.
- - - - - - - - - - - -

Give a mark ("X") to the feature which meets at best his average behaviour on that time.

+ + talks spontaneously, is actively.
+ answers, performs tasks.
0 between "+" and "–" or dubious.
– doesn't answer, performs a task only when urged.
– – obsessed, immobilized.

Weeknr:		++	+	0	–	– –	Particular details:
MON	8-10						
	10-12						
	12-14						
	14-16						
	16-18						
	18-20						
	20-22						
TUE	8-10						
	10-12						
	12-14						
	14-16						
	16-18						
	18-20						
	20-22						

etc.

Došen, A., Van Gennep, A., Zwanikken, G.J. (Eds.) (1990). Treatment of Mental Illness and Behavioral Disorder in the Mentally Retarded. Proceedings of the International Congress, May 3rd & 4th, 1990, Amsterdam, the Netherlands. Leiden, the Netherlands: Logon Publications.

Chapter 29

Training of social skills with mildly mentally retarded persons with severe behavioral disorders

A.L. le Grand

Introduction

"Hoeve Boschoord", the institution where I am working, is a treatment institution for so-called mildly mentally retarded persons with severe behavioral disorders. In other words, people who function on a sub-normal mental level (IQ-range between 50 and 90) with serious social problems and/or psychic disturbances or dysfunctions.

With these patients one sees severe forms of disturbing behaviour, criminality, severe forms of verbal and physical agression, severely destructive behaviour, suicide attempts and automutilation, sexually overactive behaviour, extremely withdrawn behaviour and addictions.

Beside this, there are problematic personality disturbances, severe contact disturbances, problems with impulse and agression regulation, fear disturbances, mood disturbances, depressions, neurotic and (borderline) psychotic disturbances.

The disturbance needs to be of the kind that the person can no longer be kept in his surroundings nor can be treated within his own context. Although previous attempts for treatment usually have been tried and failed, for admittance to the institution a treatment perspective needs to be present.

The age of our population ranges between about 18 and 55 years.

About half of the patients have been admitted through judiciary measures.

Why train of social skills

A large amount of our patients have difficulties to maintain themselves adequately in our society. Social situations quickly lead to problems, since these situations are too complex and call for too large a skill of abstraction. It is assumed that a part of these behaviour problems partly result from deficiency in mastering social skills (for example inadequate ability to make a contact, inadequate conflict resolution, etc.) and the secondary consequences of this (for example feelings of insufficiency as a result of the many rejections; negative self-image; overcompensation of feelings of insufficiency, feelings of loneliness; boredom; the inability to instigate change in the situation; (borderline)criminal behaviour, etc.).

One of the therapeutic interventions with such a population is training of social skills. Arnold Goldstein developed such a method; a structured learning therapy. It would lead us too far to go deeper into the theoretical backgrounds of this method. In this respect I refer to the literature which has been published about this subject.

The method we use is a revised derivation of Goldstein's structured learning therapy, which was developed by the Department of Psychology of the University of Groningen.

This specific method meets the needs as well as the capacities of a number of our patients, because this therapy is, as you may well know, relatively simple (social skills are broken up into small steps), it is structured, goal-oriented and pragmatic. It emphasises concrete behaviour instead of complex and abstract verbalisations. Beside this, group processes play a relatively small role, which reduces feelings of fear and tension for the individual members.

Procedure

Since October 1988 we are using this training program, in combination with other forms of therapy. By now we have started our third group.

For selection of the group members we use the following criteria of indication:

a) IQ equal or above 70.
b) Scores on the S.S.V. (Screeninglist Social Skills) and the G.B.I. (Behaviour Assessment Instrument).
   At this moment (with our third group) we use, because of its higher validity, the S.A.S.-A. (Social Fear Scale for Adolescence) and the S.I.G. (Scale for Interpersonal Behaviour).
c) Some reading and writing skills.
d) An awareness of own restricted social skills.
e) Motivation to participate.
f) No display of disturbing behaviour, in the sense of obstructing the therapy-group.
g) An indicated stay of at least half a year in the institution.
h) A talk with the trainers in order to confirm the indicatory assessments with personal impressions.

Pre- as well as post-assessment of the trainees takes place on two levels:

a) Social behaviour in general. With groups 1 and 2 we used the Behaviour Assessment Instrument. At this moment we use the Scale for Interpersonal Behaviour.

b) Specific social skills. With groups 1 and 2 we used the Screening list Social Skills. At this moment we use the Social Fear Scale for Adolescence.

The questionaires are filled in by two of the staff, except for the Scale for Interpersonal Behaviour, which is filled in by the patient himself (sometimes with help of a staff member).

Some technical information on the training

- Each group consists of 5 members.
- There are 2 trainers.
- Once a week there is a session of 2 hours, with a break of 10 minutes.
- The total amount of training session is usually 30 to 35.
- On average we use about 4 sessions to teach and train a skill.

Characteristics of the selected members

- Age range: 21-35 (group 1), 22-28 (group 2)
- IQ-range: 64-94 (group 1), 65-83 (group 2)
- All participants were male.
- All had a history of severe psychosocial deprivation during childhood (broken homes, marital disharmony, violence, brought up in children's homes, history of criminality in the immediate family as well as the urban environment, etc.).
- All had a history of multiple behavioral problems resulting from childhood.
- Reasons for admission to the institution were:
  5 (50%) were admitted following a sex offence.
  3 (30%) were admitted following arson.
  2 (20%) were admitted following theft.

Some brief information about the training program

The training program deals with the following skills:

1. To introduce yourself.
2. To ask something.
3. To say no / to refuse.
4. To discuss something.
5. To criticize.
6. To be criticized.
7. To handle disappointment.
8. To handle anger.
9. To give compliments.

The construction for each skill is as follows:

1. Instruction: information about how one should act in certain situations and what the effects of these actions are.
   Complex social skills are broken up into behaviour units as concrete as possible. Models on a video-tape demonstrate this particular skill, how it can be applied in the right and in the wrong way.
2. Practice: the skill is practiced by means of role-play; firstly imitating the video-tape and secondly using personal situations.
3. Feedback: feedback is given to these role plays, both by the participants and by the trainers. For this we also use video.
4. Transfer: it is planned that these skills are then to be trained in everyday life by means of homework.

Programwise the training of a skill is structured in the following parts:

1. Introduction of the relevant skill, that means a general talk about the various situations in which the ability to apply this particular skill is needed.
2. This leads to a number of learning points, which are concrete behaviour units. For example the skill 'to ask something':
   a) Think about what you would like to ask exactly.
   b) Say that you would like to ask something.
   c) Ask your question.
   d) Explain why you ask.
   e) Listen carefully to the answer.
   f) Tell what you think of the answer.
3. Next a videotape demonstration is given of a social situation, in which the skill we are practicing is showed in the wrong way.
4. After this there is an evaluation, analysing and comparing the earlier learning points with the demonstrated situation.
5. The same social situation is showed again, this time using the learning points in the right way.
6. Again the learning points are checked.
7. Then the demonstrated right example is imitated in the form of a role-play.
8. Again there is an evaluation, using the learning points.
9. Then social situations from the people's own lives, in which this social skill is required, are practiced. First by having the person observe how others show his situation in role-play, using the learning points.
   After feedback is given, the person concerned will role-play his own situation. If necessary, it is differentiated to several degrees of difficulties.
   Some examples of situations which have been trained by the patients:
   - ask the unit-head to be allowed to buy a new motorbike.
   - ask another patient to turn the music down.
   - ask for a raise in salary.

- ask for work at the labour exchange (especially questions about working history and current residence call for a lot of tension).
- refuse to take a beer in the disco.
- have fear of heights and nevertheless be forced to climb a ladder to paint the roof, refuse in a right way.

10. After this the role-play is evaluated.
11. In the form of homework the trained skill needs to be applied in the week (for example at work, at the sports club, in the living situation, etc.).
12. In the next session, the homework is evaluated using the learning points.
13. If necessary, that means in those cases where the homework failed, an other so-called 'reconstructing role-play' is applied.
14. Then a new social situation requiring social skills is trained. (see 9-13).

Some experiences and considerations

As to motivation: from the fact that the attendance was very good we should be able to deduct that there was enough motivation with the participants. It is not clear how much the fact that we are dealing with forced detainment is playing a role in the motivation of the participants. We have to consider that the treatment team thinks that it is useful for the patient to participate in the Goldstein therapy and it is them who are enrolling the patient. Based on the influence (and maybe the pressure) from the staff there might be cases in which we have to speak of external motivation, rather than the patient's own motivation. However, one should also consider that the participant is not only participating because another person thinks that it is important for him to participate, but also that he needs to be motivated himself, because he experiences the lack of social skills and that he is willing to work on change. This then could be called internal motivation.

Influence of the psychopathology and/or psychiatric disturbances

We were confronted with the fact that, during the selection, we did not take into sufficient consideration the influences of psychopathological and/or psychiatric disturbances. For example:

a) There was a manic-depressive patient. Afterwards we can say that this was a contra-indication. During the period of enrolment he was depressed and on this basis sub-assertive. This was not based on his lacks of social skills. After the depressive phase, there was a period in which he functioned on a manic basis: he showed extremely active and apparent-assertive behaviour. In the group he demonstrated himself in a very disturbing way: he interrupted and interjected, was vividly associating, overrated himself extremely and provoked many conflicts.
This irritated the other participants, asking a lot of their comprehension and adaptability. Besides, it required a lot of energy and tact from both trainers to lead the group and individual processes in the right direction.

And last but not least, it appeared that this investment did not lead to noticeable increase of his social skills.

b) Symptoms as a part of the Psychopathiform Syndrom (Antisocial Personality Disorder, according to the DSM III 301.70), like
   - overcompensation of feelings of insufficiency;
   - tendency to flight;
   - low confrontation tolerance;
   - difficulties in making a relationship.

Two participants (one in group 1 and one in group 2) did not experience themselves as someone who has problems in social situations. They had the tendency to pose themselves as superior. Assertive behaviour was experienced as a synonym for 'win the game' / 'get what you want'.

Based on these experiences we can conclude that in cases in which such a psychiatric or psychopathological picture dominates:

1. the diagnostic criteria needs to be sharper.
2. it can be extremely disturbing and obstructive for the other group members.
3. it can lead to little benefit from such a form of therapy for this particular participant .

Influence of the mental capacities

Both in group 1 and in group 2 we had one participant with an I.Q. that was lower than the indicated norm (respectively 64 and 65). We wanted to give them a chance, because we had the impression that these patients would benefit from the training program. During the training it turned out that they had relatively more difficulties than the other participants. This was demonstrated in the fact that their thought processes ran on a even more concrete level than those of the other participants (for example less introspective capacities, less empathising capacities, etc.).

They were less inventive in looking for alternative possibilities and were often stuck in the given training situations, without the ability to transfer the trained skills to other situations. This forced the trainers as well as the other participants to translate on even more simple and concrete levels.

Based on this experience we can say that

1) it is not recommandable to have too large a range in mental levels;
2) I.Q. below 70 is a contra-indication.

Cooperation with the staff

It turned out to be of high importance that the staff knows what is happening in the therapy. Reasons for this are:

- they can help with thinking up new training situations;
- they can help with writing down of homework;

- they can show interest for what is going on; this works in a stimulating way and has a reïnforcing function;
- it increases the relationship between the staff and the patient;
- it provides possible access points for talking.

The confidentiality

It is of utmost importance that the therapy has a confidential character. It is our experience that the participants need to overcome a certain shyness in order to be able to bring in examples of their own lives (too private, having too many relations to well-known others within the institution, etc.). There was the fear that any one of the group members or one of the trainers would not keep the information confidential and would talk to other people.
Without confidentiality, certain parts of the program become difficult to train (for example 'to criticize', 'to discuss something' and 'to say no').

Transfer

"Hoeve Boschoord" turned out to be a difficult training context. The majority of our patients reacts less 'reasonable' and more primary than in the average society. Consequence: there is a lack of transfer.

Positive feed-back

Finally we need to state that all participants indicated at the final evaluation that they had experienced this course as meaningful and useful and all felt a need to go on and regretted the end of it.

Post-assessment-results

A week after the training program we asked, as indicated already, two of the staff to fill in the S.S.V. and the G.B.I.. With 3 of the 10 participants this has not been done by the same staff members as with the first assessment, as these participants have been placed in other groups. We may expect that this has biased the reliability of our results.

Results were as follows:

Group 1:

	S.S.V.*		G.B.I.*	
A	(20)**	46 =+130.00 %	(118)	87 = +26.27 %
B	(35)	62 = +77.14 %	(96)	93 = +3.13 %
C	(37)	63 = +70.27 %	(92)	53 = +42.39 %
D	(34)	31 = −8.82 %	(96)	92 = +4.17 %
E	(40)	47 = +17.50 %	(98)	50 = +48.98 %
Total	(166)	249 = +50.00 %	(500) 3	75 = +25.00 %

* S.S.V.: The lower the score, the less social skills.
G.B.I.: The higher the score, the less social skills.
** The scores between brackets are the first assessments.

Group 2:

	S.S.V.		G.B.I.	
A	(25)	60 = +140.06 %	(86)	69 = +19.77 %
B	(47)	34 = −27.66 %	(109)	96 = +11.93 %
C	(35)	55 = +57.14 %	(121)	86 = +28.93 %
D	(43)	32 = −25.58 %	(71)	84 = −18.31 %
E	(40)	74 = +85.03 %	(69)	45 = +34.78 %
Total	(190)	255 = +34.21 %	(456)	380 = +22.79 %

The scores on the S.S.V. are related specifically to social skills, which have been trained in the training program.

The scores on the G.B.I. are related to a larger area of social behaviour. In other words, by the indications of the S.S.V., an appraisal of the effect of the skills as trained in the therapy is given; the G.B.I. can provide clues to whether there has been any generalizing effect.

According to the assessments with the S.S.V. as well as with the G.B.I. we can see an increase of social skills.

At the S.S.V. an increase of 50 % and 34.21 % respectively for group 1 and group 2, at the G.B.I. an increase of 25 % and 22.79 % respectively for group 1 and group 2.

It would not be right to relate this increase only to the participation in the training program. Without doubt there are other variables that will have had their influences. Which ones these have been and in which way they influenced the situation, we don't know exactly.

Conclusions

1. Participation in the training program has a positive influence on the development of some specific social skills and on total assertive behaviour in general.
   N.B. The number of patients that participated in the training program until now is too small (2 x 5) to draw scientifically sound conclusions. However, our experiences are promising.
   Research at the University of Groningen supports our findings.
2. In order to reach optimal results out of the training program, it turned out to be of great importance to have good indications for therapy, based on precised diagnostics, to which aim one should use clearly defined criteria.
3. Contra-indicative, based on our experience with the two groups, are the following:
   a) IQ lower than 70;
   b) A manic-depressive appearance;
   c) Some symptoms as a part of the psychopathiform syndrom.
4. Spreading the mental levels too wide is not to be recommended. It works obstructive in the progression and can lead to irritation of the other group members.
5. Good cooperation with staff embers turned out to be of great importance.
6. As with any form of psychotherapy, confidentiality has shown to be important. It seems to be a necessary condition to get a good working relationship in order to gain maximal benefit of the Goldstein therapy.

References

Bandura, A., 1977, Social learning theory. Englewood Cliffs, N.J., Prentice Hall.

Beekers, M., 1982, Interpersoonlijke vaardigheidstherapieën voor kansarmen. Lisse, Swets & Zeitlinger.

Goldstein, A.P., 1973, Structured learning therapy, toward a psychotherapy for the poor. New York, Academic Press.

Molen, H.T. van der, 1984, Aan verlegenheid valt iets te doen. Een cursus in plaats van therapie. Deventer, Van Loghum Slaterus.

Molen, H.T. van der, en S.A.M. van der Zee, 1985, Sociale redzaamheidsprogramma's voor minderbegaafde jongeren. Rijks Universiteit Groningen, Vakgroep persoonlijkheidspsychologie.

Došen, A., Van Gennep, A., Zwanikken, G.J. (Eds.) (1990). Treatment of Mental Illness and Behavioral Disorder in the Mentally Retarded. Proceedings of the International Congress, May 3rd & 4th, 1990, Amsterdam, the Netherlands. Leiden, the Netherlands: Logon Publications.

Chapter 30

Clinical treatment of behavioral problems in mildly mentally retarded persons with severe personality disorders

G.J.C.M. Verberne

Introduction

In this paper I want to review some of the literature on personality disorders, on dynamics and treatment in general, and with respect to the mentally retarded in particular. I shall especially speak from own experience however.

I shall make a distinction between some groups of personality disorders which has significance as to the choice and possibilities of various treatment methods.

In the so-called extremely behaviour disordered mentally retarded one often encounters personality disorders.

In discussions our patients with colleagues and in supervision contacts there turns out to be little agreement about how to manage severe behavioral problems when they are accompanied by severe personality disorders. Literature proves to give little help, as little is known about personality disorders in the mentally retarded (Menolascino, 1977).

Personality disorders

DSM III R defines personality disorders as disorders in which personality traits (APA, 1987) are inflexible and maladaptive and cause either significant functional impairment or subjective distress.

Personality traits are enduring patterns of perceiving, relating to, and thinking about the environment and oneself and are exhibited in a wide range of important social and personal contexts.

The manifestations of personality disorders are often recognizable by adolescence or earlier and continue throughout most of adult life, though they often become less obvious in middle or old age.

The diagnostic criteria for personality disorders refer to behaviors or traits that are characteristic of the person's recent (past year) and long-term functioning since early adulthood.

The constellation of behaviors or traits causes either significant impairment in social or occupational functioning or subjective distress.

So far DSM-III-R. (APA, 1987). DSM-III-R is not a logical system of diagnosing however. It is descriptive (with some exceptions) and has little relevance with respect to treatment possibilities.

Personality disorders are diagnosed in DSM-III-R on a special axis, axis II, together with amongst others mental retardation.

This could create the impression that personality disorders are not psychiatric diagnosis as such.

However, some personality disorders have underlying mechanisms that make them more similar to some psychotic disturbances, to neurotic disturbances, to the so called dissociative disorders, etc.

In DSM-III-R personality disorders have been grouped into three clusters. The first cluster, referred to as cluster A, includes paranoid, schizoid and schizotypal personality disorders. People with these disorders often appear odd or excentric.

Cluster B includes anti-social, borderline, histrionic and narcissistic personality disorders. People with these disorders often appear dramatic, emotional or erratic.

Cluster C includes avoidant, dependent, obsessive-compulsive and passive agressive personality disorders. People with these disorders often appear anxious or fearful.

Finally there is a residual category that can be used for other specific personality disorders or for mixed conditions, that do not qualify as one of the specific personality disorders described above (APA, 1987). This categorization was made on the base of symptomatology, not of underlying dynamics.

There is a huge gap between diagnostic descriptions in DSM-III-R and psychiatric and psychodynamic literature on personality disorders, defense mechanisms associated with them, etc. (e.g. Van den Brink, 1990; Widiger et al, 1988). This is very clear with respect to the borderline personality disorder, e.g. when one compares DSM-III-R with the psychodynamic approach of Otto Kernberg (e.g. Fahy, 1988; Kernberg, 1978).

In psychodynamic tradition, personality disorders can be viewed as having to do with conditions in which the structure of personality is principally affected, as a result of which functions of ego and super ego are disturbed as well.

This becomes evident when one looks at defense mechanisms. In general the neurotic has more ore less mature defense mechanisms, which are used so intensively and so often that they disturb social functioning and the happiness of the individual.

In psychosis, defense mechanisms are unable to protect the individual from severe anxiety and distress, the individual is not longer capable of controlling his impulses and protecting himself from internal and external stimuli. In personality disorders, defense mechanisms are more or less rigid, are often of a primitive kind, are inflexible and often lead to conflicts with the environment.

In other cases they lead to withdrawal and odd behavior.

When one looks upon personality disorders from a psychodynamic developmentally oriented point of view, it is clear that they are instances of a failure of development with severe consequences.

Personality disorders differ in severity and in nature.

Some personality disorders closely resemble psychosis and sometimes can be viewed upon as precursors of them, although science is unequivocal about this.

Borderline personality disorders and narcissistic personality disorders sometimes very much resemble dissociative disorders such as multiple personality disorders and only seem to differ from them in degree.

The difference between obsessive compulsive neurosis and the obsessive compulsive personality disorder is also often only a difference in degree.

So it seems logical to describe personality disorders from a psychodynamic point of view as having to do with a specific way of differentiation of personality, a specific constellation of preferred defense mechanisms etc. and as manifested by a number of classifiable symptoms.

I want to remark here that there are many theories on the development of personality disorders. I shall not discuss all of them but I want to say that, in my opinion, various factors such as learning history, educational background, heriditary and organic aspects, may have important influence on the etiology, and that in each individual the relative contribution of each factor may be different.

Prevalence

Maybe also because personality disorders do not exist in an absolute way, so that there is a continuum between no personality disorder and severe personality disorder, (e.g. Lerner, 1986), little is known about prevalence.

Another possible reason for the lack of information on prevalence is that personality disorders only come to psychiatric attention when they go together with severe behavioral or psychiatric problems, often after increase of environmental stress. DSM-III-R reports rather high prevalence rates.

I suppose the prevalence will turn to be somewhat lower if one speaks about personality disorders only if there are additional reasons to diagnose them in DSM-III-R categories as sufficient structural, psychodynamic abnormalities characteristic of personality disorders. It probably will be not higher than 5% in normally intelligent adults.

Personality disorders are bordering the following other psychiatric categories (e.g. Alnaes & Torgersen, 1988):

- Schizophrenia (schizotypal personality disorder, possibly schizoid personality disorder).
- Affective psychoses (borderline personality disorder, dependent personality disorder, obsessive compulsive personality disorder, passive aggressive personality disorder). (e.g. Gunderson & Elliot, 1985).
- Pervasive developmental disorder (borderline personality disorder).
- Attention deficit disorder, hyperactivity disorder (anti-social personality disorder).
- Reactive psychosis, conversion (histrionic personality disorder, narcissistic personality disorder).
- Phobias (avoidant personality disorder).
- Alcohol abuse, dependence (passive – aggressive personality disorder, borderline personality disorder, narcissistic personality disorder).
- Multiple personality disorder (borderline personality disorder).
  (See Ross & Gahan 1988 for a review of treatment techniques).

Personality disorder in the mentally retarded

I want to state here that I only speak of personality disorders if the patient fits the DSM-III-R criteria, as well as the structural psychodynamic characteristics of the personality disorder.

Little is known about prevalence in the mentally retarded. There has been little professional interest (Menolascino, 1977).

Menolascino (1985) gave an overview of 543 mentally retarded with an accompanying mental illness. 13% of them had a personality disorder. "Passive dependent" personality disorder and antisocial personality disorder were most common. Menolascino suggests that people with mild mental retardation "are most susceptible to this disorder". Elsewhere (Menolascino 1977) he states that schizoid personality disorder is rarely reported in the mentally retarded. Literature has focused especially on the antisocial personality. Here he summarizes that personality disorders do occur in the mentally retarded, have no distinct etiological relationship to mental retardation and "are not decreased in their frequency in the retarded population".

Corbett (1979) estimated, that 25% of the retarded adults in the Camberwell population study manifested a personality disorder or a severe behavior disorder. The majority of these belonged to the group of immature/unstable persons. He used an impressionistic classification.

Reid (1982) thinks there is no system of classification which can be regarded as acceptable, valid and reliable. In his opinion it is difficult to differentiate between real disorders and behavioural peculiarities. He states that some of the personality problems are organically determined.

Corbett (1979) found that personality disorders occur more frequently in epileptic mentally retarded.

Hunter (1979) thinks that the mentally retarded are prone to the antisocial, the paranoid, the obsessive-compulsive and the anxious personality disorder as he calls it.

Problem is of course to differentiate personality disorders from "normal deviation". To do this we must rely on the structural characteristics. Generally one can say that personality disorders only occur in the less severely mentally retarded (Forrest, 1979).

The more advanced, more "sophisticated" personality disorders (like borderline and narcissistic personality disorders) occur only within a more or less developed ego, so that some stability in the perception of the significant others and themselves is possible. This implies that this condition will not occur with an I.Q. of approx. 70 or less and indeed I never met a patient with these personality disorders in persons of a lower intelligence potential than an I.Q. of 70.

By the way: in the multiple personality disorder the necessary level of ego development is still higher, so that this condition does not seem to occur in I.Q. levels of 100 or lower (although this condition may be so debilitating to normal functioning that patients are viewed as borderline mentally defective persons (e.g. Lindsley, 1986, 1989).

In mildly mentally handicapped persons one can find borderline-like and narcissistic-like behavioural and personality patterns that are sufficiently circumscript for a DSM-III-R personality disorder diagnosis. However, from a structural dynamic point of view, the diagnosis of personality disorders in these cases is far less clear and symptoms are not specific enough.

In my experience, about the same what I said about the borderline personality disorder is true for the histrionic, narcissistic and anti-social behaviour disorder (Reid, 1982). They seem to occur from I.Q. level 60 to 70 onwards.

Paranoid personality disorder, schizotypal personality disorder, obsessive-compulsive personality disorder and passive-aggressive personality disorder seem to occur from I.Q. 50 onwards, according to my experience. The avoidant, schizoid and dependent personality disorders possibly occur also from I.Q. 50 onwards but here the underlying dynamics are less clear. The phenomenology of them is very familiar however to those who work with the moderately and mildly mentally handicapped.

There may be a subtype of personality disorders that is not mentioned in DSM-III-R and that seems to occur in the mentally retarded quite often. This is the immature personality in which childish, regressive behavior is prominent (e.g. McGee et al, 1984, Hunter, 1979). This patient is inclined to overreact on relatively minor, problematic situations. He often has compulsive and passive-aggressive traits and poses large problems in handling him, especially when this environment wants him to act in a specific way. There is a strong tendency to refuse what the environment wants him to do and this refusal easily becomes tyrannical. Mentally retarded persons seem to be more liable to emotional disturbances than other people; it is also probable that they have less effective defenses, so that they manifest their anxiety sometimes in acting out or attention seeking ways, whereas more intelligent people will develop a neurotic or psychosomatic illness (Forrest, 1979, Clarke & Clarke, 1975, Konarski & Cavalier, 1982).

I shall not dwell on diagnosis, but do want to state here that structural diagnosis is essential for treatment planning.

When patients do not fit exactly in DSM-III-R and structural psychodynamic criteria, but do fit the phenomenology of them, one should often conclude that the personality is too immature to be called a personality disorder and one should, exactly as in children, call the problem conduct disorder, avoidant disorder of childhood or adolescence, or an identity disorder.

Treatment

I should like to introduce the following major dimensions:

A. Focal versus diffuse.

B. Dynamic versus a-dynamic, energetic versus flat.

Let me explain:

In some patients there seems to be a traumatic focus or a point in time which seems to have had critical influence on personality development.
In the most extreme case there is a dramatic change in behavior after a very traumatic event or series of events, from which factual or imaginary escape was not possible.

In other cases this is less clear.

In the latter cases there often seem to be genetic influences, interactions with neurological and neuropsychological abnormalities, or there is a long-standing history of childhood neglect and abuse from very early childhood onwards.

Focality may be found in some cases of borderline personality disorder and narcissistic personality disorder, incidentally also in histrionic personality disorders and obsessive-compulsive personality disorders.

In other personality disorders it is seldomly found.

The dynamic structure of the personality disorder may vary in the degree of dynamicity. At the one extreme end one finds the patient in which structural interview, careful psychotherapeutic exploration and projective test investigation point at a process of active defense when the situation is not very predictable and structured.

The defense mechanisms are of a primitive kind and may consist of splitting, projective identification, and dissociation, idealization and active repression.

This kind of defense costs a lot of energy, which one encounters in the kind of reaction to an emphatic client-centered reaction: mostly aggressive and/or anxious, sometimes warm and sad, especially after a very emphatic confrontational interview following a series of seemingly neutral interviews. Dynamicity and energicity are keywords at this end of the spectrum.

At the other end is the patient with defense mechanisms like denial, reaction formation, regression, who frequently is avoidant, regressive and flat, anenergetic. It is hard to elicit feelings in these patients, although sometimes one can elicit diffuse intense dysphoria (often with automutilation or severe agression) after hurting him in his feelings of omnipotence, or frustrating an important, often physically important drive like food or smoking.

In my opinion, where there is more focality and dynamicity, treatment should be more psychotherapeutic and relationally oriented, supplemented by other treatment methods. At the extreme end of this dimension may be treatment of the personality disorder itself.

Where there is less focality and dynamicity, treatment should be more pragmatic, aimed at teaching new behaviours, controlling behaviours, finding the adequate surroundings and ways of managing disturbing behaviour, etc..

In the remainder of this paper I firstly shall discuss treatment of patients with high focality and dynamicity and after that, I shall discuss treatment of patients with low focality and dynamicity.

Patients with high focality and dynamicity are relatively rare, and include some borderline personality patients, some narcissistic patients, rarely some histrionic and obsessive-compulsive patients. They seldomly or never have I.Q. potential lower than 70, although the factual I.Q. number may be 60-70.

Trauma which has been the focus is severe. As two examples I want to mention a patient who saw his mother committing suicide, and who was placed in a children's home the day after this, never to be again in his native place, nor at the cemetary, and another patient who was victim of incestuous and threatening acts in her family during many years.

In normally intelligent persons, outpatient psychotherapy quite often proves to be very difficult, especially with respect to the tendency to avoid emotions and stress by these patients. In the mentally handicapped this is even stronger the case. Treatment should be given in a specific psychotherapeutic unit. (Verberne, 1989a; Day 1983, 1988).

Treatment should focus on the "here and now" and have strong interactional features. The treatment unit should provide the patients with structure, enough to give reassurance and to avoid extreme anxiety, not so much however, that no transference occurs.

A certain degree of openness and lack of structure promotes transference of significant former events or persons to the treatment unit and its staff. This also invites the patient to use his defense mechanims like splitting. Confronting the patient with his defense forces him to deal with his anxiety in an other way. Holding techniques may be used; the sociotherapist is warm but at distance. Besides this psychotherapeutic unit there is formal psychotherapy which often includes individual as well as group psychotherapy. Individual therapy is supportive, group psychotherapy is confronting and directed at feeling, corrective experiencing, etc..

As therapy goes on, real relationships develop between the patient and his psycho-therapist and socio-therapist. It is important to avoid treating the patients without an orientation of "here and now" concerning the past. The patient will not be able to bridge the gap in time and will use the situation to disarm the therapist.

Only when a real affect is elicited in the "here and now" after confrontation (often a significant transference-based event has occurred) a moment of real contact is possible. The therapist may try to intensify this contact by asking whether this feeling and/or situation reminds the patient of significant events or persons from the past. Very important in treatment is acceptance of the patient as a person, not of his often quite destructive and abusive behaviour.

Rivalry often gives a great deal of trouble in these therapeutic groups. It will be handled therapeutically by naming and confronting, but sometimes limits must be set very firmly, because otherwise the anxiety underlying abusive and provocative behaviour may become so extreme, that the risk of severe aggresive/destructive or autoaggressive behaviour becomes too high.

To avoid cumulation of anxiety it is also recommendable to arrange that more therapists and therapeutic nurses work with the same patient. An individual relationship may be too threatening, because of the strong transference which develops. On the other hand, more therapists and significant caregivers will provoke splitting. This must be carefully taken into account, because splitting can be very destructive to therapeutic teams and therapeutic communities.

More should be said of this kind of treatment, but the space available will not be enough for this.

For the Dutch speaking readers I want to refer to my paper: "Over diagnostiek en behandeling van de borderline persoonlijkheidsstoornissen bij licht geestelijk gehandicapten" (Verberne, 1989a).

Another discussion about treatment techniques in borderline personality disorders in the mentally retarded is given by DesNoyers, Hurley & Sovner (1988). A practical overview of treatment methods in the non-retarded is given by Tucker et al (1986).

What I just said refers especially to focal borderline personality disorders, but also applies to patients with other focal dynamic personality disorders. Splitting is often less serious then, but more attention must be paid to mechanisms such as "role fixation" and "projective identification". In narcissistic personality disorder, regular evaluation of treatment with the patient in positive terms, as well as prevention of too much offending and hurting his feelings of worth and dignity (and omnipotence) are important. When the patient feels hurt in these feelings, paranoid behaviour may develop and be directed to the entire therapeutic community and the entire hospital, sometimes even with psychotic features.

For all the patients at this psychotherapeutic pole, reassurance is often very important. It is important that much effort is made to prevent isolation of problems which are difficult to handle for the patient, for instance by turning intrapsychic conflict into interpsychic/interpersonal conflict. Besides this there is a basis of treatment which is also found in the other group, and includes art therapy, providing developmental stimuli, bringing the patient to more realistic expectations and self knowledge. Also it is important that the patient has an environment with enough exciting activities and fun. Without these problem behaviour unnecessarily occurs because this also has a function in dealing with feelings of emptiness and boredom (e.g. Reid, 1982).

Treatment at the other extreme end of the continuum, i.e. of *the patient with a personality disorder with low focality and dynamicity,* is fundamentally different. In these patients treatment is not so much directed at the personality disorder as such, but at regulating behaviour, preventing conflicts, etc..

More structure is provided in daily environment. Learning new activities, concurrent behaviour to the maladaptive behaviour and management training e.g. with respect to anger, frustration, etc., is strongly emphasized. A training for social abilities, for instance according to Goldstein, may be useful in these patients. It is very important to be very careful to prevent regression, because in this case the patient is no longer reacting normally to more or less normal stimuli and reinforcers. Often it is possible to make some real contact with the patient and to communicate with him in a development-oriented way, if the patient has the feeling that some of his needs for dependency and reassurance are reinforced and if his tendency to discuss borders and to pass limits and to manipulate the environment, is adequately handled. The latter may be achieved by using a so-called behavioral regulation system, in fact a response cost system which has about the following structure: some problem behaviours are defined, which characteristically include some non-problem behaviour, such as self care activities, behaviour which has to do with too much self-determination and overestimating oneself, and behaviour which has to do with eliciting conflicts with the environment. So a list is made of these behaviours and each behaviour is checked once a day or more often, at first occurrence of negative behaviour or when a specific limit is trespassed, for instance threatening nursing personnel more than 3 times, or not complying with a reasonable demand within some minutes. When the patient has less than 70 or 80% of the possible positive score at the end of the day, he loses a privilege. Some variations on this kind of behaviour regulation systems are possible.

In these patients it may also be necessary to train specific behaviours, such as delay of gratification of wishes. It is possible to make a training schedule, in which the patient gets a possibility to postpone desirable activities such as smoking some times a day, and the staff draws the patient's attention to such opportunities and reinforces successful behaviour by tangible reinforcers. In antisocial personality disorders it sometimes is necessary and desirable to make very clear to the patient the norms of the department and of society. It may be advisable to make a list of 15 to 20 basic rules, and each time the patient trespasses the limits of these rules, the staff mentions this trespassing, also explains why it is serious to disobey rules and what are the consequences of it, and then the patient has to do some compensatory activity, which can have, in some cases, the character of overcorrection. Eventually the patient is asked to recall the text and consequently is stimulated to incorporate this in his own thinking.

In some patients use of relaxation techniques may be useful (e.g. Verberne, 1989b).

In general it is important to prevent the patient from losing the little basic motivation he had when he came into psychiatric attention. It seems desirable to work with treatment contracts and start by offering the patient a limited degree of facilities of freedom, and give him more freedom, more possibilities, and more rewards when treatment goes on and he complies with the treatment programs.

I think it is very important to prevent the occurrence of unnecessary conflicts about patients rights. I think it should be very clear whether the patient is in the clinic on a voluntary basis or on the basis of some decision of court.

When the latter is the case, and when the patient is not motivated for treatment, he should not be treated; on the other side it is possible to provide these patients with necessary nursing care and a basic discipline while preventing the development of struggle with staff and avoiding escalation of conflicts by giving the patient opportunities to get in a more comfortable situation by working at goals set by the hospital.

Of course I have not been able to discuss all possible treatment techniques. In working with motivated patients with personality disorders, especially with high focality and dynamicity, a good alternative may to work with rational emotive therapy, but I do not have much experience with this technique. In my experience it may be very useful as a supplementary technique.

There is little in the literature on treatment possibilites of patients with personality disorders. This is true for the non-retarded but even more for the mentally handicapped. Therefore I have given you an overview of techniques, based primarily on experience, in which I have tried to give the link with the basic scientific literature.

References

Alnaes, R., Torgerson, S. (1988), The relationship between DSM III symptom disorders (axis I) and personality disorders (axis II) in an outpatient population. *Acta Psychiatrica Scandinavia,* 78, 485-492.

American Psychiatric Association (1987), *Diagnostic and statistical manual of mental disorders.* (3rd ed., revised). Washington, A.P.A.

Brink, van den, W. (1990), Persoonlijkheidsstoornissen; conceptualizering, operationalisering en onderzoeksthema's. *Tijdschrift voor Psychiatrie,* 32 (2), 105-125.

Clarke, A.D., Clarke, A.N. (1975), *Recent advances in the study of subnormality* London, Gaskell Press.

Corbett, J.A. (1979), Psychiatric morbidity and mental retardation. In: James, F.E., Snaith, R.R.: *Psychiatric illness in mental handicap*. London, Gaskell Press.

Day, K. (1983), A hospital-based psychiatric unit for mentally handicapped adults. *Mental Handicap,* 11, 137-143.

Day, K. (1988), A hospital-based treatment program for male mentally handicapped offenders. *British Journal of Psychiatry*, 153, 635-644.

Des Noyers, Hurley, A., Sovner, R. (1988), The clinical characteristics and management of borderline personality disorders in mentally retarded persons. *Psychiatric Aspects of Mental Retardation Reviews,* 7 (7 + 8), 43-49.

Fahy, T.A. (1988), The diagnosis of multiple personality disorders, a critical review. *British Journal of Psychiatry*, 153, 597-606.

Forrest, A.D. (1979), Neurosis in the mentally handicapped. In: James, F.E., Snaith, R.R., *Psychiatric Illness in Mental Handicap*. London, Gaskell Press.

Gunderson, J.G., Elliott, G.R. (1985). The interface between borderline personality disorder and affective disorder. *American Journal of Psychiatry,* 142, 277-288.

Hunter, H. (1979), Forensic psychiatry and mental handicap. In: James, F.E., Snaith, R.R.: *Psychiatric Illness in Mental Handicap* London, Gaskell Press.

Kernberg, O.F. (1978), Object relations, theory and clinical psychoanalysis. New York, Aronson.

Konarski, E.A., Cavalier, A.R. (1982), Current models of psychopathology In: Matson, J.L., Barrett, R.P.: *Psychopathology in the mentally retarded.* Orlando, etc., Grune & Stratton.

Lerner, H. (1986), Research perspectives on psychotherapy with borderline patient. *Psychotherapy,* 23, 57-69.

Lindsley, H.L. (1986), The diagnosis of multiple personality disorder. Paper read at the conference "bridging the gap", of the NADD at Hershey, Pennsylvania.

Lindsley, H.L. (1989), Multiple personality disorders in persons with developmental disabilities. *Psychiatric Aspects of Mental Retardation Reviews,* 8 (10), 65-71.

McGee, J.J. et al (1984), A model inpatient psychiatric program. In: Menolascino, F.J., Stark, J.A.: *Handbook of mental illness in the mentally retarded.* New York, Plenum.

Menolascino, F.J. (1977), *Challenges in mental retardation.* New York, Human Sciences Press.

Menolascino, F.J. (1985), Mental illness in the mentally retarded: diagnostic and treatment issues. In: Stark, J.A., Menolascino, F.J., Albarelli, M., Gray, V.: *Mental retardation and mental health, classification, diagnosis, treatment, services*. New York, etc., Springer.
Reid, A.H. (1982), *The psychiatry of mental handicap*. Oxford etc., Blackwell.
Ross, C.A., Gahan, P. (1988), Techniques in the treatment of multiple personality disorder. *American Journal of Psychotherapy,* 42 (1), 40-52.
Tucker, L., Bauer, S., Wagner, S., Harlam, D., Sher, I., (1986), Long term hospital treatment of borderline patients: a descriptive outcome study. *American Journal of Psychiatry,* 144, 1443-1448.
Verberne, G.J. (1989a), Over diagnostiek en behandeling van de borderline persoonlijkheidsstoornis bij licht geestelijk gehandicapten. Paper read at the NIP symposium at Berg en Dal.
Verberne, G.J. (1989b), Relaxatietechnieken bij licht en matig geestelijk gehandicapten: een literatuuroverzicht. *Gedragstherapie,* 22 (3), 205-217.
Widiger, T., Frances, A., Spitzer, R., Williams, J., (1988), The DSM-III-R personality disorders: an overview. American Journal of Psychiatry, 145, 786-795.

Došen, A., Van Gennep, A., Zwanikken, G.J. (Eds.) (1990). Treatment of Mental Illness and Behavioral Disorder in the Mentally Retarded. Proceedings of the International Congress, May 3rd & 4th, 1990, Amsterdam, the Netherlands. Leiden, the Netherlands: Logon Publications.

Chapter 31

Effects of Gestalt therapy and drug therapy in hyperactive severely mentally retarded children

L. Igric
N. Sikic
D. Burusic

Introduction

A lot of studies which were carried out in the last few years suggest that mentally retarded persons are more susceptible to psychic disturbances than nonretarded (Menolascino, 1984). Among mentally retarded persons in residential settings the frequency of mild disturbances is 60%, while the frequency of psychosis is 10%. The relationship between mental retardation and psychic disturbances can be manifold (Chess, 1971): 1. mental retardation with no behavioral disturbances, 2. mental retardation with behavioral disturbances caused by cerebral dysfunctions, 3. mental retardation with reactive disturbances, 4. mental retardation with neurotic disturbances, 5. mental retardation with psychosis.

The symptom of hyperactivity is included by the same author in the category of mental retardation with cerebral disfunctions. Although data show that around 15–20% of the mentally retarded express hyperactive syndrome (Payne, 1968), there is still a lot of indistinctness about this syndrome.

According to the DSM III Classification (1986), hyperactivity is characterized by attention difficulties, impulsiveness and exaggerated activity.

Došen (1983) made a distiction between six basic diagnostic categories of psychic disturbances in retarded persons, one of which is the hyperkinetic syndrome. Since psychic disturbances decrease already limited potentials for social and cognitive development in mentally retarded, in the rehabilitation process it is important to work on the decrease and the elimination of such disturbances. The most frequent treatment of psychic disturbances in mentally retarded persons today, especially if they are in the residential setting, is drug therapy. According to the literature (Lipman, 1978; Freeman, 1970; Marker (in Szymansky & Tanguay, 1980)) around 50% of the mentally retarded in institutions receive psychotropic drugs, which are applied at the staff's request with the purpose of eliminating behaviours dangerous for the child and the environment. Some investigations point out that the use of drugs frequently isn't justified, since the therapy became less frequent after regular psychiatric consultations were introduced (Rivinus, 1978). In this way, drugs frequently are exchanged for any other treatment. In hyperactive children, neuroleptics cause more calm behaviour, but which price has to be payed for this? (Szymansky & Tanguay, 1980)

Psychotherapy in the mentally retarded has its place if is viewed as a complete process with therapeutic, educational and rehabilitational aims. Beside behaviour therapy a lot of other approaches are used today, such as play therapy, music therapy, art therapy, relation therapy and others which serve to diminish and to eliminate psychic disturbances in mentally retarded persons. One of the recent attempts to adapt of psychotherapy for the mentally retarded is by Besems and van Vugt (1989). This work concerned the use of Gestalt therapy in severely mentally retarded persons. Authors started from the principle that man is a bio-psycho-social unity in which these three aspects are closely connected. The therapy offers the opportunity to the patient to have experiences so that he can get acquainted with himself, in order to establish the connection with himself and others. Not only undesirable behaviour is treated, but there is an attempt to discover what the child shows through such behaviour, in other words the child's behaviour is studied. Since there is the connection between cognition, body and psyche, a mentally retarded person needs more time to learn how to walk, sit, stand up etc., not only as a result of slower physical development, but because of the slower emotional development. The adaptation of Gestalt therapy concerns primarily the development of those physical activities which are going to lead to the development of self-perception, self respect and, in the end, self-responsibility.

The aim of the investigation

This investigation wants to test the effects of the modified Gestalt therapy in mentally retarded children showing hyperactive syndrome.

The effects of Gestalt therapy are compared with the effects of drug therapy on hyperactive behaviour in severely mentally retarded children.

Methods of work

Sample of cases (subjects)

This investigation was carried out at the Centre for rehabilitation Stancic, near Zagreb. This institution houses 540 moderately, severely and profoundly mentally retarded children. They are aged from three years to adulthood. 155 persons work in the direct care of the mentally retarded. Only 170 inhabitants are included in the rehabilitation program.

Table 1
The sample of cases (subjects)

Group	Cases	Sex	Age	Cognitive development	Other impairments	Placement in years	Family's visits
Exper.	1	m	11;8	V SM*	sight, Epy. GM	2	regular
	2	m	11;7	4–5 MA⁺	Epy.	2	rare
	3	f	6;5	VI SM	Epy.GM	3	none
Contr.	4	m	11;5	VI SM	Dif. lesia CNS	10	rare
	5	m	8;10	VI SM	Dif. lesia CNS	2	rare
	6	m	14;10	IV SM	Epy. GM	7	regular

* Senso-motor phase according to Piaget
⁺ Mental age

All cases suffered from prenatal brain damage, except case 2, who suffered postnatal damage caused by an infection.

Family circumstances were varied. They ranged from bad to good socioeconomic conditions.

All of the subjects selected were included in the regular rehabilitation treatment. The experimental group received Gestalt therapy, while the control group received drug therapy.

Investigation method

All six children were observed during a period of three months in 18 time spots in two structured situations (the group and the meats). Previously defined hyperactive behaviours were registered during this time. Six hyperactivity variables were estimated for each child.

Each day the experimental group was in Gestalt therapy for 20–30 minutes in a special room chosen for this purpose. The methods of work were adapted from Besems & van Vugt (1989) and Ouklander (1978).

The control group received drug therapy regularly (neuroleptics), subjects 5 and 6 also received antiepileptic therapy. In the experimental group all three subjects received antiepileptics.

Data processing

Frequencies of hyperactive behaviour were registered for each of the 18 time spots and for each child separately.

Data were processed through the INDIFF statistical program (Momirovic & Karaman, 1982), which serves to analyze the changes of the state of an object described under cluster of quantitative variables.

The component analysis of the states of an individual object in certain time intervals provides us with an insight into the structure of changes – relationships between variables and the components of changes, as well as an insight into the relations between time spots.

Results and discussion

The effects of Gestalt therapy

Case 1. Therapeutic work was based on establishing trust through physical experiences (the therapist's touch) which was soon accepted by the child. In joint continuous movements the child expressed resistance in the beginning, but after some time he led the therapist himself. Rolling and pulling on the floor with the purpose to develop the awareness of body weight, relaxed the child so much that he demanded to continue the exercise and reacted to music, to its beginning and end. The child accepts body stimulation and massage, during which he developed the perception of physical tension and relaxation.

During work it became obvious that the child directed his attention toward some objects much better, that the therapeutic room was more attractive and that he liked the contact with the therapist. While at the beginning of the work he escaped from physical contact, at the end of the treatment he showed dissatisfaction when the session was finished. Previously the child hit himself, but after the therapy was finished he stopped doing this.

If we consider the therapy process in all three cases,[1] we can conclude that all three children established confidence. Their individual ways were different and while at the beginning of treatment Case 2 did not seem to develop this confidence and accept touch till the end, it did happen although in the last session. This child had the highest cognitive ability, which explains his sudden psychosocial improvement.

The other two children are in their cognitive development about 18 months of age, so their psychosocial development is in harmony with the cognitive development.

In this way the confidence in the therapist was established, the process of self-perception was initiated, as well as the development of the sense of being accepted and protected, experiences that were lacking in early childhood. Speaking in general, the therapist and the therapeutic space became important to children. They gladly came to the therapist and protested when the session was finished. Although the three month-period was too short to achieve greater results, these observations stress the usefulness of psychotherapy in institutions for mentally retarded.

Comparison of effects of Gestalt therapy and drug therapy on the hyperactive behaviour

Components of changes for each subject were analyzed in the 18 time spots in the structured situation of the rehabilitation group. (For the structure of the components of changes, see Table 2 in the Appendix)

Case 1. Analysis of the change in hyperactivity in this case during the three month-period can lead to the conclusion that from the six hyperactivity variables, only two components remained explaining 75% of the total variance in the system. The share of each of them is approximately equal.

The first component of changes is mostly attributed to variables showing *extreme hyperactivity*, which was expressed through the escape from the situation, hitting, oral stimulation (putting hands into mouths), expression (laugher, screaming and crying).

Figure 1.1 provides us with a graphic representation of changes in the extreme hyperactive behaviour. The trend of decrement in hyperactivity is obvious in 18 time spots. Variations are more frequently present in the first part than in the second one, where these behaviours occur more rarely. In this situation the influence of the environmental factor on the behaviour is obvious in time, for example in the third interval where the hyperactivity is the highest during the observation made after return from the hospital.

1. Since the number of pages is limited, the other two cases aren't present.

Figure 1.1
Trajectory of first component of changes

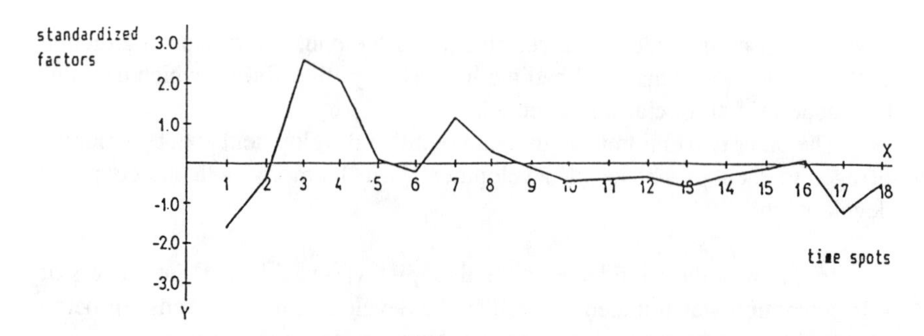

The second component is primarily composed of variables pointing to *hand movements and sound production.* The changes in time aren't expressed as much as they are in the first component.

In this situation, the influence of the environmental factors is also present, such as the exchange of the teacher (fig. 1.2.).

Figure 1.2
Trajectory of second component of changes

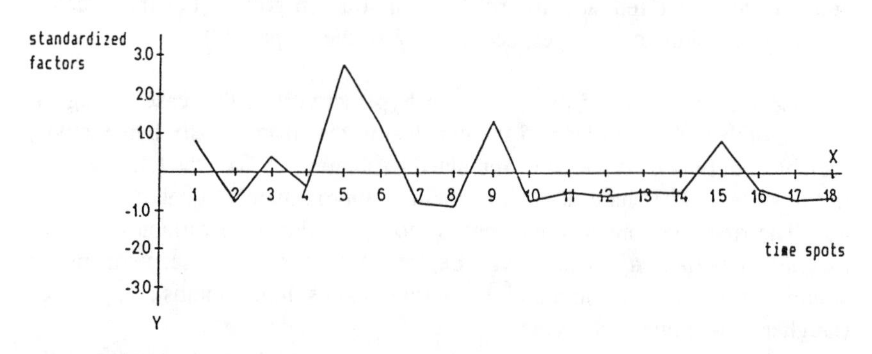

Case 2. In the projection of the components of changes on the vectors of variables, two components can be identified as explaining hyperactivity.

The first one consists of variables of escape from the situation, variables, variables of movement, distractibility and the variable of the oral-facial expression. This component is the basic object of the measurement with 48% of explained variance in the system and can be called the *general hyperactivity.*

Its trajectory[2] points to a trend of decrement. Spots with higher hyperactivity are covering the duration of a child's stay in his own group, with the familiar teacher and in the familiar environmental where its hyperactive behaviour is the usual way of behaviour.

The second component with 17% of common variance is determined by the variable of movements and can be regarded as a *factor of movement*. The trajectory of this factor shows the tendency of stabilisation in activity (i.e. the decrement in the oscillations) regardless the circumstances.

Case 3. The projection of the components on vectors of variables extracted one component of changes. It consists of variables referring to fine hand movements, sound production, body movements and oral-facial expression. For this reason, the factor can be called *general motion*. The graphic representation of the trajectory shows gradual stabilisation of motion, so that we can find the same level of motion in the second part of the experiment and no higher variations.

Analysis of the components of changes in the first three cases from the experimental group that were included in the Gestalt therapy shows very mild decrement in hyperactivity. Some of the aspects of hyperactivity show greater decrement than others.

In Case 1 the extreme hyperactivity is decreased, but other aspects aren't decreased to such an extent (such as hand movements).

Similarly, what was shown in the structured situation of the rehabilitation group happened in the meal situation (which isn't presented in this paper). It is obvious that in the chosen structured situations significant changes didn't happen in the period of three months. Obviously the transfer of behaviour from the therapeutic environment to other environments was too weak.

Case 4. In this case, two components of changes, explaining 58% of the common variance of the system, were extracted. The greatest contribution to the first components is made by the variable of movement such as "body movements" and "escape". The oral-tactile stimulation has the greatest projection on this component. For this reason it can be regarded as a *factor of movement*. Its trajectory shows the trend of decrement (after the ninth time spot the frequency of movement is decreased).

2. Since the number of pages is limited, not all graphic representations can be presented.

The greater contribution to the second component is made by the variables "looking around" and "oral-facial expression", in the sense of shouting, laughter and articulation. In this way it primarily concerns the *distractibility of attention.* The trajectory shows that within the longer period of time the greater level of distractibility is being delayed, but after the thirteen spot, it decreases.

Case 5. Two components were isolated on the basis of the six hyperactivity variables and explain 62% of the total variance.

Figure 2.1
Trajectory of the first component of changes

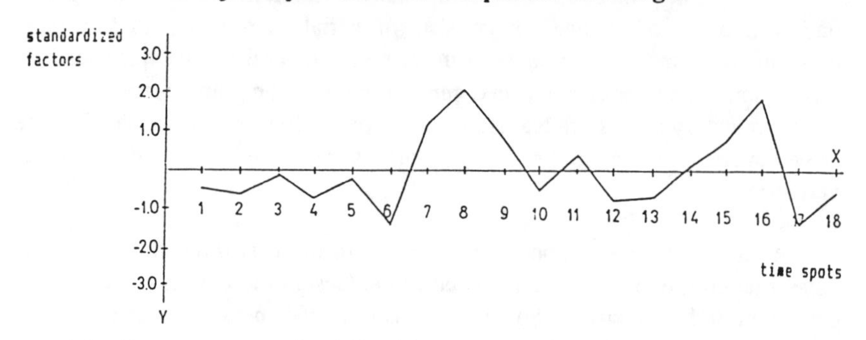

The first component is defined best by variables of movement of hands and body, and can be called the *factor of motion.* The graphic presentation of changes in time (Fig. 2.1.) shows the relation with circumstances in certain time spots, for example the work of others or illness of the subject.

Figure 2.2
Trajectory of the second component of changes

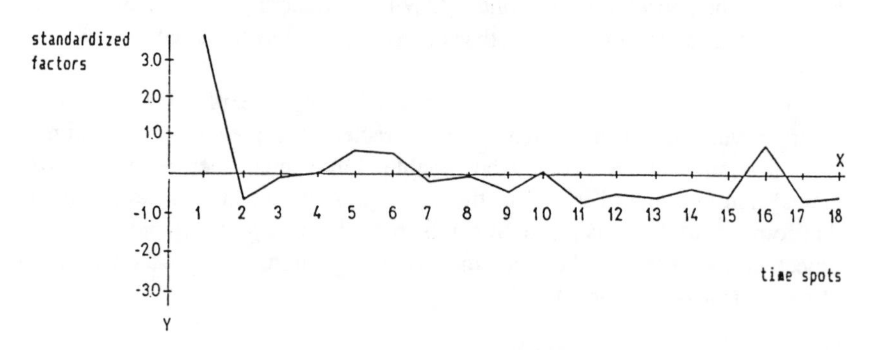

The second component consists of the variables of *distractible attention,* which follow "putting food in the mouth". Changes over time are small and the distractibility is almost equally frequent during the whole experiment, except in the first observation. This could be influenced by the presence of new persons in the group (Fig. 2.2.).

Case 6. The projection of the components of changes on the vectors of six variables extracted two factors which are explaining 63% of the total variance.

Variables which define the first factor refer to hand movements, movement in space and include the variable "hitting". This factor can be called the *factor of movements*. Its graphic presentation shows the trend of decrease in movements after the ninth time spot. Since we are talking about the child receiving drug therapy, this direction of changes isn't easy to explain. It looks like the bare fact that when the child had been included into the experiment, he was influenced to a greater extent by being more involved in the institution. The child was regularly observed in the group and the students examinators were involved with the child.

The second component consists of variables pointing out the distractibility of attention and the child's expression, the activities with longer duration such as looking out of the window. This can be called the *factor of attention distractibility*. Its trajectory doesn't show the trend of decrement until the end of the investigation.

In subjects from the control group who were receiving drug therapy (neuroleptics), the general motion decreased, while the attention distractibility remained at the same level. If we try to explain the trend of decrement in general motion, we cannot attribute that to the therapy because subjects were receiving therapy before the beginning of the experiment. Much more is explained by the fact that they were included into the experiment. This fact itself brought some changes into the child's environment and influenced it. Similar to the situation of the rehabilitation group, this happened in the meal situation.

Our subjects received psychoactive substances like 47% of the other mentally retarded in the institution. Approximately this matches data about drug prevalence in other similar institution in the world (Rivinus, 1978). The aim of this therapy was to calm down psychomotor restlessness. But there remains the question of the effects of psychofarmaca especially in the area of pharmacokinetics, or in other words: is there a genetic regulation of drug behavior in the organism of healthy and sick persons?

Since our subjects have combined disturbances, the genetic determination of drug behaviour in the organism is possible, or the number of receptors is eventually decreased (Haase, 1985; Lerer, 1987; Rudorfer & Potter, 1987) and all of this can decrease the effects of drug therapy.

Conclusion

The investigation was carried out in six severely mentally retarded children with hyperactivity syndrome placed in the institution, with the aim to estimate the effects of Gestalt therapy and to compare the effects of Gestalt therapy and drug therapy on hyperactive behaviour. During three months of daily Gestalt therapy with three children, some positive effects have been noticed in the development of the child's confidence, the development of selfperception and the acquiring experience of being protected and accepted. The process and the effects of the therapy were closely related to the child's cognitive ability. Comparison of the effects of the two different therapies on hyperactive behaviour through the analysis of components of changes in 18 time spots showed that there is somewhat more decrement in hyperactivity in the experimental group than in the control group, where decrement of only particular ways of hyperactivity happened. It is obvious that the effects of Gestalt therapy haven't been transferred to other situations, to which the short duration of therapy and the cognitive ability of subjects contributed. This makes it more difficult to transfer the behaviour from one to another situation. Therefore it is necessary to include elements of psychotherapy into other situations, especially into the rehabilitation group, which is emphasized by Brown (1971) on the basis of his experiment in conducting confluent education.

On the other hand the group receiving drug therapy, in which no changes during the experiment were expected since this was the continuance of the already existing therapy, showed a decrement of some aspects of hyperactivity, probably due to other factors. This therapy has its place in the elimination of psychic disturbances in mentally retarded people, especially in institutions during continuous psychiatric supervision. The use of individual psychotherapy in our institutional condition is too expensive today, but it should still have a place in the rehabilitation of the mentally retarded.

Appendix

Table 2
The structure of the components of changes

Group	Cases	Variables	Abbreviation names	aturations	
				Factor 1	Factor 2
Experimental	1	Hand movements	HANDMOVE	.08	.80
		Escape from the situation	ESCAPSIT	.85	.26
		Oral stimulation	ORALSTIM	.74	– .51
		Producing sounds	PRDSOUND	.00	.94
		Hitting	HITTING	.79	.41
		Expression	EXPRESSN	.68	– .33
	2	Hand movements	HANDMOVE	.43	– .36
		Body movements	BODYMOVE	.71	.58
		Looking around	WATCHING	.77	– .13
		Oral-tactile stimulation	ORLTACST	.54	– .34
		Escape from the situation	ESCAPSIT	.85	.45
		Oral-facial expression	ORLFACST	.76	– .45
	3	Fine hand movements	FHANDMOV	.84	
		Body movements	BODYMOVE	.66	
		Looking around	WATCHING	.65	
		Gross hand movements	GHANDMOV	– .55	
		Producting sounds	PRDSOUND	.70	
		Oral-tactile stimulation	ORLTACST	.62	
Control	4	Hand movements	HANDMOVE	– .53	.19
		Body movements	BODYMOVE	.64	.10
		Looking around	WATCHING	.03	.91
		Escape from the situation	ESCAPSIT	.79	.49
		Oral-tactile stimulation	ORLTACST	.42	.11
		Oral-facial expression	ORLFACST	– .68	.62
	5	Hand movements	HANDMOVE	.85	.06
		Body movements	BODYMOVE	.90	.07
		Looking around	WATCHING	– .16	.90
		Oral stimulation	ORALSTIM	.07	.90
		Seeking attention	SEEKATTN	.57	– .19
		Oral-facial expression	ORLFACST	– .37	– .18
	6	Longer activities	LONGACTV	– .13	.39
		Body movements	BODYMOVE	.76	– .25
		Looking around	WATCHING	.60	.62
		Hand movements	HANDMOVE	.86	– .29
		Hitting	HITTING	.78	– .27
		Expression	EXPRESSN	.51	.65

Literature

American Psychiatric Association: *Diagnostic and Statistical Manual of Mental Disorders (DSM III)*, Washington, DC, 1986.

Besems, T., van Vugt, G. (1988). Gestalttherapie mit geistig behinderten Menschen, Geistige behinderung, Teil 1, (pp. 1–24).

Besems, T., van Vugt, G. (1989). Gestalttherapie mit geistig behinderten Menschen, Geistige behinderung, Teil 2, (pp. 1–24).

Brown, G.J. (1971). *Human teaching for human learning: an introduction to confluent education,* An Escalen Book, New York.

Chess, S. (1971). *Treatment of emotional problems of the retarded child and of the family*. In Menolascino F.J. (Ed.): Psychiatric aspects of the diagnosis and treatment of mental retardation, Seattle, Special Child Publications.

Došen, A. (1983). *Psychischehe stoornissen bij zwakzinnige kinder,* Swets i Zeittinger B.V., Lisse

Freeman, R.D. (1970). *Use of psychoactive drugs for intellectually handicapped children.* In N.R. Bernstein (Ed.): Diminished People: Problems and Care of Mentally Retarded, (pp. 277–304), Little, Brown & Co., Boston.

Haase, H.J. (1985). *Neurolepticus.* In: Blanker M., The action of neuroleptic drugs, Elsevier, Amsterdam

Lerer, B. (1987). *Neurochemical and other neurological consequences and treatment of affective disorders.* The third Generation of Progress, Raven Press, New York.

Lipman, R.S., DiMascio, A., Reatig, N. and Kirson, T. (1978). *Drugs and mentally retarded children.* In: M.A. Lipton, DiMascio and K.F. Killam (Eds.) Psychopharmacology: A Generation of Progress, (pp. 1437–1449), Raven Press, New York.

Menolascino, F.J., J.A. Stark (1984). *Handbook of mental illness in the mentally retarded,* Plenum Press, New York.

Momirovic, K., Karaman, 2. (1982). *INDIFF – Model, algorithm and the program for the analyze of status of an object described over the cluster of quantitative variables.*, Kineziologija, 13, (pp. 5–8).

Ouklander, V. (1978). *Windows to our children,* Real People Press, Moab, Utah.

Payne, D. (1968). *Regional cooperation in mental retardation data collection,* Ment. Ret., 6, (pp. 52–53).

Rivinus, T.M. & Harmatz, J.S. (1979). *Psychiatric effects of the anticonvulsant regimens.* In: R.I. Shader (Ed.) Psychiatric Complications of Medical Drugs, Raven Press, New York.

Rudorfer, M., Potter, V.W.Z. (1987) *Pharmacokinetic of Antidepressants in Mother,* Psychopharmacology, The third Generation of Progress, Raven Press, New York.

Szymansky, L.S., P.E. Tanguay 1980). *Emotional disorders of mentally retarded persons,* University Park Press, Baltimore.

Došen, A., Van Gennep, A., Zwanikken, G.J. (Eds.) (1990). Treatment of Mental Illness and Behavioral Disorder in the Mentally Retarded. Proceedings of the International Congress, May 3rd & 4th, 1990, Amsterdam, the Netherlands. Leiden, the Netherlands: Logon Publications.

Chapter 32

Running program for severely mentally retarded men with behaviour disorders

W. Blesch
A. Metzger

Theory and objectives

There are no final answers to be found in literature as to the causes of aggressive, self-abusive and stereotypical behaviour.

There seems to be an interaction of different factors that cause the behaviour problems, one of them certainly being brain damage. Communication problems can add further to the described behaviour. Another cause of aggressive and self-abusive behaviour as well as restlessness and stereotypical behaviour appears to be deprivation of adequate sensory and motor stimulation.

It should be noted that the situation of severely mentally retarded residents is especially likely to show such deprivations. The described behaviour problems can thus be understood as a means for the residents to create such perceptual and motor stimuli on their own.

This last factor we took as the starting point of the running program.

The objective of the program was to give residents the opportunity for regular sensory and physical activities and experience as well as physical exertion.

Our goal was to achieve that the participants furthermore wouldn't have to rely as much as before on perceptual and physical experience which might harm themselves or others. However, we like to stress that our running program, besides reducing behaviour problems, also has another important objective. It is supposed to be an enjoyable, stimulating and compensating experience.

The residents should experience their own physical reactions. In addition, everyday life is structured better. The participants get the important experience of tension and relaxation. Also, getting familiar with the surroundings, buildings and nature is an important goal.

Another aspect is that being together in a group also means being related to others, to care about them and being cared about, to accept a role in the group and having to face certain social demands.

Participants of the running program

Let us briefly introduce the four male residents that take part in the running program. They all have strongly limited mental capabilities and have to be described as severely imbecile with a mental age of less than 3 years. Three of the four residents don't have as yet therapy by special staff members.

Ralf S.: He is 26 years old and comparatively independent. He is restless and moody and suffers from epilepsy. Sometimes he shows extreme behaviour problems such as aggressiveness and self-abusive behaviour.

Siegfried K.: Most of the time he is friendly and creates few problems. On the other hand he shows striking restlessness. He hardly ever sits still, he runs up and down the hall, turns around and so on. Siegfried is 37 years old.

Ralf G.: Ralf is 34 years old, and has shown self-abusive behaviour like banging his head for many years, injuring himself badly. Other residents of his group are disturbed by his very loud screams.

Heinz A.: He is 34 years old and has lived at the Johannes-Anstalten since 1964, almost all of the time in the same group. He is very often in a good mood but even then only staff members he is familiar with are able to activate him. He typically keeps to himself and sometimes shows strong aggressiveness.

Besides four regular participants there are one or two other group members who irregularly take part in the running program.

Details of the program

The program covers an approximate one hour circuit walk with slopes in the surroundings of the Johannes-Anstalten.

The pace is adjusted to the physical abilities of the slower participants and can be described as more or less fast hiking not jogging. The running should provide the participants with exertion but not exhaustion. In order to give the physically fitter participants adequate exertion, they carry a backpack or pull a cart. Sometimes a resident with walking problems is allowed to sit in the cart. Then however a staff member will pull the cart, occasionally supported by a resident.

At the end of the program the residents are offered beverages and opportunities to relax (for example: waterbed, playground).

Data and results

Several weeks before the start of the program the participants were observed to show extreme self-abusive and aggressive behaviour. In the course of the program data were taken during and after the one-hour walk. The most important results are shown in table 1.

Table 1

Name	Shown behaviour problem	number of behaviour problems (June-Nov. 89)	number of behaviour per day (June-Nov. 89)	per day before June 89
R. Sch.	aggressive self-abusive behaviour	121	0,69	1,4
S.K.	self-abusive behaviour	15	0,09	0,2
R.G.	self-abusive behaviour	392	2,24	3,9
H.A.	aggression	120	0,07	0,09

Our intention of running on a daily basis could not be achieved completely. On average, the running took place on four days a week. Furthermore, body weight and heart rate were measured before and during the program. Special behaviour problems were recorded.

Discussion

The most important result is first of all the obvious reduction of aggressive and self-abusive behaviour of R.Sch. and R.G. between June and November 89.

The number of fits on the days without running did not differ from the number on running days. These results could be interpreted in the sense that physical exertion does not at once but only in the long run lead to a reduction of the described behaviour. Possibly the physical exertion was not sufficient, or in other words the observed reduction could be a general result of offering alternatives and stimulation.

A positive side effect is the stabilisation of R.G.'s heart rate as well as H.A.'s weight reduction. In fact it was H.A. who evidently took most pleasure in his daily running. Especially with him it wasn't sure whether he could be motivated at all. During the six months it could be observed that the outsider tried more and more to communicate with the other residents.

Even though the documentation and evaluation of the data was not easy to handle and some interrelations remain unclear, it still shows in our opinion that such a regular running program is an important, reasonable and promising offer for the population of severely mentally retarded with behaviour disorders.

References

Ayres, A.J. (1979), Sensory Integration in the Child. Western Psychological Services.

Fröhlich, A.D. (1978), Dokumentation zur Situation Schwerstbehinderter. Kemper Verlag.

Fröhlich, A.D. (1981), Die Förderung Schwerstbehinderter. Erfahrungen aus 7 Ländern. Verlag der Schweizerischen Zentralstelle für Heilpädagogik, Luzern.

Kane, J.F. (1986), Körperliche Aktivierung von Menschen mit Selbstverletzungsverhalten. Vortrag Neuenkirchener Work-Shop.

Kane, J.F. (1987), Bewegung, Stereotypie, Selbstverletzungsverhalten. Vortrag Internat. Autoagressionssymposium, Viersen.

Kiphard, E.J. (1986), Mototherapie – Teil I und Teil II. Verlag modernes lernen.

Zeitschrift Zur Orientierung: (1989, Heft 3, 13. Jg.), Körper und Bewegung in der Arbeit mit behinderten Menschen.

Došen, A., Van Gennep, A., Zwanikken, G.J. (Eds.) (1990). Treatment of Mental Illness and Behavioral Disorder in the Mentally Retarded. Proceedings of the International Congress, May 3rd & 4th, 1990, Amsterdam, the Netherlands. Leiden, the Netherlands: Logon Publications.

Chapter 33

Psychotherapy of multiply handicapped persons

C.J.M.Lindner-Middendorp

Introduction

"How real is real?"... is a question asked by Watzlawick in 1973. In his book with this title he describes the consequences of misunderstanding in communication. By coincidence I started in Bartimeushage with psychotherapy in the same year- 1973. We tried to discover the possibilities of treatment of multiply handicapped persons with emotional or behavioral disorders. As these persons are mentally and visually handicapped they conceive reality in a different way. This paper is not the result of scientific research with a large population; it is rather the result of an enquiry in a small population and on the N=1 level. Therefore my contribution to the discussion on the Congress Theme will not be the statement: "Psychotherapy of multiply handicapped persons is possible...."; I only can state: "Psychotherapy of multiply handicapped persons is **not impossible**!" I want to support this statement by: 1. discussing the definition "multiple handicap," 2. giving short examples of the development of emotional or behavioral problems in which being multiply handicapped is an important factor, 3. describing the conditions to make various psychotherapeutic methods available for multiply handicapped clients.

A multiply handicapped person

5 to 8 % of the mentally handicapped population in the Netherlands is also visually handicapped. These persons may be described as multiply handicapped. Other combinations of handicaps can also lead to the diagnosis Multiple handicap. The most used description at this moment is the **definition** of de Jong in a 1988 report of the NZI, a national institute for hospital management in the Netherlands. A multiply handicapped person has:

- a combination of serious function disorders,
- which are interfering with each other's compensations in a negative way

or are even excluding each other's compensations,

– by which a specific way of existence is caused, not reducible to the existing function disorders.

The definition of multiple handicap consists of several steps. At first, there are at least two defects of wich each should lead to a handicapped existence. In addition, the definition says that for each of these defects a special program has to be developed. The next step says that the programs that have been designed for the various defects stand in the way of each other. This is called the heart of the multiple handicap problem. Personally I don't see this problem just as a problem, but more as a special challenge. A new program has to be developed for each kind of combination of various handicaps. The often abstract and crumbling information with wich a blind person must form a picture of the world is in contrast with his defective intelligence. In education a multiply handicapped child needs specific program. Intrapersonal interaction of sensory input and cognition results in a personality structured in a specific way.

Personality development and psychopathology

Each kind of handicap and its severity has an influence on personality development. Each combination of handicaps results in a different structure. This structure has to be understood as a whole. A total structure is more than the sum of its elements. This law in the Gestalt theory is also applicable when we see personality structure as a whole, as "Gestalt". Besides intrapersonal problems this handicap forms a breeding ground for misunderstanding. For most people who are not used to communicate with multiply handicapped persons this way of existence is mostly confusing. If parents or other caregivers are not able to understand how a child is conceiving its reality, they will use other signs in communcation or will perhaps deny the expressions of the child. The consequences of such a communication are disturbing in the process of attachment and in developing a satisfying identity. Watzlawick describes very clearly how psychopathology is caused when parents are denying a child's perceptions of "reality". What is happening if parents think they cannot communicate with their blind infant? These people – as we all do – are looking at the facial expression. If they trained themselves to look at the baby's hands, they would be able to communicate in a better way. This is an example of the causation of interpersonal problems. The next example makes it clear how the multiple handicap is of influence in intrapersonal aspects. A moderate mentally handicapped girl whose vision was limited to a distance of 30 centimetres looked at herself on video. She sat at a short distance of the television and said: "Look at me...... That is how I walk!" She has never been able to see herself as a whole in the mirror and she was not able to compose a picture of herself in combination with her haptonomic and kinetic experiences. Being multiply handicapped is a breeding ground for psychopathology. These people are more vulnerable to intrapersonal problems and to misunderstanding by their caregivers. Even very professional experts in the field of mental retardation give evidence of misunderstanding behavior of multiply handicapped persons. Most striking is an article in the American Journal of Mental Deficiency in 1986. Here a description is given of an investigation of maladaptive behavior of institutionalized mentally retarded individuals. No difference was made between visually handicapped mentally retarded individuals and mentally retarded persons with normal vision. For all residents the same determinants of maladaptive behavior were chosen. Self-directed behaviors were weighted less than determinants like "throwing objects". People who are able to interpret behavior of blind mentally handicapped persons will understand that these persons don't express their maladaptation by throwing objects they cannot see lying somewhere. The outcome of this investigation is predictable: having a visual handicap is related to a lower score on maladaptive behavior. Writers of this article call these results "puzzling". Actually, it is questionable whether this study can be considered valid, because no differentiation was made between determinants of maladaptive behavior of mentally and of multiply handicapped persons.

The specific way of existence has always to be taken into account in the **etiology** of mentall illness in this special group. The multiple handicap is always playing a more or less important part in the development of emotional and behavioral disorders. This can be illustrated by a case of a boy with a dog phobia. Assessment showed that he could see a dog only when this animal was very nearby. He also was not able to control his feelings of fright and did not know how to handle such a situation. Combination of both factors was the cause of the conditioning of phobic behavior. In trying to get a good diagnostic judgement, the use of classification methods like DSM or ICD do not seem to have a high validity for our clients. The notation on different axes of the visual and the mental handicap does not correspond with the definition of multiple handicap. On the other hand, the discussion on the conformity of symptoms in mentally retarded, multiply handicapped and non-handicapped people is not closed. I prefer the diagnostic system of Oudshoorn, a Dutch psychiatrist. He distuingishes 6 levels in which problems can occur. In this system the consequences of the multiple handicap can be worked out and it is suitable for a dynamic and treatment-oriented approach. Especially in the case of multiply handicapped persons the abilities to use in psychotherapy are to be discovered as soon as possible, because it sometimes takes a lot of time to adapt or fabricate materials you will need in therapy. So far definition and etiology.

Psychotherapy

In Bartimeushage I work part-time as psychotherapist. Psychotherapy is mostly the last step taken in treatment of emotional or behavioral disorders. First choice is an educational approach or special guidance in the everyday living situation. Beside this, music therapy and psychomotor therapy are part of the program. Sometimes psychopharmaca are used. My approach in psychotherpy is eclectic. I use methods like behavior modification, experiential therapy and hypnotherapy. If a systemic therapy is necessary, this is used in consultation with the proper orthopedagoge/psychologist. Other methods are not used, not because of supposed impossibilities in the clients but because of lack of training in other methods by the therapist. Although very tempting I will not engage here in the discussion of indications and usefulness of the various methods of treatment in itself. My purpose is to discuss the conditions for psychotherapy with this special group of clients. In case of the boy with the dog phobia, I chose a strategy of a combination of behavior modification and experiential therapy. The principles of both methods were applicable, I just had to find the right means to use them. For example: I had to find pictures that he could perceive. I could not take the risk that he would interpret a picture of a gently looking dog (in our eyes) as a terrifying monster, if this was not a projection. We worked with a sound-tape with barking sounds, and later on with real dogs ...first a small one, later a big shepherd.

I had to vary the distance from the dogs in a way that was adapted to his visual possibilities. My presence if he needed me and my way of modelling also had to be adjusted to his possibilities of registration. Is this therapy different from a phobia treatment with a nonhandicapped or a mentally handicapped boy? My opininon is that the answer depends on the **level of abstraction** at which we answer this question. If we analyse what happened at a higher abstraction level, we have to conclude that there is no difference; I was using the same methods I would have chosen if I was working with a nonhandicapped or a mentally retarded boy. At a lower level of abstraction we **do** observe differences. In all variables that are of influence in the use of psychotherapeutic methods, difference is observable. The following variables can be distinguished: a. the therapist b. material c. space d. time In the case of the boy with the dog phobia it is obvious that by knowing how this boy is perceiving, the therapist behaves in such a way that he can follow what is happening; my voice is an important instrument, not only for verbalizing my behavior or things that are happening, but also to express feelings empathically. Using sounds is also a means to let the client know where the therapist is. But this is not the only way; I always use a perfume and use physical contact or being at a short distance to give proof of my presence.

Material is chosen selectively or adjusted. In this case it was necessary to give more contrast to pictures and to have pictures with as little details as possible. I think the use of a sound tape with barking sounds is not unique for this boy; I would have used it also with non-multiply handicapped clients if the barking was one of the anxiety-provoking stimuli. Surroundings were especially chosen. Starting inside in a rather small room, he could explore in a fairly short time. Later on we used a familiar environment, followed by walking in the village and an unfamiliar wood. In changing the distance from the dogs we had to consider his abilities to perceive them. In this case time was only a different variable in sofar it demanded extra investigation to find out how he forms his concepts. Besides it took more preparation to get the right pictures and to adapt them.

In another case of a blind mildly retarded boy with very agressive and destructive behavior, image communication was applied in the form of radio play. He started to make the background sounds like rain, storm, cars. When I took over these sounds, he played the leading parts. After a few rehearsals the emotions that belonged to his chosen images decreased. At the end of this play he said relieved: "Now I can play in a normal way again." In this case a well-known psychotherapeutic method was applied; the difference in the use of the method is the **operationalization**. This is adapted to the way the client conceives and reproduces reality. Communication has to be adapted to this way of perceiving.

Conclusion

Psychotherapy of multiply handicapped individuals is not impossible if the following conditions are taken into account:

1. Knowledge of the consequences of the multiple handicap and experience in dealing with multiply handicapped persons is required to understand the experiences of the multiply handicapped person.
2. The use of communication forms, language styles that are completely adapted to the possibilities of the client.
3. Use of spatially and materially adapted media like we saw in the use of special pictures. This part of the therapy is very time-consuming.

In fact the conditions mentioned refer to a very client-oriented approach, in which the client variables are utilized in a very direct way to lead the process of optimal application of the other variables. It is my personal experience that training in hypnotherapy a la Erickson offered me the best equipment in reading the communicational signs of multiply handicapped people. By using formal therapeutic technics, procedures and verbatims we don't reach what we want. Working in a naturalistic way and according to the utilization principle like Erickson and Araoz, we make use of the possibilities the client (any client) shows at that moment. Resuming: psychotherapy of multiply handicapped persons is not impossible, if a harmonizing communication can be developed based on a shared ... **reality.** In fact, besides psychotherapeutic expertise it is a matter of ... and now I'll give a last double bind: common sense.

Došen, A., Van Gennep, A., Zwanikken, G.J. (Eds.) (1990). Treatment of Mental Illness and Behavioral Disorder in the Mentally Retarded. Proceedings of the International Congress, May 3rd & 4th, 1990, Amsterdam, the Netherlands. Leiden, the Netherlands: Logon Publications.

Chapter 34

Anger Management Training

B.A. Benson

Introduction

Anger management training is a structured, skills-oriented program to teach self-control skills to adults with mental retardation. Approximately 30% of the referrals to an outpatient mental health clinic for persons with mental retardation were for anger outbursts and aggressive behavior (Benson, 1985). Deficits in self-control skills can result in serious problems on the job, at home, and with peers.

The anger management (AM) program is based on Raymond Novaco's work on anger control for nonretarded adults (Novaco 1975; 1978). According to his model of anger arousal, external events are filtered through a cognitive labeling process which may or may not result in anger arousal and in behavioral reactions. The AM program includes components to address the cognitive, behavioral, and physiological aspects of anger arousal.

The AM program for adults with mental retardation is designed for persons functioning in the mild to moderate range of intellectual functioning (Benson, 1986; Benson, Rice, & Miranti, 1986). The program has been used with individuals and with groups. The group format calls for 15 sessions, once per week, for 1 1/2 hr. per session. There are 6-10 group members and two therapists. The AM program includes four parts: identification of emotions; relaxation training; self-instructional training; and problem solving skills. A session outline is included in Table 1. Each section of the program is described below.

AM Group and Identification of Feelings

Self-control training requires that the individual respond to early signs of tension with techniques to manage arousal. A first step in accomplishing this goal is to be aware of one's feelings. It is explained that anger is one of many feelings that everyone experiences, that it is natural to become angry at times. However, what one does when angry is a different matter and may result in negative consequences for the individual. The AM group is a way to learn different things to do when one is upset.

The first phase of the AM program focuses on identification of feelings (See Ludwig & Hingsburger, 1989). Group members are asked to consider three basic feelings, happy, sad, and mad (angry). Questions are offered for discussion, such as, "What things make you feel (happy, sad, angry)?" What do people (you) do when you feel (happy, sad, angry)? "How do people look when they feel (happy, sad, angry)?" "How would you feel if .... (you won a prize; your best friend moved away; you accidentally broke your radio)?" An assignment is given to monitor feelings daily by marking one face each day on a form that contains happy, sad, angry, and neutral faces. Subsequent group sessions begin by reviewing the assignment and discussing the relationship between events, feelings, and behavior.

Relaxation Training

The rationale given for relaxation training is that anger is invariably accompanied by muscle tension. Relaxation training helps to reduce muscle tension, one part of anger arousal. In addition, muscle tension can be a signal that one is becoming upset. The signal can be used to prompt self-control strategies before one loses control.

To address the tension and arousal aspects of anger, a muscle tension/release method of relaxation training is taught using ten muscle groups. The group leaders demonstrate the exercises first, observe the group members performing the exercises, and physically guide them, if necessary. The relaxation exercises end with slow, deep breathing and the self-statement "Relax." Role playing of anger-arousing situations is introduced in which role play actors practice relaxation. Other group members observe bodily signs of tension or relaxation in the role play actors. When group members are proficient in practicing the relaxation exercises in the group, an audiotape of the exercises is provided for home practice.

Self-Instructional Training

Self-instructional training is included to address the cognitive labeling process that occurs in anger arousal. Group members are told that we are always thinking about what is going on around us. Sometimes what we think can make us feel upset, whereas other things that we think can help us stay in control. The two types of self-statements are identified as "coping" statements and "trouble" statements. The goal of the AM program is to substitute coping statements for trouble statements in anger-arousing situations.

Examples are provided of coping statements and trouble statements. Group members are encouraged to choose their own coping statements. Role playing of anger-arousing situations follows in which coping statements are repeated first out loud, then silently.

Problem Solving Skills

The techniques included in the AM program thus far are primarily aimed at reducing impulsive responding to anger-arousing events. The last portion of the program seeks to improve the group member's ability to find alternative solutions to problem situations. Anger is described as a signal that there is problem to solve.

The method of teaching problem solving skills is similar to the "Think Aloud" program developed for nonretarded children (Camp, Blom, Hebert, & Van Doorninck, 1977). A four-step plan is introduced that includes these components: What is the problem? What are some solutions? Choose and follow a plan. How did I do?

The group leaders enact problem situations and ask group members to first, define the problem in objective, concrete terms from the point of view of each person in the problem situation. Role reversal in role playing is used to assist group members in taking the other person's point of view. Second, group leaders suggest alternative solutions to the problem and ask group members for their ideas. Silly and inappropriate choices are included in the list of alternatives to illustrate that there are many ways to handle a situation. Third, each alternative is examined in turn and the expected consequences of that course of action are considered. Group members are asked to draw upon their previous experience and expectations in anticipating what the consequences may be. Next, one alternative is chosen that appears to offer the most positive consequences for all parties. The method of implementing the alternative is discussed in detail and practiced in the group.

In the final step, the plan is re-evaluated after it has been tried and the outcome is compared to expectations. If the outcome is satisfactory, group members are encouraged to use positive self-statements. If the outcome is not satisfactory, coping self-statements are used and the problem solving steps repeated.

For individuals who find the four-step plan to be too abstract or complicated, repeated practice of similar situations is offered as a method of acquiring "If-then" guides for behavior. For example, "if the other worker keeps bothering me, I will tell the supervisor."

Termination

During the final sessions, practice of relaxation, self-statements, and problem solving occurs through role playing. Group members discuss efforts to apply the new skills at work and at home. Participants tell what they learned in the group and what they found helpful. Methods of maintaining contact with other group members, if desired, is discussed.

Conclusion

Teaching self-control skills to persons with mental retardation offers an alternative to staff-administered behavior management programs. Encouraging initial findings suggest that learning self-control skills can reduce aggressive behavior in adults with mental retardation.

References

Benson, B. A. (1986). Anger management training. Psychiatric Aspects of Mental Retardation Reviews, 5(10).

Benson, B. A. (1985). Behavior disorders and mental retardation: Associations with age, sex, and level of functioning in an outpatient clinic sample. Applied Research in Mental Retardation, 6, 79-85.

Benson, B. A., Rice, C. J., & Miranti, S. V. (1986). Effects of anger manage ment training with mentally retarded adults in group treatment. Journal of Consulting and Clinical Psychology, 54, 728-729.

Camp, B. W., Blom, G. E., Hebert, F., & Van Doorninck, W. J. (1977). "Think Aloud": A program for developing self-control in young aggressive boys. Journal of Abnormal Child Psychology, 5, 157-169.

Ludwig, S., & Hingsburger, D. (1989). Preparation for counseling and psycho therapy: Teaching about feelings. Psychiatric Aspects of Mental Retardation Reviews, 8(1).

Novaco, R. W. (1975). Anger control: The development and evaluation of an experimental treatment. Lexington, MA: Lexington Books.

Novaco, R. W. (1978). The cognitive regulation of anger and stress. In J. P. Foreyt & D. P. Rathgen (Eds.), Cognitive behavior therapy (pp. 241-285). New York: Plenum.

Table 1
Anger Management Training
Session Outline

Session	Topic
1	Introduction and rationale. Identification of emotions.
2	Identification of emotions. Relaxation Training.
3	Relaxation Training.
4	Relaxation Training with roleplaying.
5	Relaxation Training with roleplaying.
6	Relaxation Training with roleplaying.
7	Introduction to Self-Instructional Training.
8	Self-Instructional Training, statements out loud.
9	Self-Instructional Training, statements out loud.
10	Self-Instructional Training, statements silently.
11	Introduction to Problem Solving Skills.
12	Problem Solving Skills.
13	Problem Solving Skills.
14	Problem Solving Skills. Prepare for Termination.
15	Termination and Review.

Došen, A., Van Gennep, A., Zwanikken, G.J. (Eds.) (1990). Treatment of Mental Illness and Behavioral Disorder in the Mentally Retarded. Proceedings of the International Congress, May 3rd & 4th, 1990, Amsterdam, the Netherlands. Leiden, the Netherlands: Logon Publications.

Chapter 35

Aggressive behaviour among people with learning difficulties – the nature of the problem

P. Harris
O. Russell

Introduction

The management and treatment of people with learning difficulties who present severely aggressive behaviour poses a major challenge to service providers. Few systematic studies of the extent or frequency of such behaviour have been completed outside of institutional settings. Studies of interventions have been mainly limited to single case studies. In this paper we shall report on the progress of a study within the United Kingdom which seeks to provide a comprehensive account of the way in which services intervene and provide treatment for this group of people in a single health district with a total population of 370,000.

The first stage of the study concerning the nature, extent and circumstances of aggressive behaviour is now complete. A survey of the health district identified 168 people as presenting aggressive behaviour. This total indicated an overall prevalence rate of 12.3%. The lowest rate of aggressive behaviour was identified in day services (9.7%) and the highest in hospitals within the health district (38.2%). The prevalence rate for schools was 12.6%. Six people were identified as having been recently involved in incidents which resulted in severe injury to others. They represented less than 0.5% of the total population of people with learning difficulties from the district (or 1.6 per 100,000 population). Eighteen people were said to present extreme problems of management. This represented 1.3% of people with learning difficulties from the district (or 5 per 100,000 population). The results of the first stage are described below.

The second stage of the study will evaluate the effectiveness of treatments and interventions which are intended to alleviate the difficulties and change the behaviour. Work on this stage has began and the findings will be reported at a later date.

How was the data collected?

Having decided to confine the study to a single health district the first task was to identify the people with learning difficulties who were presenting problems of aggressive behaviour. This was done by defining aggressive behaviour and circulating the definition to the appropriate facilities.

Defining aggressive behaviour

A definition of aggression was developed with the help of service providers and incorporated into the following sentence which appeared in the initial letters to all the facilities contacted:

> "While we are primarily interested in identifying people who present serious problems such as biting, kicking, scratching etc. which result in injury to others, for example bruising, bleeding, or other tissue damage, we would also like to include all individuals whose actions such as shouting/screaming at others, or violence towards objects may not necessarily result in injury but do present serious management difficulties because of the threat or risk of injury to others."

Conducting the survey

A range of facilities and service providers were contacted including all head teachers of SLD schools, managers of ATC/RAC's, leaders, local authority, private and voluntary homes and hostels, community mental handicap teams, psychiatrists, psychologists and residential service managers. Pre-school children and the prison population were not included in the survey.

Screening the people identified

The screening stage consisted of following up the people identified as presenting problems of aggressive behaviour and conducting interviews with service providers using a structured interview schedule.

The interview schedule was developed and piloted especially for this purpose and consisted of four sections. The first section was concerned with the disabled person's characteristics such as age; sex; self-help, communication and social skills. In the second section there were checklists of aggressive and other disturbing behaviours. The checklist items were rated for frequency, intensity and management difficulty. The third section was about the physical resources of the facility and staffing resources were the subject of the fourth section.

The interviews with service providers took place between May and November 1988. The reliability of the method of data collection was determined by conducting a number of repeat interviews. At all stages, participants were assured that all information arising from the study would be treated confidentially and that no identifying characteristics would be given when the results were analysed.

What were the findings?

All known facilities for people with learning difficulties associated with the health district were contacted and the response rate was 100%. A total of 200 people were identified but after a preliminary examination of the completed interview schedules some 16% of cases showed no evidence of aggressive or any other type of disturbing behaviour. Interview schedules describing the remaining 168 individuals were included for the data analysis.

How many males and females were there?

Contrary to expectations there was not a strong association between the person's sex and the presence of aggressive behaviour. About 69% (n = 116) of the group were male but given that there were more males (59%) than females from the health district, this difference was only just statistically significant. There was no significant evidence of an association between the person's sex and the presence of aggressive behaviour within the schools or the hospitals.

How old were they?

The average age of the group was 34 years and their ages ranged from 8 to 85 years. Thirty-four percent of the group were between the ages of 15 and 29 years and six people were over 70 years of age.

Figure 1 shows the distribution of the group by sex and age: the numbers tend to rise during the teenage years and peaked in the late 30's.

Where did they live?

As can be seen from Table 1 over half of the people were living on hospital wards (55.4%). About a quarter of the group were living in the family home and these were mainly children and teenagers. Most of the others (17.3%) were living in staffed housing or hostels.

Figure 1
The distribution of the group by sex and age

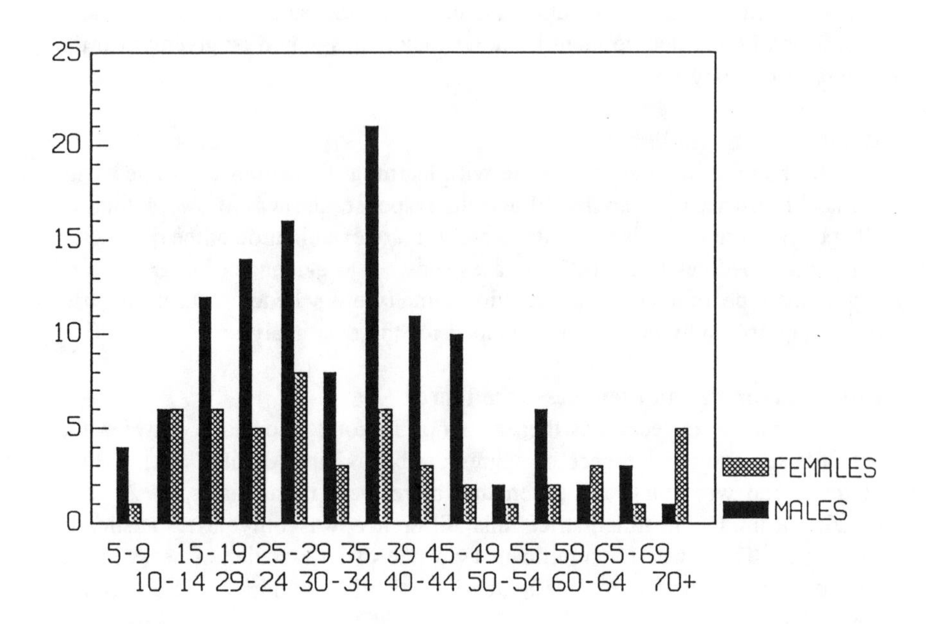

Table 1
Type of residence (n = 168)

	Number	Percent
Family home	41	24.4
Foster home	1	0.6
Hospital ward	93	55.4
Staffed house/hostel		
SSD	2	1.2
NHS	18	10.7
Private	6	3.6
Voluntary	3	1.8
Other	4	2.4
Totals	**168**	**100.0**

What sort of behaviour did they engage in?

The most common physically aggressive behaviours reported are shown in Table 2. It is evident that hitting-out at others (ie punching/slapping/pushing/pulling people) was the most frequently occurring behaviour: about half the group were said to have engaged in this type of interaction during the past month. There was a much lower incidence of behaviour such as biting (12.6%), headbutting (7.1%) and using weapons (6.5%).

Table 2
Frequency of aggressive behaviours as a percentage of the group (n = 168)

Behaviour	*Past Month* (%)
Hitting	50.6
Kicking	23.4
Pinching	21.4
Scratching	20.2

Details of other challenging behaviours were also collected and it was found that self-injury, withdrawal, stereotypical and ritualistic behaviours were quite common among this group (Table 3).

Table 3
Frequency of other challenging behaviour as a percentage of the group (n = 168)

Behaviour	*Past Month* (%)
Self Injury	35.7
Withdrawal	38.1
Stereotypical	36.3
Ritualistic	35.1

It was clear that the individuals in the group tended to engage in complex behaviours and that physical aggression may not necessarily be the most distressing aspect of the person's behaviour. In order to understand the people concerned it is probably more useful to look at the motives and context of all the challenging behaviours not just the aggressive ones.

Injury to others

Table 4 shows the degree of injury to others resulting from incidents of aggressive behaviour. About 40% of the group had never injured anyone. On the other hand, "serious" and "very serious" injuries were all accounted for by eight people in the survey. It was evident that two of these people no longer presented problems of aggression, the last serious incident having occurred a number of years ago. The six remaining people had all been involved in recent incidents resulting in severe injury to another person. They represented 0.44% of the total population of people with learning difficulties from the district.

Table 4
Number of people involved in incidents resulting in injury to others

	N	%
No Injury	67	39.9
Minor Injury	45	26.8
Moderate Injury	48	28.6
Serious Injury	6	3.5
Very Serious Injury	2	1.2
	168	100.0

An examination of the biographies of the six individuals showed that they tended to have had a long history of distressing behaviour. Typically their lives were characterised by traumatic life events, lack of control over the environment, insecurity and anxiety and poverty of circumstances. Robert was one of the people who was said to have caused a serious injury. The profile below is intended to give some insight into his circumstances:

A Profile of Robert

Robert is eleven years old and has profound disabilities. He has severe learning difficulties, he is blind and usually has at least one major epileptic seizure per month. It was suspected that he was severely battered during infancy although this has never been substantiated.

Robert is completely dependent upon others for toileting, washing and dressing and he needs help with food and drink. Although he is quite capable of walking he needs guidance because of his blindness. He can communicate to a very limited extent using a small range of signs and gestures but even people who know him well have difficulty understanding what he is trying to say.

For the past 18 months Robert has lived in a special residential school some considerable distance from his home town. He sleeps in a dormitory with four other children and often gets up during the night. During the day he attends school class, there are four other children in the class. His favourite activity is swimming which he does at least once a week. He never participates in group activities and is mostly indifferent to other students. He is usually negative in his relationships with staff at the school.

The staff felt that Robert required a one-to-one staff ratio but believed that this was not possible because of his aggressive behaviour. Robert engages in a wide range of aggressive and distressing behaviours. He frequently bites, pinches and scratches as well as headbutting and pulling people's hair. Often he bangs his own head and bites and scratches himself although this does not usually result in injury because staff always intervene. Furthermore he often screams and displays ritualistic and stereotypical behaviour and usually soils himself when agitated or upset.

Despite this behaviour, Robert's class teacher did not find him difficult to manage. Most of the staff found Robert's repeated smearing of faeces the most difficult behaviour to cope with. Many of the staff felt defeated in their efforts to understand the reasons for his behaviour and concerned by the limited degree of contact they were able to establish.

There was said to be a programme for meeting Robert's needs but this was poorly developed. Robert did not take medication for his behavioural disturbances but was said to have a programme of behaviour modification although this was not an agreed written programme. There was no other treatment or intervention plans. His teacher was satisfied with the present methods of managing Robert's behaviour but thought that this could be improved by finding an environment which was better suited to provide for Robert's needs.

What conclusions were reached?

This and other information from the study suggested that in terms of the development of aggressive behaviour over the lifespan, the general picture was that the behaviour often started early in life although serious difficulties may not be apparent at this stage. Aggressive and other distressing behaviour tended to become more unmanageable during the teenage years and often continued into adulthood. In the past, the people themselves have usually been referred to secure accommodation in hospital settings. In this way the difficulties were contained but with little evidence of effective development for the individuals concerned.

The study found very little evidence of an expressed need for more secure accommodation. The challenge for the future was seen as one of providing new and effective services within community settings. A crucial aspect of these services will be to intervene early in the person's development to reduce aggressive behaviour and increase his or her quality of life.

Finally, this stage of the study suggested that the causes and maintenance of aggressive behaviour are inextricably bound up with the person's quality of life. In general, supportive, compensatory and normalising environments help to eliminate aggressive behaviours; whereas deprived, stressed and poorly stimulated circumstances tend to exacerbate early difficulties.

References

Harris, P. and Russell, O. (1989), The prevalence of aggressive behaviour among people with learning difficulties (mental handicap) in a single health district: interim report. University of Bristol: Norah Fry Research Centre

Harris, P. and Russell, O. (1989), The nature of aggressive behaviour among people with learning difficulties (mental handicap) in a single health district: second report. University of Bristol: Norah Fry Research Centre

Harris, P. and Russell, O. (1990) Rising to the challenge? The lives of five people with very challenging behaviour: third report. University of Bristol: Norah Fry Research Centre.

Došen, A., Van Gennep, A., Zwanikken, G.J. (Eds.) (1990). Treatment of Mental Illness and Behavioral Disorder in the Mentally Retarded. Proceedings of the International Congress, May 3rd & 4th, 1990, Amsterdam, the Netherlands. Leiden, the Netherlands: Logon Publications.

Chapter 36

Treatment of sexually deviant behaviour in mildly mentally retarded adults

G.J.C.M. Verberne

Introduction

In this paper I want to discuss some more or less frequently occurring types of sexually deviant behaviour in the mentally retarded as well as treatment techniques. Especially I want to discuss some underlying dynamics which are important in respect to treatment planning. I shall emphasize that sexual disorders occurring in the non-retarded also occur in the mentally retarded, but that it is possible to meet the same sexually deviant behaviours in the mentally retarded which have different underlying dynamics and contributing factors (and which demand other considerations with respect to treatment). I shall discuss this from a developmental point of view.

I work at Nieuw Spraeland as a clinical psychologist. Nieuw Spraeland is an institute which has served as an in-patient clinic for the moderately and mildly mentally retarded during 15 years, but at this moment is developing towards an institute for the so-called extremely behavioural disordered mildly mentally handicapped.

In this paper I shall only speak only about the mildly mentally retarded, i.e. if the I.Q.'s are within the 50 to 70 range.

In Nieuw Spraeland we quite often treat sex offenders as they are called in American literature.

Most often it concerns pedophiles, occasionally also exhibitionism, transvesticism, rape and voyeurism. I shall speak from my own clinical experience, as rather little is scientifically known. This may sound strange, because these kinds of behaviour disturbances occur more often in the mentally retarded than in the non-retarded population. The number of mildly mentally retarded sex offenders seems to be growing, as is the need for proper treatment. Therefore there seems to be good reason for thinking about the problem.

Sexual disorders

DSM-III-R (A.P.A. 1987) divides the so-called sexual disorders into two groups. I quote: "the paraphilias are characterized by arousal in response to sexual objects or situations that are not part of normative arousal-activity patterns and that in varying degrees may interfere with the capacity for reciprocal, affectionate sexual activity; the sexual dysfunctions are characterized by inhibitions in sexual desire or the psychophysiologic changes that characterize the sexual respons cycle".

The paraphilias essentially concern "recurrent sexual urges, and sexually arousing fantasies generally involving either:

1. non-human objects
2. the suffering or humiliation of oneself or one's partner, or
3. children or other non-consenting persons.

The diagnosis is made only if the person has acted on these urges and is markedly distressed by them".

The latter notion is important in respect to the mentally retarded. About the prevalence little is known; presumably the prevalence in the community is far higher than that indicated by statistics from clinical facilities. Generally the paraphilias are seldomly diagnosed in women. For the diagnostic criteria I want to refer to the DSM-III-R. (A.P.A., 1987).

Generally the paraphilias are looked upon as neurotic or character-neurotic disturbances from a psychodynamic point of view. In some instances there seems to be a relation to developmental problems (often having been victim of sexual abuse in childhood. (e.g. Groth & Bairnbaum, 1978). For a number of impressive case descriptions I want to refer to O'Brien (1986). In the experience of Groth (Groth & Bairnbaum, 1978) sexual aggression towards children is one of four possible ways to cope with own former victimization. He calls it the "vampire syndrome" as the offender repays others for his own victimization. For an extensive discussion of treatment aspects in the non-retarded see Breer (1987), Slater (1988), Porter (1986), Knopp (1984).

Severe sexually deviant behaviour may also have to do with poor educational socio-economic situations. This sometimes is found in low-structure families with a poor socio-economic status and which are poorly functioning in several respects (e.g. Brandt & Zlotnic, 1988, Frenken & van Stolk, 1987). In my experience, more property offenses and sexual offenses are seen in these families. The sexual offenses are often of an immature kind, such as incest, rape and sodomy.

These sexual offenses typically occur in young adolescence, and are often strongly related to immaturity and defective social learning. Treatment models based on learning theories are discussed by Knopp (1984).

Sometimes sexually deviant behaviour seems to be related to organic factors. Brain tumors and frontal lobe damage, for instance, may release repressed primitive drives and inhibit normal control (Lishman, 1987), but this seldom leads to serious sexual offenses. Sometimes sexually deviant behaviour is a result of temporal lobe epilepsy (Bear et al, 1984; Lishman, 1987). Sexually deviant behaviour may also be a response to imperative hallucinations in schizophrenia. This seems to be a very rare complication.(For an overview of the relation between criminal behaviour and mental disorder see Gunn, 1977).

Sexually deviant behaviour in the mentally retarded

Sexually deviant behaviour seems to occur in the mentally retarded more often than in the non-retarded. Studies with prison populations as well as studies with community populations point at higher prevalence of sexual offenses and arson (e.g. Tutt, 1971, Gibbens & Robertson, 1983; see Reid 1982 and Power, 1969 for discussions of studies). Prevalence of pedophilia seems to be unknown; sometimes one gets the impression that it is growing.

Which are factors that contribute to this high incidence?
I wish to focus your attention to 5 relevant points of view.

1. Immature sexuality.

First I will remind you what of old Freud already said; the young child is a polymorph perverted person; i.e. sexuality is not yet directed at a specific person, nor is it focused at the own genitals. Sexual pleasure occurs in all kinds of plays and may take various forms, including some that are called deviant in adults. During development the sexual energy, the libido, is directed at more specific objects, mostly persons, as well as at more discrete own bodily zones. One could imagine that in the disturbed personality development of the mentally retarded arrest may occur in this development, also that sexual energy is not directed at significant adults in childhood and peers later on, and not at own genital body parts, so that there is a gap between the primitive sexual directivity (or indirectivity as I should say), and the biological sexual arousal, as manifested by penile erection. It would not be strange if a mentally retarded person would react to this by diffuse but energetic sexual activity such as undressing, rubbing his genitals to persons or objects, etc., would it?

2. Immature personality development.

Another aspect of personality development on which I want to speak concerns the development of regulatory structures of personality such as the ego and the super-ego.

During development and education the ego is formed as a structure capable of providing stability in the organism by providing cognitive schemes as well as adaptive mechanisms to environmental stresses and changes and ways of relating to the environment, also of providing ways to achieve equilibrium between biological drives and the super-ego, which represents the demands and norms of the parents and, generally speaking, of society. It has often been investigated and concluded that in the mentally retarded ego generally develops slower and achieves less sophistication and maturation (e.g. Webster, 1970). In the profoundly and severely mentally retarded super-ego may be absent, but in the mildly mentally retarded a primitive punitive super-ego may also be found. Overly disinhibited poor impulse control as well as overly inhibited behaviour could be presumed to occur in the mildly mentally handicapped and this indeed seems to be the case. Of course this also applies to the inhibited and overly inhibited sexual behaviour. (e.g. Mitchell, 1985, 1987). Because of poor ego functioning, mania and hypomania in the mentally retarded may lead to sexual recklessness, which may easily become threatening to others.

3. The third point of view I want to discuss concerns the learning aspects of behaviour.

As you know learning mechanisms play a role in behaviour development. These include classical and operant (instrumental) conditioning and modeling.

It has been demonstrated that mentally retarded individuals can learn in the same ways as the non-retarded, but contiguity and the perception of the relation between the behaviour and the reward or between the model-behaviour and irrelevant behaviour are more important. It is important to give extra attention to this, especially in social learning, and experience with Goldstein training of social behaviour seems to underline this.

The entire complex of simple communication skills, dating skills, etc., is highly dependent on this kind of social learning and generally little attention was paid to this until recently (e.g. Menolascino, 1977). I refer to various recent papers on sex education and training in prosocial behaviour as examples of how ideas have changed (e.g. Craft, 1987, Szymanski & Jansen, 1980).

I want to remark here that in families of the mildly mentally retarded there is often a poor socio-economic situation which may play a negative role in socialization. In other ways also learning aspects may be important, for instance with respect to learned anxiety for the other sex.

4. The fourth point of view I want to discuss concerns *pecularities in neuropsychological functioning*. Neurological and neuropsychological research has demonstrated that the structures in brain which develop latest often do not become as stable and mature in the mentally retarded, as they do in the non-retarded. As a result of this, most mentally retarded individuals have difficulties in complex spatial skills, symbolic thinking, abstract thinking, planning, self-evaluation and verbal regulation of his or her behaviour (e.g. Luria, 1963).

There is more however. In many mentally retarded individuals, the structures, which play an important role in providing the cortex with a stable basic tension, are not as flexible as in the non-retarded. As a result of this, mentally retarded are more dependent on the environment as to stability of stimulus input. They lose control more easily when there is an increase of internal and external stimuli, get aroused more easily and have a harder job in controlling this arousal. This often interacts with poor possibilities of verbal self-regulation. (Verberne, 1990).

More often than in the non-retarded, there is evidence of pre-natal, peri-natal or post-natal brain damage, other than the immaturity belonging to mental retardation itself, and which often accentuates the pattern I mentioned before. In the non-retarded, there is evidence that sociopathic individuals more often have signs of brain damage than non-offenders.

5. Then there is also a *specific developmental factor*. Psychodynamic development seems to follow a rather normal, but more vulnerable and slower course than in the non-retarded. As a result of this the barriers of the developmental phases sometimes provide the mentally retarded with many problems. When the mentally retarded individual is between 15 and 25 years of age, factors such as closing childhood and approaching adulthood, a new desire for independence, achieving a higher-level sense of sexual identity are often accompanied by many doubts about this, existential doubts and anxieties, the anxiety of a changing body, of sexual passions and phantasies that easily become a source of much stress (e.g. Mitchell, 1987, Menolascino, 1983, Gilson & Levitas, 1987), sometimes so large that psychosis develops.

In my experience mildly and borderline mentally retarded in this period often try to keep off anxiety by anti social, attention-seeking and thrill-seeking behaviour, which is often coloured by the underlying sexual drives and conflicts. There is something more: mentally retarded children have an enhanced risk for sexual victimization, which of course has a tremendous influence on psychosexual and personality development. Maybe another remark belonging to this category is that deviant behaviour, including sexually deviant behaviour, can be an inapproperiate way of seeking help for other problems, which often are of a developmental kind. Quite often in the mentally retarded person with sexually inappropriate behaviour one can meet an anxious person, desperately seeking contact.

These are five important aspects which enlarge the possibility of the mentally retarded individual to achieve less control over sexual impulses, less control over how to achieve satisfactory social and sexual relations and which lessen the diference between normal and abnormal sexual behaviour.

What I want to state here is that understanding of these kinds of developmental and maturational aspects are of crucial importance in assessing and treating the mentally retarded sex offender and the mentally retarded with other, less criminal sexually deviant behaviour.

However, the more serious sexual disturbances which are found in the non-retarded, may also occur in the mentally retarded, although not in my experience in the moderately retarded and seldom in the mildly mentally retarded.

Treatment

In those cases of true paraphilia treatment should be structured along the same dimensions as in the non-retarded (which is more easily said than done!). Psychotherapy and behaviour therapy can be important in those cases. Alas, success of psychotherapy in those cases is dependent on the degree in which working through of complex transference and insight are possible and this seldom proves to be the case.

In my experience regulating behaviour, providing the individual with new behaviour skills and leisure skills, and finding a way of making life less stressfull, may constitute a treatment program which brings enough rest to make possible a more flexible and a less maladaptive way of living. Sometimes medication may help to achieve this goal (e.g. Provera, Griffiths et al, 1985).

There is a borderline area between the paraphilias and the reactive immature behavioural disturbances I discussed above.

In those cases there is often sufficient evidence for a supplementary diagnosis of a personality disorder, mostly of a schizoid or anti-social kind.

Treatment depends on the diagnosis of underlying mechanisms.

I have discussed some treatment-issues of the true paraphilias already. In this borderline area the same issues apply. It is of crucial importance to search for possibilities of further emotional and personal development. Sometimes it is possible to treat the underlying personality disorder but this is rare in my experience. Sometimes it is possible to treat underlying neurotic mechanisms by group psychotherapy and art therapy. Group psychotherapy is generally more suitable than individual psychotherapy.

More often it is recommendable to reduce environmental stress, to achieve control over behaviour tendencies bringing the mentally retarded into trouble such as unrealistic ideas of living independently, overestimating one's possibilities, controlling drinking habits, to learn to look at masturbation as a normal way of dealing with sexual impulses; reinforcement of environmental structure as well as behavioural regulation by response cost systems are sometimes appropriate. (Mitchell, 1985, 1987).

Sometimes relaxation techniques can be useful (Verberne, 1989b) in the context of stress management training (Benson, 1986). Sometimes rational emotive therapy can help. However, it is very hard to treat these (often young) people, especially when there is an additional diagnosis of anti-social personality disorder. Working in a treatment unit you can easily come into conflict with your conscience sometimes, knowing that the risk of recidivism is high when the period of court based treatment is over. The management of special psychotherapeutic units and their effectiveness is discussed by Day (1983, 1988). I shall make some more remarks on these patients later on, when I speak more specifically about rape and child molest.

However, in the majority of the patients with sexual behaviour disturbances I have treated, developmental problems and disabilities such as the five factors I mentioned before play the leading role.

As to the respective factors I want to review some aspects important in treatment briefly.

In case of immature sexuality social skills training may be appropriate (Craft, 1987, Hingsburger 1989), as is proper sexual education (Craft, 1987, Hingsburger, 1987, 1988), of course depending on general intellectual and maturational level. Inappropriate forms of expression may be treated by behaviour modification, preferably by a way of differential reinforcement. I refer here to the textbooks of Whitman et al (1983), Barrett (1986), Cipani (1989). Besides this, of course, proper stimulation should be given with respect to psychosocial development in general (Mitchell, 1985, 1987).

It is often important to reduce sexually exciting stimuli such as video movies, proximity of female staff.

As to the *immature personality development* the same applies. Ego functioning may be stimulated by preventing overstimulation and understimulation, by allowing the individual to make choices he is able to handle, to stimulate him, to promote interests and hobbies, etc. Art therapy can be important in this process. Providing the individual with additional structure as to predictability of the environment, clear setting of limits are of fundamental importance. In those individuals with overinhibited behaviour, psychotherapy can help to reinforce ego functioning, to develop adaptive mechanisms, and so forth.

As to the *learning aspects of behaviour:* When there is evidence for influences of disturbed learning processes, behaviour therapy will often be the treatment of choice. Depending on the specific situation of the individual, one might choose behaviour modification, sensitization, systematic desensitization, discrimination training, positive practice, social skills training, assertiveness training, rational emotive therapy, training in coping with stressful stimuli, relaxation training, etc.

Role playing may be of particular importance, as is behaviour rehearsal. Token economy systems may be a good therapeutic device if they are carefully designed. In general it is important to work step by step, not to overestimate the capacity of the individual for generalization of learned skills. For the treatment of sexual improper behaviour in the severely and profoundly retarded I want to refer to textbooks like that of Whitman et al (1983), Barrett (1986), Cipani (1989) and Mitchell (1985).

As to *the neuropsychological aspects* it may be important to restructure the environment, so that there is more stability in auditive, visual and emotional stimuli, to teach the individual to achieve relaxation, to teach him to plan, to use internal speech as a way of regulating his behaviour. Sometimes medication may be useful here.

With respect to these patients in which the more or less leading role in the problem is played by the *developmental problems* mentioned above, treatment should try to develop and strengthen the individual in the respective areas (e.g. Hunter, 1979). Herein one should make a judgment about the need to adjust, train and treat. In this judgment, I.Q.-level, discomfort of the individual about the problems, the degree to which the problems obstruct further development, and danger or discomfort for the environment are important. For a general overview I refer to Santamour & Watson (1982). Besided this, it is important to create a living environment which offers enough support (e.g. Griffiths et al, 1985, Schramsky, 1987). Sometimes psychotherapy is indicated to help the individual going through a developmental phase.

So far for the general aspects.

Most of them apply especially in pedophilia.

Exhibitionism has a strong narcissistic background, as has transvesticism. Behaviour regulation by response cost systems etc. may be useful in combination with concurrent stimulation of more adequate pro-social behaviour. It is important, however, to recognize the need for attention underlying the behaviour and the need for dependency. Generally it is recommendable to provide the client with opportunities for getting narcissistic attention in a more acceptable way and regularly evaluate his behaviour in a positive way. In transvesticistic behaviour it is important to pay attention to the attentional aspects of it. So, dressing oneself in women's dress may be permitted in the own bedroom, but within time limits. No communication about it in the living group is allowed. Besides this, emphasis must be placed upon prosocial behaviour such as enlarging the amount of time spent in the living group and in interacting with others. Enlargement and deepening of interests should also be stimulated.

As to rape, a differentiation should probably be made between the sociopathic rapist and rapists with social needs but lack of social skills. The same is true for the more aggressive types of child molest. The sociopathic rapers and molesters generally have a poor prognosis, unless there is a tendency towards remorse and insight, also in own dynamics, which alas is seldom the case. In general these people are not motivated for treatment. The neurotic raper and molester often seem to have doubts about their own sexual identity, often have been victims themselves, just as in the sociopathic offenders (e.g. Groth & Bairnbaum, 1978). However, in the neurotics more contact is possible with the examiner and generally there are indications of remorse. In psychological and psychiatric investigation more differences show up as to the kinds of defense mechanisms etc.. For these individuals, individual and group-psychotherapy are indicated. This does not mean that treatment is easy, or always very successful. Often these youngsters are aggressive, reluctant as to cooperation and disclosure! Generally, psychotherapy alternates directive questioning, and confrontation with a client-centered approach (e.g. Breer, 1987).

Another type of sexually deviant behaviour may be prostitution, especially when this is a pathological way of dealing with emotional problems. This can be encountered in people with borderline personality disorders (Verberne, 1989a, Des Noyers, Hurley & Sovner, 1988, Tarnopolsky & Berelowitz, 1987), and people who have been victim of sexual abuse (Leehan & Wilson, 1985). Treatment is not fundamentally different from the non-retarded. Excellent overviews of treatment of victim-prostitutes are given by Jehu (1988) and Gilbert (1984).

What I have tried to clarify is that in the mentally retarded one can hardly recognize such a person as "the" sexual offender or "the" pedophile. True paraphilias occur albeit rarely. The average mentally retarded individual with sexually deviant behaviour is a person with developmental difficulties and should be treated as such. Thorough analysis of personality structure, course of development, mechanisms underlying the behavioural problems, learning and neuropsychological aspects of the behaviour problems are of crucial importance for planning treatment programs. I have not yet mentioned explicitly that treatment should take place in a comprehensive, integrated treatment program. I thought it would not be necessary to explain this, because the developmentally oriented way of thinking inevitably leads to these kinds of programs. In the same way I think it is superfluous to plead for group homes for mildly mentally retarded adults with sexually abnormal behaviour, who cannot be succesfully treated but who can live in the community with extra support (e.g. Schramsky, 1986).

References

American Psychiatric Association (1987) *Diagnostic and statistical manual of mental disorders, 3rd e.d. revised.* Washington, American Psyhiatric Association.

Barrett R. (ed.) (1986) *Severe behavior disorders in the mentally retarded, nondrug approaches to treatment.* New York & London, Plenum Press.

Bear, D., Freeman, R., Greenberg, M. (1984). Behavioral alterations in patients with temporal lobe epilepsy. In: D. Blumer: *Psychiatric aspects of epilepsy.* Washington, American Psychiatric Press.

Benson, B.A. (1986) Anger management training. *Psychiatric Aspects of Mental Retardation Reviews,* 5 (10), 51-55.

Brandt, D.E., Zlotnick, G.J. (1988) *The psychology and treatment of the youthful offender.* Springfield illinois, C.C. Thomas.

Breer, W. (1987) *The adolescent molester.* Springfield Illinois, C.C. Thomas.

Cipani, E. (1989) *The treatment of severe behavior disorders,* Washington, American Association on Mental Deficiency.

Craft, A. (1987) *Mental handicap and sexuality: issues and perspectives.* Tunbridge Wells, Costello.

Day, K. (1983) A hospital-based psychiatric unit for mentally handicapped adults. *Mental Handicap,* 11, 140-147.

Day, K. (1988) A hospital-based treatment programm for male mentally handicapped offenders. *British Jounal of Psychiatry,* 153, 635-644.

Des Noyens Hurley, A., Sovner, R. (1983) Treatment of sexual deviation in mentally retarded persons. *Psychiatric Aspects of Mental Retardation Reviews,* 2 (4), 13-16.

Des Noyers Hurley, A., Sovner, R. (1988) The clinical characteristics and management of borderline personality disorder in mentally retarded persons. *Psychiatric Aspects of Mental Retardation Reviews,* 7 (7 + 8), 43-49.

Frenken, J., van Stolk, B. (1987). *Hulpverleners en incestslachtoffers.* Deventer, Van Loghum Slaterus.

Gibbens, T.C., Robertson, G. (1983) A survey of the criminal careers of hospital order patients. *British Journal of Psychiatry,* 143, 362-369.

Gilbert, M.H. (1984) Treatment of prostitute victims of sexual assault. In: Stuart, I.R., Greer, J.G.: *Victims of sexual aggression.* New York, Van Nostrand Reinhold.

Gilson, S.F., Levitas, A.S. (1987) Psychosocial crises in the lives of mentally retarded people. *Psychiatric Aspects of Mental Retardation Reviews,* 6, (6), 27-31.

Griffiths, D., Hingsburger, D., Christian, R. (1985) Treating developmentally handicapped sexual offenders. *Psychiatric Aspects of Mental Retardation Reviews* (4 (12), 49-52.

Groth, A.N., Bairnbaum, H.J. (1978) Adult sexual orientation and attraction to underage persons. *Archives of sexual behavior, 7,* 175-181.

Gunn, J. (1977) Criminal behavior and mental disorder. *British Journal of Psychiyatry, 130,* 317-329.

Hingsburger, D. (1987) Sex counseling with the developmentally handicapped *Psychiatric Aspects of Mental Retardation Reviews (9),* 41-45.

Hingsburger, D. (1988) Clients and curriculum: preparing for sex education. *Psychiatric Aspects of Mental Retardation Reviews,* 7, (3), 13-17.

Hingsburger, D. (1989) Relationship training, sexual behavior and persons with developmental handicaps. *Psychiatric Aspects of Mental Retardation Reviews,* 8 (5), 33-38.

Hunter, W. (1979) Forensic psychiatry and mental handicap. In: James, F.J., Snaith, R.P. *Psychiatric illness and mental handicap,* Londen, Gaskell.

Jehu, D. (1988). Beyond sexual abuse, therapy with women who were childhood victims. Chichester etc, J. Wiley & Sons.

Knopp, H. (1984) *Retraining adult sex offenders, methods and modes.* Orwell, Sater Society Press.

Leehan, J., Wilsons, L. (1985) *Grown-up abused children,* Springfield Illinois, C.C. Thomas.

Lishman, W.A. (1987) *Organic Psychiatry,* Oxford etc., Blackwell.

Luria, A.R. (1963) *The mentally retarded child.* Oxford etc. Pergamon.

Menolascino, F.J. (1977) *Challenges in mental retardation.* New York, Human Sciences Press.

Menolascino, F.J. (1983) Overview. In: Menolascino, F.J., McCann, B.M.: *Mental health and mental retardation, bridging the gap.* Baltimore, University Park Press.

Mitchell, L.K. (1985) *Behavioral intervention in the sexual problems of mentally handicapped individuals in residential and home settings.* Springfield, Illionois, C.C. Thomas.

Mitchell, L.K. (1987) Intervention in the inappropriate sexual behaviour of individuals with mental handicaps. In: Craft, A.: *Mental handicap and sexuality: issues and perspectives.* Tunbridge Wells, Costello.

O'Brien, S.J. (1986) *Why they did it: stories of eight convicted child molesters.* Springfiels Illinois, C.C. Thomas.

Porter, S. (1986) *Treating the going male victim of sexual assault.*

Syracuse, Safer Society Press.

Power, D.J. (1969) Subnormality and crime. *Medical Science and Law,* 162, 83-93.

Reid, A.H.. (1982). *The psychiatry of mental handicap.* Oxford etc: Blackwell.

Schramsky, T. (1956) Community possibilities for treating violent sex offenders. Paper read at the congress of the NADD at Hershey, Pennsylvania.

Slater, A.C. (1988). *Treating child sex offenders and victims.* Newbury Park

etc., Sage.
Santamour, M.B., Watson, P.J. (1982) *The retarded offender*, New York, Praeger.
Szymanski, L.S., Jansen, P.E. (1980) Assessment of sexuality and sexual vulerability of retarded persons. In Szymanski, L.S., Tanquay, P.E.: *Emotional disorders in mentally retarded persons*. Baltimore, University Park Press.
Tarnopolsky, A., Berelowitz, M. (1987) Borderline personality, a review of recent research. *British Journal of Psychiatry,* 151, 724-734.
Tutt, N.J. (1971) The subnormal offender. *British Journal of Subnormality 17,* 42-47.
Verberne, G.J. (1989a) Over diagnostiek en behandeling van de borderline persoonlijksheidsstoornis bij licht geestelijk gehandicapten. Paper Read at the NIP symposium at Berg en Dal.
Verberne, G.J. (1989b) Relaxatietechnieken bij licht en matig geestelijk gehandicapten: een literatuursoverzicht. *Gedragstherapie*, 22 (3), 205-217.
Verberne, G.J. (1990) Neuropsychologisch onderzoek bij volwassen licht geestelijk gehandicapten met gedrags- of psychiatrische problemen. In: Došen A., Flikweert, D.A.: *Zorg voor geestelijke gezondheid bij zwakzinnigen Groningen, Stichting kinderstudies en N.G.B.Z.*
Webster, T. (1970) Unique aspects of emotional development in mentally retarded children. In: Menolascion, F.J.: *Psychiatric approaches to mental retardation*, New York, Londen, Basic Books.
Whitman, T.L., Scibak, J.W., Reid, D.H. (1983) *Behavior modification with the severely and profoundly mentally retarded*. New York etc., Acadamic Press.

Došen, A., Van Gennep, A., Zwanikken, G.J. (Eds.) (1990). Treatment of Mental Illness and Behavioral Disorder in the Mentally Retarded. Proceedings of the International Congress, May 3rd & 4th, 1990, Amsterdam, the Netherlands. Leiden, the Netherlands: Logon Publications.

Chapter 37

A model for staff training and clinical treatment for the mentally retarded sex offender

D. Cox-Lindenbaum

Introduction

The treatment of the mentally retarded sex offender poses a major challenge to the therapist, the client and the general community. The responsibility on the part of the therapist in building a therapeutic alliance, and the issues involved in the treatment of the client are unique.

This chapter has a two-fold educational purpose. First, it will focus on client treatment with an overview of a unique clinical model which addresses the cognitive limitations of the mentally retarded sex offender and integrates it with the underlying emotional issues and consequent dysfunctional sexual acting-out behaviors. Second, it will focus on staff training involving didactic material and affective experience in order to provide a framework for dealing with transferential issues, and thereby fostering a therapeutic alliance and positive direction for treatment of the client.

Clinical Treatment

Traditionally, clinical treatment for the mentally retarded sex offender has primarily focused on the descriptive aspects of the disorder rather than the developmental and psychodynamic issues of the person. Previous treatment often took the form of placing the client in the most restrictive environment with no recourse for therapeutic intervention.

A major obstacle to treatment was an inability on the part of the professional community to recognize a sexual disorder in a mentally retarded person. Often, sexually violent acts such as rape, child molestation, sexual masochism, sexual sadism and exhibitionism were assumed to be the result of the mental retardation, rather than severe clinical dysfunction and personality deficits. This process of "Diagnostic Overshadowing" as termed by Reiss (1982), often results in the person not being appropriately diagnosed and not receiving the necessary clinical services. With the focus primarily on descriptive aspects of the sexually coercive incidents such as the sexuality, the violence and the legality issues, the opportunity for treatment may be missed and the person may fall through the gap in the service delivery system.

Szymanski and Tanguay (1984) have indicated that mentally retarded people are vulnerable to mental disorders; yet, few clinicians in the field have acknowledged this in their treatment.

Most clinical services provided have focused only on the cognitive modules with the assumption being that the "sexual misconduct" was due to a lack of sexual information, opportunities for sexual interaction and sexual counseling. Through the process of deinstitutionalization and community living, it has become clear that some mentally retarded people who repeat sexual offenses and have received comprehensive sex education programs have not been able to integrate this information in order to modify their sexually violent behavior. They require a more comprehensive clinical treatment approach.

The Social/Sexual Group Treatment Program is one part of a total treatment process which may include individual therapy and psychopharmacological intervention. The program is a clinical intervention comprised of cognitive modules and experiential process. The cognitive modules are not classroom instruction but rather the presentation of material and the integration of this information through an interpersonal dynamic process. This process is crucial to the program and utilized by the therapist and client in creatively continuing to discover and refine treatment for this complex disorder.

The Social/Sexual Group Treatment Program utilizes cognitive modules comprised of Feeling Identification, Relaxation Training, Anger Management, Cognitive Restructuring, Social Skill Training and Transition Planning. The structure of these didactic exercises sets the foundation on which to build the experiential process. Through sharing amongst the group members, the bonding process occurs allowing each client to identify stressors and patterns of self destructive behaviors, to explore more responsible alternative behaviors and to connect and be intimate with peers in a socially appropriate manner.

This treatment focuses on the developmental life cycle of the mentally retarded person who has learned to use sex and violence dysfunctionally and as an expression of his inner conflicts. The program examines his mental retardation disability as a source of his alienation from society and one of the sources for his feelings of rage. It explores his acting out sexually as a symptom of psychological dysfunctioning associated more with conflict and severe stress than with pleasure and satisfaction.

It is my clinical assumption that sexually violent behaviors are complex and require a multi-faceted treatment approach. These behaviors represent underlying psychological differences and are manifested in impaired social-sexual relationships. The most prevalent issue of paraphiliacs, whether mentally retarded or not, is the visible absence of close, emotionally intimate relationships. The goal of the group process is for the client to make a connection with his peers and bond with other group members.

Prior to any treatment there must be an assessment of the person. It is through this assessment process that the therapist can begin to determine the clinical needs to be addressed and possible treatment interventions to reduce, inhibit or eliminate the sexual assualtiveness of the client.

The "Social-Sexual Evaluation Profile" developed specifically for the mentally retarded adult was designed by Dr. Charles Perroncel (1989). It is an instrument utilized by the clinician to assist in identifying the psychological deficits of the client. It measures gender identification, recognition of social cues, ego-dystonic and ego-syntonic sexual expressions, sexual seductions experienced and seductions used, coercion experienced and coercion used, distortions regarding consenting sexuality, and distortions regarding violence and coercion. This information provides the necessary data to establish an individualized treatment plan for the client.

Based upon the assessments of numerous clients who were mentally retarded sex offenders, the results indicate that they had poor social skills, lack of knowledge about sexuality and poor judgment. These deficits provide the content areas for the cognitive modules utilized in the treatment. In addition, the assessment information along with the overt symptomatology of the offender suggests that he is incapable of bonding with peers. Dealing with this issue through the group process by developing social skills and fostering intimate relationships is the central theme in treatment.

The organization of treatment consists of three stages. Stage I consists of Feeling Identification, Relaxation Training and Anger Management. Stage II consists of Cognitive Restructuring and Social Skill Training;; and Stage III is Transition Planning.

In Stage I the module begins with *Feeling Identification*. The appropriate labeling of feelings are essential to the understanding and identification of the antecedents to sexually aggressive behavior. In the case of the mentally retarded sex offender, the focus becomes the identification and exploration of feelings of rage and shame associated with their cognitive disability. The exploration of these feelings are the experiential part of the program. Group members seem to have in common the defense mechanism of denial in which they not only deny their disability but also, in this initial stage, any acknowledgement of the pain associated with it.

Relaxation Training is another part of Stage I. It enables the clients to identify emotional and physical stressors and to develop stress reduction life plans. Simultaneously, the experiential group process begins to allow the clients to identify their own level of anxiety and through instruction, visual imagery and information sharing help themselves to reduce this level of stress.

The third part of Stage I is *Anger Management Training*. Utilizing a modified version of Benson's (1986) Anger Management Program, this training enables clients to overcome their denial and identify their anger and rage related to their disability, cognitive limitations, family dysfunction, own victimization, restrictive placement and sense of powerlessness. Through assertiveness training, self instruction, understanding one's own antecedent feelings and events leading to anger, rage and self-destructive behavior, the client learns to control his emotions and find more appropriate, responsible ways of expressing these feelings.

Stage II of treatment utilizes *Cognitive Restructuring* and *Social Skill Training*. In Cognitive Restructuring focused feedback is used in the interactions amongst the group members and becomes part of their interpersonal style. Clients explore their own self destructive cycles and their perceptual distortions. This phase addresses their emerging sense of depression and loss, their alienation and rejection of peers as an expression of their own self hate. Through self examination and feedback the goal is to explore perceptual distortions and self destructive style, increase awareness and accept responsibility for one's own sexual behavior.

In Social Skill Training their sense of fear and anxiety regarding peer interaction manifests itself as well as their own conflicts regarding their sexual identify. The goals are developing communication skills, enhancing interpersonal relationships with peers, giving and receiving constructive feedback and assertiveness training.

Stage III involves *Transition Planning*. During this stage of treatment the client identifies coping strategies, recognizes safety cues, recognizes and overcomes distortions, accepts dependency issues and utilizes supportive peer interactions in a positive way. The ability to accept one's dual diagnosis and commitment to manage it through the participation in the treatment process, becomes the focus of the program with regard to aftercare. The prevention of any relapse is an integral part of the transitional planning process in the group.

Staff Training

One of the most difficult issues for the clinician in working with the Mentally retarded sex offender is identifying and accepting his "Dual Diagnostic" status. When there is this identification, then there are opportunities to provide guidelines and organization to our treatment so that the mentally retarded person has the same treatment opportunities as a non-handicapped person.

It is important for clinicians who treat the mentally retarded to begin to be able to conceptualize violently sexually acting out as behaviors that may be rooted in a sexual disorder. Facing our own distortions, disappointments and denial regarding the client's acting out behavior is essential in treating sexual disorders in a mentally retarded person. However, it is often easier for staff to see themselves as advocates for the retarded, vocal against the sexual injustice of the past decade. We would prefer to assume the role as caretakers, rather than clinicians involved in a treatment alliance where the prognosis is extremely guarded. Dismissing sexual Coercive behaviors as misconduct resulting from poor sexual opportunities, with rationalization of these incidents as "single accidents", does not assist us in the task at hand and, in effect, may become an obstacle to the client's treatment.

The Staff Training involved in the Social-Sexual Treatment and Training Program identifies and addresses the underlying issues involved in treating the Mentally Retarded Sex Offender.

The Program is comprised of a formal Didactic/Cognitive Module, with an Experiential Component. The entire program stresses commitment, involvement and responsibility on the part of both client and staff member(s). Guidelines for operating as a Group are established. Didactic material involving an Overview of the Group Treatment Program, Methodology of Treatment, Responsibility of Leaders, Review of DSM IIIR Diagnostic Psycho-Sexual Disorders, and articles involving etiology of sexual offenses are reviewed. Strategies of group process with emphasis on confrontation, defense mechanisms, engaging and bonding principles are stressed. As the didactic clinical information is presented, assignments involving staff attitudes and values awareness are introduced. These surveys involve sexuality in general, and sexuality and the mentally retarded.

Through an attitude and value survey staff trainers begin to identify their own bias, prejudice, assumptions, and attitudes and values regarding themselves and the mentally retarded. Specific issues of sexuality such as masturbation, orgasm, sexual style, sexually transmitted disease, etc. are reviewed. Values and beliefs regarding sexual preference, variations, incest, rape, are additionally considered. A personal review of such material allows an assessment of each trainee's values and knowledge to emerge. Self-assessment becomes a stepping stone to further exploration of counter-transferential issues further on in client treatment. The processing of the staff self-evaluation becomes the link between the Staff Training Program and the Client Treatment Program. Personal and therapeutic style in confronting resistive behavior between staff becomes apparent and is a concrete experience for group process which can then be utilized with clients.

As the Training Program continues and the task becomes the formation of client treatment Groups, staff attitudes continue to emerge. Through client case presentation and intake review, the initial process is often thwarted with the rationalizations for the referring violent sexual behaviors. The client's retardation is acknowledged and then utilized to deny his capabilities and functional level. Client's incidents of molestation, coercion, exhibitionism, and sadism are cloaked as "accidental." It is only through careful review of the material, that the Staff Trainees begin to identify their own resistance, as a defense against their own sense of fear, and overwhelming sense of responsibility in treating and working with a population of sexual offenders who are also mentally retarded. With support, their own insecurity regarding issues related to client confrontation, rage, bonding with a sex offender, violence, maintaining control in group, working with dependency issues, client deprivation and suicidal depression begin to emerge. Acceptance of the treatment issues involved in the Program become more reality-based. This process of professional growth takes place in an atmosphere of bonding, trust and mutual respect for the human condition, which in turn, becomes the framework from which the client-therapist alliance will develop. Over time, the trainee accepts the client's dual diagnosis and can focus on the complex clinical needs of the clients who presents a psychiatric disorder, with the complication of cognitive limitations.

Working with the staff's sense of self, the trainer prepares the therapist to deal with the sex offenders destructive defense system and enables them to gain the necessary clinical skills to establish a therapeutic alliance with clients.

Issues of one's own rage with clients and the identification with their victims is a counter-transferential issue that needs to be dealt with in the training process. This breakthrough in the trainee's denial system then allows them to confront the client in his denial of irresponsible behavior. Increasing confrontational skills in a firm, consistent engaging manner, devoid of anger, replaces the denial or authoritative control which come from the therapists own emotional needs. Relentless exploration of powerlessness are dealt with through the clients' issues regarding their mental retardation. Trainees become more experienced with their ability to bond with clients and facilitate clients bonding with each other. Ongoing clinical supervision is a necessity for providing support to the clinician in working with the challenges presented by this population.

As the client becomes more involved in the treatment, and defenses lowered, repressed memories of abuse, trauma, fear, alienation, and rage emerge. Such emotional catharsis lends itself to client depression and despair. The anger, rage and denial gives way to a state of anxiety, panic, helplessness, emptiness and dependency on the therapist. Dealing with these client emotions are extremely draining and require treatment team and supervisory support.

Conclusion

With a knowledge of the Phases of Treatment for the Mentally Retarded Sex Offender, the staff is better able to advocate for the client's safety from his own destructive cycle as well as the safety for the Community. The trainee along with the client also identifies negative patterns of behavior which precipitate the sexual acting out. An awareness of this sexual acting out on the part of the clients often creates dependency on the staff for protection from their own impulses. Support in working with those dependency issues is a crucial part of the therapeutic process for the client and the supervisory process for the staff.

In accepting that we will not cure this disorder but hopefully help the client to manage it, the therapist no longer becomes the enabler to self destructive and violent behavior but rather establishes an alliance with the client which is engaging and therapeutic in nature.

References

Benson, B.A., Rice, C.J. and Miranti, S.V. 1986, "Effects of Anger Management training with Mentally Retarded adults in Group Treatment." *Journal of Consulting and Clinical Psychology*, 154, 728-729.
Groth, N.A. *Men Who Rape*, Plenum Press, NY, 1979, pp 215-218.

Perroncel, CC. 1989, "The Social-Sexual Evaluation Profile." Torrington, Connecticut.

Reiss, S., Levitan, G.W. and McNally, R.J. 1982, "Emotionally disturbed Mentally Retarded People," *American Psychologist* 37(4): 261-367.

Szymanski, L. and Tanguay, P.E. 1980 *Emotional disorders of Mentally Retarded Persons*. Baltimore: University Park Press.

Došen, A., Van Gennep, A., Zwanikken, G.J. (Eds.) (1990). Treatment of Mental Illness and Behavioral Disorder in the Mentally Retarded. Proceedings of the International Congress, May 3rd & 4th, 1990, Amsterdam, the Netherlands. Leiden, the Netherlands: Logon Publications.

Chapter 38

Comparison of maladaptive behaviour between mentally handicapped adults with and without epilepsy

S. Deb
D. Hunter

Introduction

It is fair to say that the relationship between psychiatric illness and epilepsy is far from clear. Not long ago epilepsy itself was diagnosed as a type of psychiatric illness. Some of the beliefs regarding the commonly associated characteristics of epileptics had their origin in ancient times and survived till today without much scientific evidence for them. Although in ancient Greece epilepsy was called the sacred disease, the person who suffered from that disease was considered to be far from sacred; on the contrary the epileptic himself was unclean and whoever touched him might become a prey to the demon.

So far some association between epilepsy and increased general psychopathology has emerged. The concept of a global "epileptic personality" held earlier this century, has generally fallen into disfavour. The pendulum has swung from the constitutional concept, via the denial of any mental abnormality (Lennox, 1960) to the contested identification of a specific temporal lobe syndrome (Gibbs, 1957; Geschwind, 1979). A critical review of studies using standardized objective tests however has been unable to confirm the position of TLE in psychopathology. It appears on the other hand that patients with epilepsy demonstrate more emotional and psychiatric problems than normal individuals and other medical groups; but this does not appear to be greater than for persons with other chronic neurological or medical conditions (Whitman et al, 1984).

However, the literature on the psychopathology of mentally handicapped epileptics is sparse and fraught with methodological loopholes. Eymen et al (1969) studied the mental handicap population in three large hospitals in the USA and showed hyperactivity along with other factors such as aggression, speech problems and difficulties in eating/dressing to be more common amongst institutionalized mentally handicapped epileptics. In another study Le Verne Capes and Moore (1970) compared twenty-one factors of maladaptive behaviour between a group of 229 epileptic and a non-matched control group of 511 non-epileptic mentally handicapped patients in Arizona Children's Colony. They showed significant differences in sixteen out of twenty-one factors (mainly hyperactivity, withdrawal and aggression directed to others, self or objects).

On the other hand, Corbett (1981), in the Camberwell study, did not find any significant difference in the frequency of behaviour disturbance between epileptic and non-epileptic children with severe mental handicap. This finding was also supported by our previous study (Deb et al, 1987) where we were unable to find any significant difference in the rate of maladaptive behaviour between epileptic and matched control group on non-epileptic adults in a mental handicap institution. In a recent controlled study conducted by Espie et al (1989) involving mentally handicapped epileptic in-patients and out-patients, no overall significant difference in maladaptive behaviour was found between epileptics and non-epileptics, although a subgroup of poorly controlled epileptics presented greater behavioural management problems.

Methods

We studied psychopathological aspects of mentally handicapped people with epilepsy under the headings of (1) Maladaptive behaviour (2) Psychiatric Illness and (3) Personality disorder. Because of the limited time, I shall only present some of the findings in the maladaptive behaviour section. We studied 300 mentally handicapped adults in Leicester, U.K., half of whom were epileptics and the other half being the individually matched control group. Out of 150 epileptics, 100 were institutionalized and 50 lived in the community. Matching was done according to (1) age (2) sex (3) level of intelligence as measured by various psychometric tests (4) level of communication (expressive speech, comprehension and clarity of speech) (5) Sensory impairment (eg. vision and hearing) (6) living environment (7) length of hospitalization or attendance at Day Centre and (8) associated chronic physical illness.

We used Profile of Abilities, and Adjustment schedule as a rating scale for Adaptive and Maladaptive behaviour. This scale was designed by Dr Lorna Wing and her colleagues from the MRC Social Psychiatric Unit, London in 1988. This is an observer rated questionnaire which has 13 subsections under problem behaviour section, each subsection was scored on a ranked scale. The inter-rater, inter-informant and test-retest reliability of this scale had been thoroughly tested and the scores lay between 78% and 93%. We gathered information from either ward staff or a carer who knew the mentally handicapped person at least for the previous 3 years or more.

The epileptic group contained 77 males and 73 females, the mean age being 40 years, SD 13 years and an age range between 20-77 years. Seventy-five were severely mentally handicapped (IQ < 35), 49 mildly (IQ 70-50) and 26 moderately (IQ 49-35). In the hospital there was a significantly higher proportion of severely mentally handicapped people ($p<0.001$) and an older age group compared with the community population but no such difference emerged in the distribution of sex. Non-epileptics had a significantly higher chromosomal cause ($p<0.01$) for their handicap whereas epileptics had a higher pre-natal cause and a significantly higher ($p<0.001$) post-natal cause compared with the non-epileptics.

Sixty-five per cent (n=98) sustained generalized epilepsy compared with 17% (n=25) who suffered from partial epilepsy; in the remaining cases seizure type remained undetermined. Fifty-eight patients sustained no seizures in the 12 months period previous to the study, and they were called non-active epileptics. Out of the 92 active epileptics, 35 patients sustained less than one fit per month and 56 sustained more than one fit per month, and in one case the frequency of fits remained unclear. The majority of epileptics had their onset of epilepsy before the age of 10, and a majority suffered from epilepsy for 20 years or more. Eighty-four patients suffered from one type of seizure whereas 39 suffered from more than one type of seizure and in 27 cases the seizure type remained unclear.

EEG findings of 100 epileptics showed predominantly focal epileptiform change (31%) compared with 21% generalized diffuse change. The EEG findings in combination with clinical picture makes us assume that most of the clinically diagnosed generalized epilepsy were in fact secondarily generalized. Drug treatment showed a tendency of monotherapy with a particular preference to Carbamazepine. Out of the 150 epileptic patients, 139 received antiepileptic medication. Eighty-seven received monotherapy whereas 52 received polytherapy. Fifty-six received monotherapy of Carbamazepine whereas 16 received Sodium Valproate and 14 received either Phenobarbitone or Phenytoin monotherapy.

Results

No statistically significant difference was detected on any of the maladaptive behaviour ratings of the PAA when the whole epileptic group (n=150) was compared with the whole non-epileptic control group (n=150) or when segregated into hospitalized controls or community controls. Active epileptics were found to be significantly less co-operative ($p=0.027$) and more echolalic when compared with their matched control. No such differences emerged when non-active epileptics were compared with their control group.

Each person was then rated according to the number of severe maladaptive behaviour rating. No statistically significant difference was found when the epileptic group (n=150) was compared with non-epileptic group (n=150) for the total number of severe ratings on the problem behaviour sub-scales of P.A.A., although a slightly higher percentage of epileptics (58%) had a higher number of severe behaviour ratings as compared with the matched control non-epileptics (52.7%). 55.3% of the total population had scored severe ratings on any of the maladaptive behaviour subsection of P.A.A.

When severe behaviour ratings were compared between the groups, the severely mentally handicapped compared with mild to moderately handicapped and the hospitalized population compared with the community based population showed significantly higher behaviour problem. When different categories of mood according to PAA scale were studied, no significant difference was found between epileptics and non-epileptics but hospitalized patients had more changeable mood.

When different subgroups of epileptic patients were compared with the corresponding matched control non-epileptic patients, in the following subgroups non-epileptics showed significantly more aggression; the severe mental handicap group (n=75, P=0.049); the group who suffered from single type of epilepsy (n=85, P=0.02); the group treated with monotherapy of anticonvulsant medication (n=87, P=0.03); the group treated with carbamazepine alone (n=56, P=0.01); and those whose EEG showed only prominent background slow activities (n=48, P=0.01). In the last group non-epileptics had also shown significantly more overactivity (P=0.04). On the other hand, epileptics whose EEG had only shown generalized epileptiform activity (n=21) had shown significantly more temper tantrums (P=0.01) and irritability (P=0.01).

When different subgroups of hospitalised epileptics were compared with their non-epileptic matched control group, a similar picture emerged as it did for the combined group of hospitalized and community group. However amongst the community based epileptics those who are mildly to moderately handicapped (n=37) were found to be significantly more destructive and irritable.

Conclusion

The main findings of our study are (1) No significant difference in maladaptive behaviour between epileptic and non-epileptic mentally handicapped adults, (2) 55.3% of the total population had shown severe rating in one or more maladaptive behaviour, (3) 58% of epileptics compared with

52.7% of non-epileptics showed a severe behaviour problem, however this was not statistically significant and (4) The subgroup of active epileptics was significantly less co-operative and more echolalic compared with the non-epileptics.

The overall findings in our study support the idea that in spite of widely held beliefs that epileptics as a group show more aggressive and other behaviour problems, scientific evidence is lacking. Previous such studies have failed to match appropriate controls. In this study we have been able to match two groups according to variables which could affect a mentally handicapped person's behaviour.

Acknowledgement

I am grateful to Sanofi UK for their travel grant, and Mrs S Wardell for typing the manuscript.

References

Corbett, J .A. (1981) Epilepsy and mental retardation. In Epilepsy and Psychiatry (eds E.H. Reynolds & M. R. Trimble). Edinburgh: Churchill Livingstone.

Deb, S., Cowie, V.A. & Richens, A. (1987) Folate metabolism and problem behaviour in mentally handicapped epileptics. *Journal of Mental Deficiency Research*, 31, 173-168.

Espie, C.A., Pashley, A.S., Bonham, K.G., Sourindhrin, I. & O'Donovan, M. (1989), The mentally handicapped person with epilepsy: a comparative study investigating psychosocial functioning. *Journal of Mental Deficiency Research*, 33, 123-135.

Eyman, R.K., Capes, L., Moore, B.C., & Zachofsky, T. (1969), Retardates with seizures. *American Journal of Mental Deficiency*, 74, 651-659.

Geschwind, N. (1979), Behavioural changes in temporal lobe epilepsy. *Psychological Medicine*, 9, 217-219.

Gibbs, F.A. (1957), Ictal and non-ictal psychiatric disorders in temporal lobe epilepsy. *Journal of Nervous and Mental Disease*, 113, 522-528.

La Verne Capes & Moore, B.C. (1970), Behaviour differences between seizure and non-seizure retardates. *Arizona Medicine*, XXVII, 2, 74-76.

Lennox, W.G. (1960), Epilepsy and related disorder. Boston: Little, Brown.

Whitman, S., Hermann, B.P. & Gordon, A. (1984), Psychopathology in epilepsy: how great is the risk? *Biological Psychiatry*, 19, 213-236.

Došen, A., Van Gennep, A., Zwanikken, G.J. (Eds.) (1990). Treatment of Mental Illness and Behavioral Disorder in the Mentally Retarded. Proceedings of the International Congress, May 3rd & 4th, 1990, Amsterdam, the Netherlands. Leiden, the Netherlands: Logon Publications.

Chapter 39

A behavioral methodology for diagnosing affective disorders in individuals with mental retardation

R. Sovner
M. Lowry

Mentally retarded persons can develop all types of affective disorders (16,17); they occur in profound and severely handicapped persons as well as those with mild and moderate handicaps (2,8). Diagnosing these disorders and assessing treatment response in this population is quite challenging, however, because the presence of developmental disabilities creates a number of methodological problems.

1. It is difficult to use self-reports for determining the presence of diagnostically relevant behavior and symptoms.

Many of the symptom criteria used to diagnose affective disorders reflect subjective changes in mood and behavior (e.g., fatigue) (11). In markedly severe cases of depression and mania, when symptoms develop acutely, the diagnosis may be obvious due to clearcut changes in psychosocial functioning (e.g., the sudden onset of a sleep disturbance). In cases in which the disorder is chronic or symptom severity is only mild or moderate, behavioral changes consistent with mania or depression may be more difficult to recognize.

Another problem is that typical affective features may present in very individualized ways. Agitation, for example, may present as pacing in one person, stereotypic behavior in another, and self-injury in a third.

Fortunately, many affective signs and symptoms lend them selves to behavioral assessment so that the diagnosis does not have to rely on client reports of subjective changes consistent with an affective disorder. Tables 1 and 2 present the *Diagnostic and Statistical Manual of Mental Disorders, Third Edition Revised* (*DSM-IIIR*) (3) symptom/behavior criteria for depression and mania. We have also listed in the tables what we believe are behavioral equivalents of many of the criteria.

Table 1
DSM-IIIR diagnostic criteria for mania and behavioral equivalents in the developmentally disabled*

Mood State:	DSM-IIIR (3) Criteria	Observed Equivalents in Mentally Retarded Persons	Objective Behaviors Which Might Be Monitored
	Euphoric/elevated/irritable mood (no minimum duration necessary).	Boisterousness or excitement may be the predominant mood state. Self-injury may be associated with irritability.	Measure rates of smiling and/or laughing.
Symptom Criteria:	At least three symptoms must be present if patient has euphoric mood. Four symptoms must be present if patient only has irritable mood.		
	(1) inflated self-esteem/grandiosity	Thought content may center around mastery of daily living skills.	Measure inappropriate remarks.
	(2) decr. need for sleep	Increased maladaptive behavior at usual bedtime or in early morning. Patient is dressed for work at 5:00 AM.	Monitor sleep pattern using 30 minute intervals.
	(3) more talkative/pressured speech	Increased fequency of vocalization irrespective of whether patient has usable speech.	Measure rates of swearing, singing, screaming.
	(4) flight of ideas/racing thoughts	Disorganized speech.	
	(5) distractibility	Decrease in workshop performance.	Use workshop performance data.
	(6) incr. goal directed activity/psychomotor agitation	Aggressive behavior and negativism may be present.	Measure aggressions, request refusals per week, pacing, etc.
	(7) excessive involvement in pleasureable activities	Teasing behavior, fondling others, publicly masturbating.	Measure intervals in which the behavior occurs.

* Adapted from Sovner & Hurley (14)

Table 2
DSM-IIIR diagnostic criteria for major depression and behavioral equivalents in subject*

		DSM-IIIR (3) Criteria [Five or more of the following symptoms must be present for a minimum of two weeks. Symptom (1) or (2) must be one of the five.]	Observed Equivalents in Mentally Retarded Persons	Objective Behaviors Which Might Be Measured
Mood State:	(1)	Depressed mood, irritable mood in children or adolescents	Apathetic facial expression with lack of emotional reactivity.	Measure rates of smiling, responses to preferred activities, crying episodes.
Symptom Criteria:	(2)	Generalized decrease in interest or pleasure by self-report or observed apathy	Withdrawal, lack of reinforcers.	Measure time spent in room, etc.
	(3)	significant decrease in appetite or weight loss (5% body weight in one month) or significant increase in appetite or weight gain (5% of body weight in one month)	------------	Measure meal refusals, change in weight.
	(4)	insomnia or hypersomnia	Change in total sleep time	Use sleep chart to record sleep
	(5)	psychomotor agitation or retardation	Agitation may present as SIB or aggression, retardation may present as passivity.	Time spent in bed, spontaneous verbizations, pacing.
	(6)	fatigue or loss of energy	Decreased energy.	
	(7)	feelings of worthlessness/inappropriate guilt	statements such as "I'm retarded."	Requires expressive language to determine if symptom is present.
	(8)	decreased concentration/ indecisiveness/ diminished ability to think	Change in workshop performance	Use workshop performance data.
	(9)	recurrent thoughts of death/suicidal ideation	Perseveration on the deaths of family members and friends, preoccupation with funerals.	Requires expressive language to determine if symptom is present.

* Adapted from Sovner & Hurley (15)

2. In mentally retarded persons, affective disorders often present with non-specific maladaptive behavior

Maladaptive behavior can sometimes be a non-specific stress response to any one or more internal conditions, including: 1) physical discomfort and pain; 2) brain-damage associated changes in impulse control, activity level, and mood; 3) overarousal associated with pervasive developmental disorders; 4) subjective distress related to classic psychiatric disorders; and 5) beha vioral side-effects of pharmacotherapy.

The onset of a psychiatric illness may therefore present as an increase in the severity of longstanding maladaptive responses (e.g., self-injury), an increase in the frequency of these re sponses, and/or their occurrence in new settings. The presence of an affective disorder may be missed unless caregivers and clinicians recognize that the changes in behavior may reflect an underlying mental disorder (11).

3. An affective disorder may represent a co-morbid psychopathological state

An affective disorder may be superimposed upon a pervasive developmental disorder (6,7,16) or other metabolic/genetic disor der (e.g., Fragile X syndrome) which may have characteristic behavioral features. These features may mask the presence of affective symptoms. Manic overactivity, for example, may present as an increase in self-stimulatory behavior in a person with autism (17).

4. The presenting problem in an affective disorder may be state-dependent behavior with cyclical increases in severity

Some behaviors occur only during periods of mania or depres sion. Reid and Leonard (9), for example, were able to demon strate that recurrent vomiting in a mildly handicapped woman was associated only with depressed phases of a rapid cycling bipolar disorder. (Rapid cycling is defined as greater than three epi sodes of mania and/or depression per year.) Unless the associa tion between affective states and the occurrence of non-specific behaviors is recognized, their diagnostic significance and rela tionship to an affective disorder will be missed.

Developing a behavioral methodology for diagnosing affective disorders

Behavioral assessment research has demonstrated that any observable behavior can be objectively measured and quantified. (1,10). The measurement process consists of operationally defi ning the behavior, selecting an appropriate data system, training observers in data collection, and analyzing the collected infor mation. Behavioral assessment methodologies are particularly well-suited to the task of diagnosing affective disorders in mentally retarded persons.

1. Behavioral equivalents of some manic and depressive symptoms are easily recognized (e.g., manic overactivity) and are, therefore, quantifiable.

The behavioral equivalents of affective disorder criteria and the kinds of objective behaviors which can be measured are presented in Tables 1 and 2. (The tables do not exhaust the possible behaviors that can reflect the presence of a manic or depressive illness.)

2. Many commonly used data systems in applied behavior analysis are suitable for measuring behavior associated with an affective disorder.

3. Direct service staff, who provide ongoing supervision to mentally retarded persons at home and work, can be trained to become reliable observers and data collectors.

4. Behavior data, collected across settings and times of day, can be pooled to provide a comprehensive picture of an individual's functioning.

A common diagnostic and treatment error is to rely on re ports from only one setting, such as the community residence, when the major behavior problems are occurring at the workshop. Objective behavioral data collected in several different settings helps to control for this problem.

5. The collected data provides a baseline with which to determine treatment efficacy.

The same data used to make a diagnosis of mania or depres sion can be used to measure treatment response. This is impor tant because there may only be a decrease in the frequency and severity of maladaptive behaviors (e.g., self-injury associated with depression), not a complete remission. Consequently, the change from the baseline rate of maladaptive behavior becomes a critical outcome measure.

Behavioral systems have been used by some clinicians to diagnose and treat affective disorders in mentally retarded per sons. Field *et al* (4) were able to develop operational criteria for assessing depression-associated behaviors in a 22-year-old woman with moderate mental retardation and measure her positive response to imipramine under double blind conditions. Hardy *et al* (5) utilized a frequency count of self-injury to determine response to desipramine in a mentally retarded 20-year-old man with major depression.

Reid and Leonard (9) used a severity rating of mania and depression to demonstrate the association between the frequency of vomiting episodes amd depressed phases in their patient with a rapid cycling bipolar disorder. They then used these global ratings of mood state to document a response to lithium. Wieseler *et al* (19) also demonstrated that global ratings of depression and mania could track the clinical course of a mentally retarded person with a rapid cycling bipolar illness.

Steps in implementing a behavior monitoring program for the diagnosis and treatment of affective disorders

The following discussion describes the steps in setting up behavioral monitoring systems.

Operationally define the behaviors to be measured

When an individual is suspected of experiencing an episode of affective illness, the first step is to define operationally those behaviors which reflect the affective disturbance. Such definitions include a written description of the behavior's physical presentation (i.e., what the behavior looks like – its topography) and any associated features (e.g., accompanying verbal expressions).

To illustrate this point, pressured speech – a characteristic feature of mania – can be operationally defined in various ways depending on individual presentation. For one person who displayed nearly continuous utterances, we defined "non-stop talking" as continuously verbalizing for at least five consecutive minutes without ever pausing for more than five seconds. In another case, in which pressured speech presented as "screaming", we defined the behavior as vocalizing or verbalizing at a volume higher than normal conversational levels. In a client for whom manic speech presented as singing, we measured melodic vocalizing of a nursery rhyme or popular song.

This approach can also be used to define psychomotor agita tion and manic overactivity. In the case of an agitated depressed person, pacing was measured by first defining it as continuously walking back and forth or in circles for more than 60 seconds at a time. For a manic client, the overactivity presented as "running" which we defined as taking long strides in rapid succession.

Choose an appropriate data collection system

Once the behaviors which are associated with the individual's affective disorder have been operationally defined, the next step is to choose a data system. The type of data to be recorded is influenced by the temporal properties of the behavior and, just as important, the availability of staff to collect the data.

Frequency Counting

In general, frequency counting (i.e., counting the instances of a behavior) is appropriate if the observer can detect discrete occurrences of the behavior, can count each instance as fast as the behavior occurs, and does not have to count inordinately large numbers (e.g., behavior which occurs several times per minute for several hours at a time).

A good example of a behavior which lends itself to frequency recording is meal refusal (the behavioral equivalent of depres sion-associated decreased appetite). Refusing a meal is a dis crete event (e.g., saying "no" and refusing to eat) that is readily observable and generally does not occur more than three times per day.

Partial Interval Recording

For most of the affective behaviors which we measure, a frequency count is not practical. Some behaviors are charac terized by a continuous flow of responses which have an ill-defined beginning and end (e.g., manic screaming can last for seconds or minutes and end without discernible pauses). Other behaviors such as stereotypic rocking may happen hundreds or even thousands of times per day, making frequency counts impractical.

Partial interval recording is a type of data system better suited for measuring most affective behaviors. The person's day is divided into a series of intervals of equal duration. Each hour, for example, might be divided into four 15-minute periods. For each interval, the trained observer records whether the behavior has occurred or not, rather than the number of times it was displayed. Partial interval techniques can also be applied to rating scales, especially those which measure global ratings of mood state or illness severity.

The limitations in the use of frequency counts do not apply to partial interval recording systems. The observer is not required to count as quickly as the behavior occurs nor count very high frequencies. For behaviors of long duration there is no need to determine when the behavior began or ended. Partial interval recording also requires less staff observation time; as soon as the behavior occurs during an interval, staff do not need to monitor that behavior until the next interval begins.

The utility of the partial interval system is illustrated by the measurement of nightly sleep pattern. Sleep data is especi ally valuable in diagnosing individuals who are non-verbal and/or have severe-profound handicaps. The night is divided into 30 minute time intervals and staff are instructed to place an 'X' in the box for a specific interval if the client is awake for any time during that period.

An examination of the time when the client was asleep or awake on any given night shows whether there was difficulty falling asleep, awakening in the middle of the night, or early morning awakening. Analysis of the total number of hours slept per night across consecutive nights reveals episodes of hypersom nia (increased need for sleep) or hyposomnia (decreased need for sleep). Another method of analyzing sleep is to select a speci fic time period (e.g., a week or month) and categorize each period with respect to the number of nights during which the client slept 4 or less hours, 4.5 to 6 hours, 6.5 to 8 hours, and greater than 8 hours. The resulting distribution can be dis played as a bar graph showing the percentage of nights within each category.

Train Staff to Use the System

One of the major advantages of behavioral measurement sys tems is their simplicity. They do not depend soley on the obser vations of highly skilled clinicians; any direct care staff person can be trained to recognize instances of each behavior and make the appropriate data entry.

The first step in the training process is to identify which staff need to learn the data system. The goal is always to have a trained person in a position to observe the client's behavior. Therefore, staff who work within the client's residence and work placement need to be trained.

For most applications, the trainer is a clinician who opera tionally defines the behaviors and establishes the data system. Direct care staff are first given a verbal description and demon stration of the behavior. Viewing a videotape of the client engaging in the behavior can be very helpful. Next, the data sheet which includes definitions of the behaviors to be measured is reviewed. The trainer describes an everyday situation in which the behavior occurs and demonstrates what data entries would be made. The staff person then practices making the proper data entries in a simulated situation. The simulations might involve the trainer role-playing the behaviors and/or the staff person viewing a videotape of the client engaging in the beha vior. When the staff person becomes proficient at making the correct data entries during the simulations, authorization is given to utilize the data system. Feedback by the supervisor on the correctness of the staff person's data entries is provided during the first few days when data are recorded and thereafter on an intermittent basis.

Data Analysis

In settings where direct service staff are working with a client throughout the day and night, a continuous stream of data can be collected. The partial interval and frequency recording systems permit an analysis of any behavior across hours, days, weeks, or months. Utilization of graphic techniques to track behaviors can reveal important characteristics of an affective disorder.

Graphed data can demonstrate relationships between various behaviors associated with an affective disorder. Figure 1 displays the sleep pattern (hours per night) and meals refused of an adult with a major depression. The data demonstrate a positive correlation between the measures (sleep time and meal refusals increase during periods of depression).

Figure 1
Relationship between meal refusals and sleep pattern in a mentally retarded woman with major depression

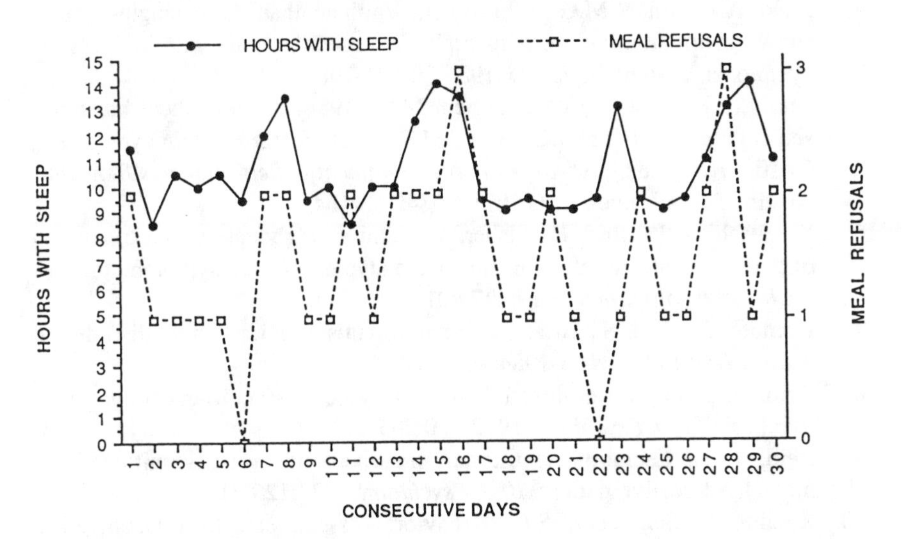

Once the pattern of behaviors is determined, the data system can be used for diagnostic purposes and to assess treatment response or the effects of medication withdrawal.

Conclusion

The adaptation of behavioral assessment principles to the diagnosis and treatment of affective disorders promises to in crease the reliability of psychiatric diagnoses in the mentally retarded and provide an objective way of determining treatment efficacy. Given the number of potentially effective psychiatric interventions, even for such atypical disorders as rapid cycling bipolar disorder (12,13), the failure to diagnosis these disor ders may deprive individuals of treatment which may drastically alter their lives for the better.

References

1. Ciminero A.R., Calhoun, K.S., Adams, H.E. *Handbook of Behavioral Assessment.* NY: Wiley & Sons, 1986.
2. Corbett J.A. Psychiatric morbidity and mental retardation. In James, F.E., Snaith, R.P. (eds.), *Psychiatric Illness and Mental Handicap* London: Gaskell Press, 1979;11-25.
3. *Diagnostic and Statistical Manual of Mental Disorders, Third Edition – Revised,* Washington DC: American Psychiatric Association, 1986.
4. Field, A.J., Aman, M.G., White, A.J., Vaithianathan, C. A single-subject study of imipramine in a mentally retarded woman with depressive symptoms. *J Ment Defic Res* 1986;30:191-198.
5. Hardy, P.M., Waters, J.M., Cohen, M.S. (1984) A biomedical basis for self-injury. In Griffin, J.C., Start, M.T., Williams D.E., Altmeyer, B.K., Griffin, H.K. (eds.), *Advances in the Treatment of Self-injurious Behavior* Austin, Texas: James C. Griffin, 1984;153-164.
6. Kerebeshian, J., Burd, L., Fisher, W. Lithium carbonate in the treatment of two patients with infantile autism and atypical bipolar symptomatology. *J Clin Psychopharmacol* 1987;7:401-405.
7. Komoto, J., Usui, S., Hirata, J. Infantile autism and affective disorder. *J Autism Devel Disorders* 1984;14:81-84.
8. Reid, A.H. Psychoses in adult mental defectives: I. Manic depressive psychosis. *Br J Psychiatry* 1972;120:205-212.
9. Reid, A.H., Leonard, A. Lithium treatment of cyclic vomiting in a mentally defective patient. *Br J Psychiatry* 1977;125:316.
10. Rojahn, J., Schroeder, S.R. Behavioral assessment. In Matson, J.L., Mulick, J.A. (eds.), *Handbook of Mental Retardation.* NY: Pergamon Press, 1983;227-243.
11. Sovner, R. Limiting factors in the use of DSM-III criteria with mentally ill/mentally retarded persons. *Psychopharmacol Bull* 1986;22:1055-1059.
12. Sovner, R. Anticonvulsant drug therapy of neuropsychiatric disorders in mentally retarded persons. In McElroy, S.E., Pope, H.G. Jr (eds.), *Use of Anticonvulsants in Psychiatry. Recent Advances.* Clifton, N.J.: Oxford Health Care, 1988;169-181.
13. Sovner, R. The use of valproate in the treatment of mentally retarded persons with typical and atypical bipolar disorders. *J Clin Psychiatry* 1989; 50 [3 supplment]: 40-43.
14. Sovner, R., Hurley, A.D. Diagnosing mania in the mentally retarded. *Psychiatr Aspects MR* 1982;8-11.
15. Sovner, R., Hurley, A.D. Diagnosing depression in the mentally retarded. *Psychiatr Aspects MR* 1982;1:1-3.
16. Sovner, R., Hurley A.D. Do the mentally retarded suffer from affective illness? *Arch Gen Psychiatry* 1983; 40:61-67.

17. Sovner, R., Pary, R.J. Affective disorders in developmentally disabled persons. In Matson, J.L., Barrett, R.P. (eds.), *Psychopathology in the Mentally Retarded, Second Edition.* Psychological Corporation, in press.
18. Steingard, R., Biederman, J. Lithium responsive manic-like symptoms in two individuals with autism and mental retardation. *J Am Acad Child Adol Psychiatry* 1987;26:932-935.
19. Wieseler, N.A., Campbell, G.J., Sonis, W. Ongoing use of an affective rating scale in the treatment of a mentally retarded individual with a rapid-cycling bipolar affective disorder. *Res Devel Disabil* 1988;9:47-53.

Došen, A., Van Gennep, A., Zwanikken, G.J. (Eds.) (1990). Treatment of Mental Illness and Behavioral Disorder in the Mentally Retarded. Proceedings of the International Congress, May 3rd & 4th, 1990, Amsterdam, the Netherlands. Leiden, the Netherlands: Logon Publications.

Chapter 40

Temperament research with mentally retarded people in the Netherlands

J.B. Blok

Introduction

Little is known about the temperament of mentally retarded people. Chess (1970) and Chess and Korn (1970) discussed the temperament of relatively small samples of mentally retarded people. Thomas and Chess (1977) define temperament as a general term referring to the "how" of behavior: "It differs from ability, wich is concerned with the *what* and *how well* of behaving, and from motivation, wich accounts for *why* a person does what he is doing. Temperament, by contrast, concerns the *way* in which an individual behaves." (Thomas & Chess, 1977, p.9). Our purpose was to adapt an already existing instrument: the "Parent and Teacher Questionnaire for children 3-7 years of age" (Thomas & Chess, 1977, p.222-232). In doing so, we chose an instrument which was developed for normal intelligent children. We followed Chess and Korn (1970) when discussing the temperament ratings of mentally retarded children 5 to 12 years old: "these average ratings are very similar to those obtained in the larger sample of normal children (...) at about age 5, an age roughly equivalent to the MA of the mentally retarded children." (Chess & Korn, 1970, p.126).

Temperament is just one of the relevant variables in the care for the mentally retarded children. Chess (1970) refers to temperament as only one feauture among other ones like degree of retardation and habitual level of functioning.

Rutter (1977) is of the opinion that for mentally retarded children in general temperamental characteristics are not different from those of children of average intelligence but that behavioral problems are much more prominent in this group.Thomas and Chess (1977) note that mentally retarded children with a so-called Difficult Child temperament pattern are prone to develop behavior disorders. They stress however the fact that the Difficult Child in general is more apt to develop behavior disorders but that the presence of handicaps increases this vulnerability.

In a more general sense Thomas and Chess pay attention to the finding that for any handicapped child new situations bring about new sources of stress. They advocate an optimal approach, which can be formulated after determining the temperamental characteristics:

> "To put it another way, healthy development for the deviant child requires special concern for consonance between his individual capacities and attributes of the environment. Furthermore, each type of cognitive, physical or other handicap may modify or change the type of management which is optimal for a specific temperamental constellation, as compared to that of the nonhandicapped child. For these reasons it is important that those responsible for the care and education of the deviant child identify his temperamental traits. Once this is done, the approach which will be optimal for that child with his specific temperament and developmental deviation can be formulated and implemented." (Thomas & Chess, 1977, p. 64).

Some results with the TVZ

In order to measure temperamental characteristics of mentally retarded people we adopted the Parent and Teacher Questionnaire by Thomas and Chess (1977). It was given the name "Temperamentsschaal voor Zwakzinnigen" (TVZ). In collaboration with Peter van den Berg and Jan Feij of the Free University of Amsterdam, data of 1200 mentally retarded people in the age of 10 to 55 years were gathered. Results were obtained from 33 of the 70 institutions for mentally retarded in the Netherlands that are registered as such. The results were processed by factor analysis. With the analysis of principal components we identified 7 factors or temperamental characteristics (see Table 1).

The first variable is **Approach**; this indicates the amount of shy behavior versus the amount of friendly or bold behavior. People with high scores on Approach tend to react as an "extravert".

Adaptability is a very important variable, because the environment can play a crucial role in reducing the effects of low Adaptability. For people with low scores on Adaptability things are going too fast: for example they go home for the weekend, but also have tot visit other members of the family and have to accompany parents while shopping. This can be organised better. A "transitional object" makes things easier for this category. In our institute many objects have this function: a doll, a Dinkey toy, a marble, a little blanket, a string of beads, a special cloth or jacket.

Table 1
Temperament variables in the TVZ
(Thomas & Chess, 1977; Blok, 1989).

Approach:
the nature of the initial response to a new stimulus constellation, be it a new person, new object or a new environment.
Example: My child is immediately friendly with and approaches unknown adults who visit our home.

Adaptability:
responses to new or altered situations; the ease with which they are modified in desired directions.
Example: If my child is shy with a strange adult he/she quickly (within a half-hour or so) gets over this.

Intensity:
intensity of reaction, irrespective of its quality or direction.
Example: When upset or annoyed with a task my child may throw it down, cry, yell or slam door, etc.

Sensory sensitivity:
low vs. high responsiveness, slow or quick reactions to sensory stimuli.
Example: My child quickly notices odors and comments on unpleasant smells.

Mood:
the amount of pleasant, joyful and friendly behaviors, as contrasted with unpleasant, crying and unfriendly behavior.
Example: He/she starts the day in a cheerful way.

Persistence:
refers to the continuation of an activity in the face of obstacles to the maintenance of the activity direction.
Example: When my child starts a project such as model, puzzle, painting, he/she works at it without stopping until completed, even if it takes a long time.

Soothability:
the ease with which one can be calmed down.
Example: My child can be stopped from pestering if he/she is given something else to do.

Intensity: In some cases high Intensity indicates "having temper tantrums", but it can also be the case that they speak and laugh louder than other people do. Scores on this variable correlate with the presence or absence of behavioral disorders.

Sensory sensitivity: this might reveal something about the inner tension of a person. When somebody reacts immediately to itchy clothes, being wet, noises, etc., this person can be considerd as "sensitive". When sensitive reactions increase, this tendency can be a forerunner of a nervous breakdown. Sources of stress must be removed in such cases.

Mood is a characteristic that in many cases doesn't get much attention. Fluctuations in mood are reflected in the score. A low score on Mood might be a reason for consulting a psychiatrist for this resident.
A high score on **Persistence** is a favorable outcome for people with a difficult temperament. One has to find an attractive task for them.

The second order factor analysis of the factor scores showed the variables Adaptability, Intensity, Mood and Soothability to constitute a factor which we called "easy-difficult". This is the same factor "easy difficult" that was found by Thomas and Chess (1968). We consider this factor to be of interest for the understanding of behavior disorders of mentally retarded people.

A second factor to be called "Attention to the environment" gets its main loadings by the variables Sensory Sensitivity, Approach and Persistence. This factor could possibly lead to a better insight in "pervasive disorders" like autism.

The results of the analyses concerning the reliability (see Table 2) indicate that the reliability of the TVZ is satisfactory. Blok (1989) and Blok, van den Berg and Feij (in press) give norms for mentally retarded people living in the Netherlands.

Table 2
Scale reliabilities (Cronbach' alpha), inter-rater reliability and test-retest reliability.

	Cronbach's alpha	inter-rater reliability	test-retest reliability
Scale	*N*=1020	*N*=62	*N*=53
Approach	.78	.68	.87
Adaptability	.83	.70	.86
Intensity	.81	.73	.87
Sensory Sensitivity	.72	.62	.87
Mood	.85	.67	.81
Persistence	.80	.73	.86
Soothability	.79	.68	.85

Three cases

I would like to introduce three residents of our institute: Haarendael. All three have lived on Haarendael for more than 15 years now. Before that, they stayed in several institutions, amongst others an "observation center": De Hondsberg. They have been selected because of their low score on the TVZ-factor "easy-difficult". Their temperamental scores on Intensity and Soothability are about the same.

> Harry is a 35 year old man, who lives in a group home in a small town. His WISC-R IQ is 66. On six of the WISC-R subtests his mental age is about 7 years, on five others about 11 years.
> Tamara is a 35 year old woman living in the institute Haarendael. Her IQ is 35 (mental age 4 years).

Peter is a 29 year old man who also lives in the institute, in a different group. His IQ is difficult to determine, probably around 20. His mental age is 3 years. The scores of these three on the TVZ are given in Table 3.

Harry has difficulties in taking criticism and shows stereotyped behaviors. If you warn him in advance, he stays rather quiet. He likes positive remarks. When he is disturbing others with his behavior, appointments use to be made. Structure, safety and information are important for him. Difficult work which requires control makes him react touchy and show restless behavior. He is impatient and has fear of failure. One says that he has an "irritating, demanding curiosity". No medication is given. He is able to live in a group home in a small town and visits a leisure club.

Table 3:
Individual scores on the TVZ.

Scale	Harry	Tamara	Peter
Easy/difficult	2	1	1
Intensity	10	10	8
Soothability	3	1	2
Mood	9	3	1
Adaptability	7	1	3
Approach	5	5	8
Sensory Sensitivity	2	8	5
Persistence	3	5	6

Tamara shows many agressive and self-destructive behaviors. She really has "temper tantrums". Some of these might correlate with epilepsy, menstrual complaints and communication problems. Tearing clothes is often reported. On the worksite fewer problems are reported.
Peter has a long history of self-destructive behavior, headbanging being the most problematic. Tearing clothes is also often reported. Epilepsy might be a causal factor in his behavior disorder. During a few years in his life he was functioning well: he was free of self-destructive behavior and was able to work at a worksite, where he could perform on a relatively high level.

Conclusion

We see some common traits among these people. They react loudly and are difficult to calm down. These are not the only disturbing reactions, but the other reactions seem to correlate with their developmental level. We see that a mentally retarded person functioning at a high level develops personality problems. At lower level, in the two other cases, much destructive behavior is reported. At the high level it is possible to make agreements and fix rules, while at the lower level these are too complex. A closer supervision is needed. It seems that, once developmental level and temperament are described, it will be easier to select a specific therapy or to set certain goals that these people can attain.

References

Blok, J.B. (1989). Temperament bij zwakzinnigen; Constructie van een meet instrument. Lisse: Swets & Zeitlinger.

Blok, J.B., Berg, van den P.Th., & Feij, J.A. (in press). Handleiding bij de Temperamentsschaal voor zwakzinnigen (TVZ). Lisse: Swets & Zeitlinger.

Chess, S. (1970). Emotional problems in mentally retarded children. In F.J. Menolascino (Ed.), Psychiatric approaches to mental retardation. London: Basic Books (p. 55-67).

Chess, S. & Korn, S. (1970). Temperament and behavior disorders in mentally retarded children. Archives of General Psychiatry, 23, 122-130.

Rutter, M. (1977). Individual differences. In M. Rutter & L. Hersov (Eds.), Child psychiatry: Modern approaches. Oxford: Blackwell (p.3-21).

Thomas, A. & Chess, S. (1977). Temperament and development. New York: Brunner/Mazel.

Thomas, A., Chess, S. & Birch, H.G. (1968). Temperament and behavior dis orders in children. New York: University Press.

Došen, A., Van Gennep, A., Zwanikken, G.J. (Eds.) (1990). Treatment of Mental Illness and Behavioral Disorder in the Mentally Retarded. Proceedings of the International Congress, May 3rd & 4th, 1990, Amsterdam, the Netherlands. Leiden, the Netherlands: Logon Publications.

Chapter 41

From punishment and treatment to living and residing as normally as possible

G. van Hove

This case-study concerns integrative and active interaction with serious psychic and behavioural problems in a slightly mentally handicapped woman.

I would like to tell you my story about A.

A. is a 54 year old, mentally handicapped woman. She belongs to that category of people which are generally described as mentally handicapped with behavioural and psychic problems.

Before actually beginning my story I want to lay special emphasis on the fact that it is 'my' story, a story which is composed of objective data (e.g. reports of those people who referred A. to different institutions, chronological reports from the project of sheltered housing where A. to date lives under supervision) but which, besides, is based on my own methods of observing and explaining her behaviour.

To give a wider perspective to my interpretations I will, in the second part of my story, briefly look into a number of approaches which have clearly influenced my observation methods.

A. was born on the 24th of March 1936 in a family of 5 children. At the time, her mentally handicapped mother was 33 years old and unmarried.

At the age of five A. was taken up by a medical pedagogical institution.

Not much is known about this period. However, all of this should be viewed in the context of the state of orthopedagogic care just before and after the second World War which was at that time still scarcely out of the egg.

Her mother was taken into a psychiatric institution as a patient when A. was 8 years old due to a measure of compulsory internment.

At the age of 16 A. herself was admitted to a psychiatric institution as a patient (also due to a measure of compulsory internment). At the time the following reason for her admission was given: mental handicap and character problems. A. had very little school education: she was illiterate and innumerate.

A. left the hospital when she was 29 years old.

She went to live with an aunt and uncle; this was a shippers-family. During this period she worked e.g. in a knitting-workshop and as a cleaning lady in a school.

During this same period A. showed many physical complaints and was frequently absent from work.

Two years later she went to live with her brother. He was divorced from his legal wife and entertained several relationships. Two other women lived with him.

Very soon it became clear that the reason for taking in A. was the "financial benefit" that could be obtained.

The same year A. leaves her brother.

She moves in with a man with whom she has recently become aquainted.

After about a year she is again admitted to an open psychiatric department. At that time A. was about 33 years old.

After a stay of about 6 years there, she is set to work in a sheltered workshop and she can reside in a group-home.

Her stay in this home is interrupted three times for admission to a psychiatric clinic.

A. has a lot of problems in the home. The following problems are mentioned: disturbing behaviour, aggressiveness towards her educators, not adhering to agreements made, kleptomania, regularly drinks too much,.... On top of all this she is dismissed from her job in the sheltered workshop because of frequent absences due to constant physical complaints. Aerophagia and deliberate constipation are mentioned.

After this series of admissions it is decided that A. cannot return to the home.

Therefore she is admitted to a psychiatric clinic . There she functions quite independently within a group of 12 slightly mentally disabled women. During her stay in this clinic she again went to work in the sheltered workshop.

From the report on this period we also learn that A. showed self-mutilation behaviour (mention is made of "vaginal scratching wounds").

By the people who were guiding her and by her co-habitants she is described as a "troublesome and annoying person" who:

- cannot handle money on her own
- tries to get out of rules and agreements made
- escapes in self-mutilation and physical complaints
- is hardly impressionable
- shows no restraints towards alcohol

At the age of 48 she is referred to a project of sheltered housing. The psychiatric centre is of the opinion that a half-way house with the necessary "structure" may be her "last chance of living in society".

In this half-way house she adapts herself rather quickly. She lives there with three others and during the day she works in a sheltered workshop.

In the house she very soon occupies the position of "a cosy lady": at the coffee-table, on holidays, trips,... A. is always present and active.

But when it comes to working, things go less smoothly. A. shows frequent absences due to illness. Her main complaints concern stomach aches. This escalates until she is admitted to hospital for a serious wound on her arm.

The diagnosis is made: there is a great suspicion of self-mutilation by repeatedly striking a pointed iron object.

This event was hard to handle for the guidance team, even if it was only because "self-mutilation" is always difficult to deal with.

Moreover, everyone had, naively, thought that all these problems belonged definitively to the past now that she was taken out of the "psychiatric atmosphere".

The whole of this situation was discussed with her in an honest and forthright manner. From these confrontations we thought we could conclude that A. could no longer stand the pressure of a full-time job. She mainly felt she had to perform a lot in her job; she could no longer come up with the energy ("I'm almost 50 and I want some peace", she said at one time).

Moreover, her three co-habitants did not work. Therefore she found it very difficult to leave the house early every morning and to return only late in the evening. She felt she missed too much of the homely cosiness during the day.

After lots of talking back and forth it was decided that A. would not go to work any longer. In return it was demanded that her "unreasonable conduct" should stop if she wanted to stay on in an integrated living-project.

Within a period of 3 years A. evolved to become a fairly independent woman.

This positive evolution was not reached without difficulties. In our opinion it was the consequence of an integrative approach:

* a lot was done to **establish a "relationship" with A.**
  Like any other person A. needs to be seen and heard. In a small unit such as a half-way house this is easily obtained. Being a supervisor one is as it were obliged to make contacts and to give individual attention to the residents. A. is clearly someone in this context.

* During her stay in the half-way house it became clear that A. **had a great need for clarity and information.** By way of residents, meetings and individual conversations the house rules and individual agreements are made transparent.

* Within this small unit A. has to do her share of the **chores**, activities which she clearly experiences as "chores" (e.g. dishes, cleaning...)
  But she is also given a number of other **reponsibilities** which fit in very well with her interests and personality. It is for example asked of her to make the Christmas decorations in the house, to offer coffee and biscuits to visitors, to take care of the hair of some of the other residents......

* Besides letting her off her outdoor-job a lot of **stress** was taken away by a very structural approach to A.'s budget.
  Possessing "a lot" of money creates a restlessness in A.
  To her, having money is synonymous with spending money. Not having any money means that she constantly has to ask to the supervisors for it.
  Starting from these data, a budget plan and an agreement system is developed which reduces A.'s restlessness to a strict minimum.
  This plan induces payments by way of standing orders and twice-weekly withdrawals for small personal expenses. It is continually emphasized that it concerns her money.

All of this together with the atmosphere in this living environment reduced her problematic behaviour to an acceptable level.

Not without importance in this context was what one could call the "**reinterpretation**" of her behaviour. We assume that if "problem-behaviour" still occurs (for us) we should give importance to the **communicative function** it has. This means that we do not merely say that A. "drinks too much" in certain periods. We consider this behaviour within a total context: what causes her drinking, does she want to convey something to us by this behaviour???

After a three year stay in the half-way house A. decides to live more independently (under observation). She rents a small appartment in town and arranges it completely. Three times a week she receives a visit from a supervisor who advises and assists her.

This continues for about half a year. This period ends in total chaos: A. neglects herself completely, spends all her days in bars and drinks too much, she is completely "destroyed" by loneliness, she misses her appointments....

At the end of this period she is admitted to hospital with a stomach bleeding.

Coincidentally, at the same time the function of the half-way house is evaluated by the guidance team. It is decided that a chance is going to be given to the people to stay on in this house.

Another coincidence is that there is a vacancy in this living-unit during A.'s rehabilitation period.

During the evaluation of the half year in which she lived indepently, A. herself comes up with the suggestion to quit. She would rather return to the house, this time with the promise that she can stay.

She immediately accepts the proposition. In a remarkable short time she resumes her place as if she had never been away.

All her complex problems are gradually reduced to surveyable proportions: A. goes through periods in which she drinks too much, A. smokes a lot although she is conscious of the fact that this will not help in reducing her stomach complaints, she also goes through periods in which she has to be pushed enormously to show some activity, she quite often nags about money-matters although everything has been clearly agreed upon,......: are these genuine behavioural problems????

At present A. still lives in this living-unit.

Recently I have seen her take on a strange role, namely that of an "understanding sister". She regularly invites her mentally handicapped brother for a day, and her other brother can really open his heart to her about his marriage problems.

Seeing that A. is able to take care of others from time to time I think she feels fairly happy these days.

Discussion

In this second part we want to make clear a number of approaches which have greatly influenced our views on and interpretation of A.'s behaviour.

1. We thought it necessary to present this case study in the form of a **biography** because we strongly believe that 'problems' and behaviour have to be considered in their **historical context**. With A. it is clear that her 'difficult' behaviour is partly determined by e.g. her emotional and pedagogic abandonment, her long stay in institutions, the great number of people whith whom she has been in contact during her life, the great number of situations in which she must have felt misused or lonely.
   We are clearly confronted here with 'problems' which have to be considered in their **developmental context.**

2. One of the typical elements of the approach within the living situation in which she actually resides is that the central concept is **structure**.
   I know that this concept is used (too?) often. If I use it here it is with the idea that offering structure equals offering security. This offered security should give people the necessary context from which they can go out on an explorative expedition. Two elements are central in the interpretation of the concept of 'structure', namely: **individualisation** and differentiation. In this way I avoid the tendancy of repression which always lies in ambush.
   If structure is given in such a pedagogic manner, one comes close to basic human attitudes such as **"respect"** and even **"endearment"** for these people.
   Thus it is on this small basis that genuine and close guidance relations can be developed.

3. Within this total approach great importance is given to **listening** to A.
   We never merely consider her problem-behaviour as behaviour, but as an attempt to communicate or, even more, as **an incapability for verbal communication.**
   A. does not talk easily and only very rarely allows us to look within 'her most profound being'.
   In a period of too much alcohol, a period with numerous physical complaints, we always have to search for the underlying meaning.
   What is bothering A., what did she fail to understand....?

4. The guidance in the living-unit in which A. resides gives a lot of emphasis to the **individual responsibility** of the occupants.
   Seen in the light of 'the quality of existence', this is a basic attitude which means that the mentally disabled human being **gets a grip on his/her life in parallel with his/her possibilities.**
   Within this context importance should be given to the individual choices which A. makes in her life.

She is, for example, very pleased that she can determine her holiday destination all by herself. It pleases her very much that she has the liberty to choose the moment for a visit to her mentally handicapped brother.
She also likes to be closely involved in the choice of her clothing and furniture.
All along great importance is given to what A. already **is able to do.**

5. To obtain a correct interpretation of A.'s behaviour it is very important that we get an insight into the **stress-inducing factors.**
After 5 years of supervision they are fairly clear with A.: e.g. uncertainty in financial matters, tensions with her brother, unfriendly treatment, too many tasks and responsibility.
Priority should be given to minimalise these factors under guidance together with A. to give her a basic feeling of peace and security.

6. Finally, I want to point out the great influence which the principles of **integrative action orthopedagogics** have on our work and attitude.
We will try here to clarify a number of these principles:

* It is important not to pin ourselves down to a (too) simple cause-effect reasoning. Behaviour is so complex that we should try to understand it through constant analysis-synthesis movements.

* We should not pin ourselves down to treatment based on a specific school of thought.
We have the obligation to adopt the useful elements of all existing schools of thought.

* The principle of **functionality**, i.e. working at the level, the interests of the handicapped person, is of great importance.

* The principle of **adaptability** is indispensible. It is necessary that we adapt ourselves again and again at all times and that we never take on an "automatic pilot" approach.

* Finally, we highlight the importance of **action.** We do not proceed to an extensive period of research and diagnosis only to act afterwards. We rather use action to come to a better approach.
This is an ever-continuing process which could be seen as a spiral movement.

Epilogue

What I will remember of this congress is that all schools of thought who presented their way of treatment laid emphasis on:

* contact
* the establishment of a relation
* a warm and good climate (some called it 'home')
* individually adapted tools and goals

Those principles found their expression in so called "relation therapy", "psycho-analytic therapy", "gentle teaching" and others.

I think, and I try to be humble as a pedagogue, that the principles above are (only) real pedagogical principles.

So I will remember that the difficult and mostly forgotten people are finally getting the treatment they deserve.

Došen, A., Van Gennep, A., Zwanikken, G.J. (Eds.) (1990). Treatment of Mental Illness and Behavioral Disorder in the Mentally Retarded. Proceedings of the International Congress, May 3rd & 4th, 1990, Amsterdam, the Netherlands. Leiden, the Netherlands: Logon Publications.

Chapter 42

Psychiatric disorders in mentally retarded patients and their treatment in a medium secure unit

M.S. Isweran
N. Brener

Introduction

In the United Kingdom over the last decade there has been a drive to develop regional secure facilities for people with mental illness.

There has been a much slower response to the development of regional secure units for patients with mental retardation. As yet, not all Regions in the UK have them. The Eric Shepherd Unit is one such Secure Unit facility. This unit has been in operation for the past three and a half years and it provides a service to the 3.5 million people of the North West Thames Region.

Psychiatric Disorders

The prevalence and the nature of psychiatric disorders in mentally retarded patients who are admitted to a secure unit is not well known.

The following study was conducted at Eric Shepherd Unit with the aim of finding the extent of psychiatric disorders using the DSM III-R criteria. All the twenty-one inpatients in this unit were included in this study, which was conducted over a three month period. All patients were interviewed by one person (N.B.), who was not involved with the day to day management of these patients. The notes were reviewed and nursing staff consulted on all subjects in this study.

The following information was collected:

1. DSM III-R diagnoses on Axis I,II and III
2. Demographic details
3. Status under the Mental Health Act 1983

4. IQ, if available
5. Index offence and past forensic history
6. Past psychiatric and family psychiatric history.

The characteristics of this group are shown in Table I. There was no statistical difference between the ages of men and women in this sample.

95.2% were being detained under a Section of the Mental Health Act 1983.

33% of the total group have restrictions placed on their detention orders by the Home Office. Only one female patient was in the hospital voluntarily. These patients have a high incidence of previous psychiatric problems (85.7%). Six patients (28.6%) gave a family history of psychiatric illness. Men were more likely to have had previous problems with the law, but this is not statistically significant.

Table I
Patient Characteristics

	Male	Female	Total
Numbers	14	7	21
Age Mean years	31.5	29.86	31
Standard Deviation	9.55	3.31	8.06 N.S.
Legal Status (under the Mental Health Act)			
Prison Sections (Sec 37, 37/41, 47/49)	8	3	11
Treatment Order (Sec 3)	5	3	8
Assessment Order (Sec 2)	1	0	1
Informal	0	1	1
Past Psychiatric History Present (%)	11(78.6)	7(100)	18(85.7) N.S.
Family History of Psychiatric Illness Present (%)	4(28.6)	2(28.6)	6(28.6) N.S
Past Forensic History Present(%)	13(93)	4(57)	17(81) N.S.

Table II shows that nine patients (42.9%) had diagnosis on Axis I of DSM III-R. Six were schizophrenic (29.8%), one patient was manic, another alcoholic and another suffering from anxiety state. Two of the six schizophrenics were classifiable under the paranoid type, the rest were undifferentiated. On Axis II, thirteen patients (61.8%) had definable diagnoses, predominantly antisocial personality disorders (42.9%). Seven patients (33.3%) had diagnoses on Axis III; only one person had confirmed epilepsy (4.75%).

Table II
DSM III-R Diagnosis on Axis I II & III

	Male	Female	Total
Axis I	5	4	9 (42.9%)
Schizophrenia	4	2	6 (29.8%)
Anxiety State	1	0	1
Alcohol Abuse	0	1	1
Manic State	0	1	1
Axis II	9	4	13 (61.8%)
Antisocial PD	6	3	9 (42.9%)
Schizoid PD	1	0	1
Antisocial Behaviour	2	1	3
Axis III	4	3	7 (33.3%)
Deafness	1	0	1
Epilepsy	0	1	1
Cardiac disorders	0	1	1
Thyroid disorders	1	0	1
Cleft palate	0	1	1
XYY chromosomes	1	0	1

Seventeen patients on the Unit had a recorded IQ. Their level of mental retardation as defined by DSM III-R is set out on Table III.

Thirteen were in the mild range (76.4%). Three patients had an IQ above this range (17.6%). None suffered from severe mental retardation; only one was in the moderately retarded range (5.88%).

Four of the five patients suffering from schizophrenia had an IQ above 55. None of the Axis I schizophrenics had Axis II diagnoses.

Table III
Degree of Mental Retardation as defined in DSM III-R

IQ Range	Male	Female	Total
Borderline	2	1	3 (17.6%)
Mild	8	5	13 (76.47%)
Moderate	1	0	1 (5.88%)
Severe	0	0	0
IQ unavailable	3	1	4

Table IV
Index Offences

	Male	Female	Total
Violence and homicide	5	1	6 (31.6%)
Sexual Offences	2	1	3 (15.8%)
Arson and criminal damage	5	3	8 (42.1%)
Others	1	1	2 (10.5%)

Seventeen patients on the Unit had a recorded IQ. Their level of mental retardation as defined by DSM III-R is set out on Table III.

Thirteen were in the mild range (76.4%). Three patients had an IQ above this range (17.6%). None suffered from severe mental retardation; only one was in the moderately retarded range (5.88%).

Four of the five patients suffering from schizophrenia had an IQ above 55. None of the Axis I schizophrenics had Axis II diagnoses.

Using the Home Office classification system for offences, patients in this study were found to have committed more offences against property than against person (Table IV), although this was not statistically significant. None of the Index Offences committed by those with schizophrenia were against persons. Two schizophrenic patients committed offences against property, including arson.

Treatment Needs

The nature and prevalence of the psychiatric disorders are important factors in formulating a treatment strategy aimed at the mentally retarded patients admitted to a secure unit. The needs of these patients are different from those who are admitted to a secure unit for psychiatric patients of normal intelligence. In our view, the patients with mental retardation have special needs to necessitate a specific treatment programme that can only be provided in a separate service.

Comparison of the patients in Eric Shepherd Unit with those in a secure unit for similar patients, but with normal intelligence, revealed that the mentally retarded patients have less defined psychiatric disorders than those with normal intelligence (J. Pendred, 1988). Mentally retarded patients also had higher incidence of juvenile delinquency and recidivism. They also tend to commit offences towards property, rather than towards persons. Mentally retarded patients also had history of long separation from both parents and come from deprived background.

In studies conducted in secure units for normal intelligence patients, the psychiatric disorders mainly consisted of psychotic problems, and personality disorders are less common (Treasaden, 1985). A similar situation exists also in special hospitals that deal with patients who require maximum security. The mentally retarded patients in secure units appear to have more personality disorders compared with those of normal intelligence.

The problems presented by mentally retarded patients in a secure unit fall within three major categories:

a) Problems associated with mental retardation including impaired social and occupational skills and consequent inability to live independently.

b) Psychiatric disorders, which, as we found, are predominantly personality disorders.

c) Criminal and aggressive behaviour with a degree of danger to the public.

Treatment programme

A treatment programme aimed at mentally retarded patients in a secure unit should be able to deal with all the above factors. There is no prescribed treatment strategy available for this group of patients. A hospital based treatment programme for male mentally retarded offender patients in a district based hospital unit has been described (Day, 1989). In Eric Shepherd Unit, during its existence over the last three and a half years, a treatment programme has been developed aimed specifically at mentally retarded patients who are admitted to a secure unit.

The treatment regime at this unit has the following ingredients:

a) A Structured environment. This is an essential part of the treatment regime and the structure provides a therapeutic function for the patients, most of whom have had very unstable and insecure life in their past, and need a secure and a stable period to work with their problems. The structure is provided by the physical security and by the fairly regimented life they have while in the unit. Privileges are given to the patients depending on their behaviour, but each patient is treated individually to prevent them becoming institutionalised.

b) Psychiatric assessment and treatment. The Psychiatric disorders are diagnosed and treated with appropriate psychotropic medication. It is also found that some patients who do not have well developed signs and symptoms of mental illness also do benefit by medication, specially if they have a high arousal level, which make them liable to over-react to a stress-producing situation.

c) Psychological Treatment Psychotherapeutic interventions in the form of counselling, individual psychotherapy and group therapy are provided wherever possible. Psychodynamic psychotherapy is often found to be difficult with this group of patients as they find the experience very painful or threatening. Some behaviour modification by behavioural therapy is occasionally given when a specific behaviour problem is disruptive to the extent of preventing patients from benefiting from other forms of treatments.

d) Occupational and Social Skills Training. These patients very often lack living skills and get into antisocial conduct as a result of their inability to lead a normal life. A workshop within the secure environment is provided for the patients so that they are able to have occupational training throughout their stay in the unit. A Social Education unit and a training flat are also available to assist with the training needed for their resettlement in the community.

e) Adult Education. A classroom with teachers who specialise in teaching this group of patients is provided.

f) Therapeutic community approach Patients spend roughly two to three years in this unit. They are encouraged to explore their feelings and behaviour in the context of their life in the unit. Therapeutic community meetings are held weekly, and patients are helped to discuss their problems and to make decisions within the constraints of the security and restrictions imposed on their life.

Including all the above elements in a single treatment strategy is a challenge. Individual patients are different in their particular therapeutic needs, but all of them should be able to benefit by the range of treatment options available for them in the unit. Individual patients' needs are discussed at the regular multi-disciplinary team meetings and decisions are made based on their individual needs. The multi-disciplinary approach with regular assessment and review of their treatment needs is an essential element in the treatment programme.

Response to Treatment

The unit has not been running for such a length of time to enable a full evaluation of the service. However, there are indications that the patients do respond to the treatment regime. The turnover of patients (Table V) is satisfactory in relation to the other services for mentally retarded people. Maintaining a good turnover is one of the main aims of the service, as this means patients who are admitted to this service with a difficult history improve to the extent that they are able to move on to a non-secure service.

Table V
Turnover of patients

	86/87	87/88	88/89
Admissions	8	7	7
Discharges	5	11	8
Readmissions	0	1	2
Transfer to special hospitals	0	2	1

Table VI
Clinical conditions in patients currently in the unit

Improved	15 (65.2%)
No improvement	7 (30.4%)
Deterioration	1 (4.3%)

On an average, eight patients are admitted and discharged every year. Three patients had to be admitted to maximum secure hospitals over the last three years, indicating a deterioration in their condition. Three patients were also readmitted during this period. All the others were discharged to less secure or open environments.

A superficial examination of the clinical conditions of patients at a particular time in the unit indicates that 65% of them have made significant improvement, judged on clinical assessment of their behaviour (Table VI). There is also a group of patients whose improvement is minimal, and make only very slow progress. This group of patients probably will require long term management in a different type of service. Even though the treatment regime appears to be satisfactory, further study to evaluate the response to this treatment regime is needed.

Conclusion

Treatment needs of the mentally retarded patients who are treated in a secure unit due to their violent and criminal tendency are not widely recognised. Assessment of the psychiatric disorders in patients who are treated in such a unit indicates that psychiatric disorders are common among them and personality disorders form the major psychiatric problem. Treatment programmes aimed at these patients should take into account the psychiatric, training, educational and the social needs of these patients.

References

Pendred, J.E. (1988) An Investigation of the Differences Between Mentally Impaired and Mentally Ill Offenders in Two Regional Secure Units. Thesis for the Diploma in Clinical Psychology.

Treasaden, I.H. (1985) Current Practice in Regional Interim Secure Units. In Secure Provision: A Review of Special Services for the Mentally Ill and Mentally handicapped in England and Wales. ed. Larry Gostin: Tavistock Publication.

Day, K. (1988) A Hospital Based Treatment Programme for the Mentally Handicapped Offenders. British Journal of Psychiatry 153, 635-644.

Došen, A., Van Gennep, A., Zwanikken, G.J. (Eds.) (1990). Treatment of Mental Illness and Behavioral Disorder in the Mentally Retarded. Proceedings of the International Congress, May 3rd & 4th, 1990, Amsterdam, the Netherlands. Leiden, the Netherlands: Logon Publications.

Chapter 43

Challenging Behaviours: Problems, Provisions and 'Solutions'

J. Dockrell
G. Gaskell
H. Rehman

Introduction

Since the mid 1970's there has been a commitment in Britain to closing mental handicap hospitals and developing community based services for people with learning difficulties (King's Fund 1980). Within South East Thames Regional Health Authority (SETRHA) the special needs of individuals with learning difficulties and challenging behaviours were recognised. To serve the 15 districts within SETRHA a Special Development Team was set up for those with severe learning difficulties and challenging behaviour (Emerson et al 1987); the Mental Impairment Evaluation and Treatment Service (MIETS), the subject of this paper, was established to facilitate successful community placements for those with mild learning difficulty and challenging behaviours. Although what constitutes challenging behaviour is relative to the service providers skills and competencies, the MIETS unit was expected to work with clients showing more extreme behaviours, e.g. physical aggression, sex offenses and arson, and/or those with psychiatric disorders.

The MIETS unit

The aims and objectives of MIETS are:

1) To provide a psychiatric assessment and treatment service for adults who have a mild learning difficulty and have serious behavioural and/or psychiatric disorders; 2) to provide clinical information about clients in order to help local district teams enable the person to participate as fully as possible in all aspects of daily life; 3) where appropriate to commence treatment or advise on the management of specific behavioural problems; 4) through contact

with the local clinical teams during a clientsadmission, provide guidance and support which will allow the team to develop new expertise and knowledge.

MIETS, with 13 beds, is located in the grounds of the Royal Bethlem Hospital. It is staffed by a multi-disciplinary team consisting of the equivalent of 1.5 full time psychiatrists, 1.5 clinical psychologists, 2 occupational therapists, 0.5 social worker and 33.1 nursing staff. The service costs about £60000 per year of which the referring district pays some £40000 with the remainder provided by SETRHA.

Districts referring clients are required to pose specific questions which the Unit agrees to investigate within a contractual arrangement. The district must accept responsibility for providing continuing care for the person once the assessment and treatment is completed by the Unit. After consideration and a preliminary assessment a client is admitted for a specific period of time, with a maximum stay of 18 months. Once admitted the client undergoes intensive assessment and treatment; liaison is maintained between the Unit and local teams concerning the client's progress. Prior to discharge the district or local authority is notified and is required to provide the appropriate aftercare as agreed at the time of referral.

MIETS began admitting clients in May 1987. To date there have been 57 referrals, 29 admissions and 19 discharges. Of the 29 clients admitted, 16 were referred for aggressive behaviour, 6 for arson, 4 for sexually related problems and 3 for other difficult behaviours.

The evaluation

The question addressed in this research concerns the efficacy of MIETS, as a special unit, in meeting the needs of the districts and contributing towards successful community placement for its clients. Answering such questions invites an evaluation perspective.

Our approach to service evaluation involves a number of inter-related dimensions. Central to the evaluation is the extent to which the service achieves its own aims and objectives and the extent to which the service meets with the requirements of its consumers, the districts professional staff who act as agents for the clients. Without a reasonable match between these two any service would face difficulties.

Focussing on the MIETS unit itself the study is monitoring the clients' functioning and behaviour prior to, during and following their period of admission. The needs of the consumers, the fifteen districts within SETRHA, are assessed by detailed interviews with managers and clinical personnel and a survey of direct care staff. In addition, there is an economic efficiency analysis assessing the traditional criteria of cost benefits and cost effectiveness. In this paper we focus on the service requirements of the districts who are ultimately responsible for the care of all people with learning difficulties, including those with challenging behaviours and/or psychiatric problems. The other aspects of the evaluation will be reported at a later date as they are completed.

This paper draws upon the data collected from a survey of *all* 15 districts within SETRHA. In each district three to six key management and clinical staff with direct responsibility for individuals with learning difficulties and challenging behaviour were interviewed (Unit General Managers, Psychiatrists, Directors of services for people with learning difficulties, Community Mental Handicap Team leaders and Psychologists). Where appropriate interviews were also carried out with direct care staff and social services personnel.

The interviews, lasting about one hour, were conducted using a semi-structured schedule. Respondents were asked about: (1) their understanding of challenging behaviour and the numbers of clients they had with such problems, specific examples were requested; (2) details of services provided locally and any gaps in existing service provision; (3) knowledge of the MIETS unit, referrals to MIETS, satisfaction with the service; (4) use of private facilities and Special Hospitals and numbers of clients placed in these units; (5) gaps in district provision, special service needs and future plans for this group of clients. This survey comprised 60 persons and provided a comprehensive description of each districts practices and service requirements.

The varying requirements of the districts

From the interviews in the districts, it is apparent that MIETS serves a range of functions both in terms of responding to explicit contractual referrals and implicit service needs. It is striking that the demand for MIETS services and the types of referrals made are very different across the districts. While it is possible that the incidence of clients exhibiting patterns of challenging behaviour varies across the districts, we consider that the reasons for the differing rates of referral go to the very heart of the philosophy of normalisation (Wolfensberger 1972) and the policies surrounding community based services.

The interviews with senior management and clinical staff have led us to the conclusion that different districts have different service needs. These needs are a consequence of three organisational factors: overall philosophy of care; technology, that is the state of service development, and leadership and communication, that is the existence of key persons and co-ordination within health service facilities and with social services. We have identified four different types of service provision (solutions) amongst the districts as of early 1990. For each type we note the numbers of relevant districts, but it is important to recognise that some districts are discussing developments which will take them into other 'solutions'.

Generally higher numbers of referrals are associated with those districts which have no clearly articulated care plans for this client group. Although their services for people with severe learning difficulties may be well developed, clients with mild learning difficulties and challenging behaviour have been of lower priority. Until recently they have relied on hospitalization for these clients. Confronted by the current problem, i.e. the closure of hospitals, there is often inter-agency conflict between health professionals, the learning difficulty services and social services. No-one is able, or willing, to accept responsibility for them. Hence there is a need for external services to contain problem clients and the MIETS unit and services run by the private sector are relied on. Thus MIETS becomes implicitly a respite facility although this is never explicitly stated in the referral. In such districts it is often said that MIETS' admission procedures are too slow, the eighteen month maximum stay too short, and the requirement to guarantee a community placement following MIETS difficult to implement. However there is a recognition in these districts that they are failing the client group and an acknowledgement that change is necessary. At present there are six districts working along the lines of what we call the 'removal solution'.

Some districts, while working within a general policy of community service, believe that certain individuals with learning difficulties need medical treatment within a secure setting. MIETS fulfils this need as it offers an assessment and treatment service drawing on a multi-disciplinary team of recognised experts. Such a perspective leads to the view that MIETS will treat the problem. Such districts often complain that while MIETS has done an excellent job in the functional analysis of the client's problem, the problem still exists. Implicitly treatment is seen to have failed whether or not treatment was part of the contract between MIETS and the district. A solution to this dilemma suggested in some districts is a local facility to contain the problem clients over an extended period of time. They believe that some clients will probably never experience life outside a local and smaller version of a hospital. There are presently three districts using what we term the 'long stay unit solution'.

For some districts working within a clearly articulated normalisation framework MIETS fills a gap in service provision because local facilities (houses, flats etc.) and competencies (trained staff) have not been fully developed. These districts are planning local services and at some point in the future expect to make no further referrals to MIETS. Their current plans derive from a commitment to community integration and to concerns about the lack of generalizability of assessments carried out in situations such as MIETS, that are not representative of the community context. There are four districts working along the lines of a 'service development solution'.

Finally, there are two districts who do not believe they need the MIETS service. They have not made any recent referrals to MIETS and do not expect to do so. Their clients with learning difficulties and challenging behaviour are catered for within the district in contexts that reflect the community care philosophy in every day practice. It is notable that they make no current use of private provisions outside the district. It clearly takes time to establish the organisational arrangements to achieve such practices. But in addition to time, there is the vital role of leadership and the commitment of a team of key persons who provide not only horizontal integration between the various health professionals and in some cases social services, but also vertical integration between senior management and the direct care staff. These two dimensions of organisational integration are crucial. Horizontal integration sets the basis for a co-ordinated multi-agency and multi-disciplinary approach; it prevents time consuming and service damaging inter-agency conflict and allows districts to maximise revenue for client care from various governmental resources. Vertical integration builds a co-ordinated and mutually supporting team in which, for example, staff turnover is low, the appointment of care workers is based on philosophical compatibility, and the care workers can rely on management for training and practical support. Crises are contained within the district and often prevented because expert team members, often from management, are readily on-call. This we term the 'local consultation and support solution'.

Although our economic assessment is in its early stages, there are interesting differences emerging between the districts. Those with established community care facilities see MIETS as an expensive service, the cost of which could be better spent developing local facilities. Other districts, and particularly those requiring treatment or out of district respite facilities, have a different perception of the costs. For them the options are limited and, as such, they have little choice.

In more general terms the four solutions that we have identified are only a subset of a range of possible solutions available to a district. The implementation of services by any particular district will depend on their own priorities, the allocation of resources and the design of service delivery. To develop appropriate client provisions districts must be able to recognise and understand the problems of this particular client group and generate alternatives to solve these problems. Choices must be made within budgetary constraints and an implementation plan drawn up. Finally to assess the viability of the alternatives services must be monitored and outcomes evaluated.

The districts' experiences with MIETS

To what extent does MIETS meet the needs of districts that require this type of service? The districts can familiarise themselves with the Unit's work by keeping in close contact as a client is assessed and treated. Post MIETS the efficacy of the service is seen variously as: adequate assessment of the client; reduction in challenging behaviours; detailed rehabilitation plans; continuing advice and support. On these criteria we see differences related to the state of service development.

Districts using MIETS as 'respite' are content with the written reports from the Unit. When the client's discharge is imminent, a crisis develops since the local facilities are ill-prepared. Further out-of-district care is organised, and, possibly, a re-referral to MIETS. The client is once again 'removed'.

The districts adopting the Long Stay Unit solution often complain of communication difficulties with the Unit. The assumption by the Unit that the districts would be characterised by strong vertical and horizontal integration leads the MIETS staff to 'talk' to the districts' senior clinical staff. In reality, these districts often tend to be rather poorly integrated with gaps in communication between senior clinicians, management and direct care staff. While the former may attend case conferences, it is unusual for them to send direct care staff to the Unit for a briefing from the experts or for a 'getting to know you' session with a prospective client. Without adequate communication within the district they are ill-prepared to devise and implement community placements along the lines of the Units recommendations.

In districts with developing services there is a different problem. They are concerned that guidance and support following discharge is limited. These districts recognise a pressing need for specialised support services to help them devise and implement techniques and services in situ. They would like MIETS to operate as a task force to help them develop skills for this client group. Such a task force would also be available at times of crisis.

Some preliminary conclusions

We return to the question posed at the beginning of this paper, can special units meet community needs? In relation to the districts in South East Thames there is no simple answer. Although all the districts are working under the umbrella of community care, their practices and facilities are very different. We have seen from the district's point of view that the MIETS Unit can be used merely as a respite and as such may act as a disincentive to develop local services, or it may serve to medicalize challenging behaviour, a view which some districts feel is incompatible with community care, or it can provide a specialist service for districts whose own provisions are not yet fully developed.

Given that many districts neither have the staff nor the organisational structures to cater for clients with learning difficulties and challenging behaviour at present, there is clearly a need for a unit of some variety. Moreover there are some districts which operate within a model requiring full treatment prior to discharge into the community (the 'long stay unit solution'). In these districts there will be a need for a specialist unit to assess and treat such clients. But if, however, it is assumed that all the districts will progressively embrace the normalisation philosophy and acquire the skills for these clients then the MIETS unit will be required in its present form only in the short to medium term. As more districts develop local services it would then be necessary to refocus specialist help away from the Unit towards the districts themselves. However, our evidence suggests that there is not a smooth transition to community care. While referrals to MIETS have declined in some districts, others are maintaining a reliance on private hospitals and the MIETS unit.

If we return to the formal objectives set out for MIETS the district survey has allowed us to draw some preliminary conclusions. For those districts who refer to MIETS there is acknowledgement of the excellent assessments and functional analyses carried out within the Unit (objective 2). There is less consensus about the advice on management of specific behavioural problems (objective 3). The districts ability to respond to this advice depends on their own competencies and facilities and the extent to which they feel management techniques are in tune with the reality of community care. districts who refer to MIETS, irrespective of their state of service development, want access to support and advice locally from the Unit following discharge (an extension of objective 4). There is general agreement that this need is not available.

It is not clear to us whether the MIETS unit can or necessarily should respond to all the needs of the different districts. As we have seen the districts vary from those operating the 'removal solution' through toy 'service development solution' with others making no calls on the Unit. It is an open question as to which of the service requirements of the districts the MIETS unit should be directed and what other arrangements are needed for those requirements that are not being met by MIETS. As it proceeds our study will lead to recommendations on these issues.

References

Emerson, E., Barrett, S., Bell, C., Cummings, R., Toogood, A. and Mansell, J. (1987), *Developing services for people with severe learning difficulties and challenging behaviours*. University of Kent at Canterbury, Institute of Social and Applied Psychology.

King's Fund Centre (1980), *An ordinary life: comprehensive locally-based residential services for mentally handicapped people* (project paper 24). London, King Edwards Hospital Fund for London.

Wolfensberger, W. (1972), *Normalisation: The principles of normalisation in human services*. Toronto: National Institute on Mental Retardation.

Došen, A., Van Gennep, A., Zwanikken, G.J. (Eds.) (1990). Treatment of Mental Illness and Behavioral Disorder in the Mentally Retarded. Proceedings of the International Congress, May 3rd & 4th, 1990, Amsterdam, the Netherlands. Leiden, the Netherlands: Logon Publications.

Chapter 44

Residential treatment of mildly mentally retarded children and adolescents with behaviour disorders, educational problems and social-affective problems

J.S.T. Niessen

Introduction

In the Reeve institute in Kampen, mildly mentally handicapped children and adolescents (5 to 21 years) are treated for:

- behavioural problems
- pedagogical problems
- social/emotional problems.

83 children are accommodated in the institute, in 8 communal houses spread throughout the town of Kampen.

The following points form the basis for treatment:

- We assume that the parent-child relationship is the only inherent relationship the children have, a relationship which is respected at all times. When this relationship has been impaired, every effort is made to repair the damage as far as possible.

- The parents are primarily responsible for their children's upbringing. The institute offers itself as a co-educator and offers its expertise to assist the parents. On this basis, the parents are involved in the care and treatment of their child.

- Treatment of the children is most effective in an environment in which the child feels safe. The form of the living environment is established against the background of the general problems experienced by the mildly mentally handicapped. This results in a well structured, small scale environment in which the child experiences the least possible hindrance from his or her handicap.

- From this safe communal group, the child is stimulated to take part in the local community to the greatest possible extent. We thus attempt to avoid a negative hospitalization process. This results in children and young people becoming dependent upon the amenities in local society. Support is given by the institute when necessary, against the background of the children's individual problems.

- With regard to behavioural and psychosocial problems, we base our treatment on attempting to allow the children to live in an environment as natural as possible for as long as possible.

Based on these principles, we formulate a view that the children and adolescents are treated by workers in their communal group. They are in turn supported by the members of staff such as psychologists and special educationalists who work according to theoretical educational and psycho-dynamic models.

Which children are treated?

In the Reeve we attempt to help children for whom daily life is too difficult. When children begin school, they have to learn complicated things and new skills: sit still, listen, relate what has been told and remember today's story tomorrow. Keep working until they're finished and not leave their seat to involve themselves with other children. Understand why they have to do something and why they may not do other things. It's a never ending list and as if that wasn't enough, they have to learn to read, write and do arithmetic. If they fall within the group of children who cannot learn or learn slowly, they regard themselves as becoming progressively more stupid and find that they are more and more often left out. The other children can all do what they can't. They don't understand why they can't do something or why the teacher sighs when she looks at their work or moans. "Why isn't that right, I've done my very best, haven't I?"

The other children jeer and laugh at you if you give an answer which they think is strange.

The school is used as an example here because it is a place where children of roughly the same age are put together and have to perform similar tasks under roughly similar circumstances. It's apparent when a child cannot keep up or is different from the rest. All those aspects which apply to school actually also apply to the living situation outside of school: the child cannot keep pace. It isn't always apparent right away because the child isn't compared with other children in the same way as at school, but when carefully observed the child is found not to be able to do lots of things which other children of a similar age can do. We can observe, for example, how lonely the child is, or how he or she only plays with much younger children. A child who can't get to grasps with a story intended for his age, such as the Little Red Riding Hood fable, is completely swamped by his daily experiences. What happens to a child who lives in too difficult an environment, who almost constantly finds that he can't join in? He can withdraw and no longer be actively involved. He's not there anymore, he's declared himself dead, in a manner of speaking. He can be very sweet so that adults don't get angry at him, but then he becomes completely dependent and doesn't learn to understand things. He can become a clown so that he won't be laughed at but can make people laugh, something which he can almost control. Once again he only really learns a few tricks and not what's important. He can assert himself in which case he becomes tough, naughty, aggressive and does things which mean that the others have to take account of him, but he doesn't learn anything. He can become "ill". His hopelessness and helplessness can be translated into physical or psychological ailments; stomach ache, fainting fits, tantrums, scratching himself to the point of bleeding, wetting the bed, smearing faeces.

In short, a child who misses contact with his world will show problematic behaviour. A child who behaves thus is incomprehensible. He cannot talk about his own problems. Every child wants to be able to do the same things as other children, all children want to be liked by others. If this isn't the case, the child cannot explain why. Not being able to do this and the possible accessory problems are even more obscure for a child than for those around him. It's made even more difficult for some children, they experience things at home about which they dare not and cannot talk and from which they can't escape. The problems can take control of the child and his parents as a curse, in which case they need help.

Which parents are involved?

Just as other people, parents are good and bad, stupid and sensible, thoughtful and impulsive, all at the same time. It goes wrong for some parents, they encounter more problems in their lives than others, more problems than they can cope with. No-one wants to behave badly towards their child so that he becomes even more miserable. Things can just happen in life which you can't do anything about. Impotence leads to desperate acts.

Parents have their own problems. The model family portrayed in advertisements does not exist. Parents have their own problems and don't exactly want additional difficulties to arise because the child is problematic at school: doesn't learn, doesn't do his best, is slow, is sneaky, behaves childishly, is troublesome.

A child whose problems cannot be solved also attracts aggression at home. Parents experience feelings of being out of control and powerless. They don't know what to do. "The teacher at school, the educational psychologist, the G.P., they all just talk, they know how to talk but we're left to pick up the pieces".

This is a simplified story. There are parents who try all sorts of methods to help their child. There are parents who themselves get more directly stuck if things go wrong with their child. There are also parents who have so many problems of their own that they don't even get around to dealing with the child. The important issue is that the parents get bogged down together with their child, can't solve the problems together with their child, and will now have to be helped together with their child.

How do we help?

In the Reeve we want to give these children a new world to live in, which suits them better. By systematically clarifying and simplifying life within the communal group, we can ensure that the children are positively aware of what is happening. Our intention is that they understand and learn from the connection within daily activities. Another objective is that they become aware that they can do more and more things themselves and can therefore learn to become responsible.

Because the children appear normal on the outside and because their behaviour is not noticeable, their handicap is often not recognized. Even professional educationalists do not always understand that learning difficulties can distort the childrens' lives. These educationalists then get the impression that their treatment has few results. They become demoralized and carry out their work in a routine fashion. Such an approach doesn't help in putting the child on the right tracks.

Counselling of parents and caregivers is aimed at directing a sense of understanding towards the children and translating this understanding into action. This understanding is the beginning of a favourable change as it makes the child and adult aware that they belong together and it helps the adult to respect the child as a person.

If children are admitted to the Reeve, it's important to work professionally. Within families, upbringing often takes place in a spontaneous, natural course of events. In the communal group we opt for systematic upbringing. Not that the educationalists will behave unnaturally. The communal group is an organized environment in which we attempt to allow the children to experience this environment as being as natural as possible.

Based on information provided by the parents, from behaviour observation by the caregivers, from examination by the psychologist or special educationalist, the behavioural problems are analyzed. A training programme is then worked out, together with the caregivers, school and parents. Such a programme, an action plan, is important when things have gone wrong at home. In the action plan we ascertain how we must deal with the children and how we can help them with their problems. This sometimes entails simple suggestions, and sometimes complicated agreements which result in operations which systematically stimulate the learning process.

The most important part of the professional work is done by the caregivers working in the communal group. They are supported and guided by their team counselors and by the members of staff. The caregivers perform particularly difficult work because they often have to jump over their own shadow in an emotional sense. They must do their work with affection, but how do they do that if they're dealing with a child who prompts negative feelings in them? How can they be nice to a child they don't like?

Guidance is therefore necessary, so that they learn to put the child's behaviour into perspective, so that they learn to be objective about their own negative feelings. Otherwise they run the risk that they will take a gloomy view of that particular child, which will result in an increasingly disapproving attitude, leading to negative feelings between themselves and the child.

Results

We cannot improve on "learning difficulties" by means of our educational help.

What we can do is to attempt to strengthen the children's self confidence by allowing them to experience the fact that they have already learnt a lot and can already do a lot for themselves. We help the children to learn those daily activities which they need in their own situation and through which they become aware that they can learn new things and that they can also do those things which other children of their own age do.

By adopting a well thought-out approach they acquire new skills: the development of personal taste, planning of time, handling money, looking after themselves as far as their appearance and own rooms are concerned, listening to each other and dealing with criticism.

By teaching children and young people to integrate with one another and to consciously learn to process pleasant and unpleasant experiences, their self-confidence grows. This positive experience processing leads them to valuing themselves.

Through encouragement and support children learn that problems can be overcome; and that they can even play a part in that process. They thus often become stronger and more able to cope with the questions posed by life in our society. They become aware that the curse which was on them – their being different and their loneliness – can be broken.

Došen, A., Van Gennep, A., Zwanikken, G.J. (Eds.) (1990). Treatment of Mental Illness and Behavioral Disorder in the Mentally Retarded. Proceedings of the International Congress, May 3rd & 4th, 1990, Amsterdam, the Netherlands. Leiden, the Netherlands: Logon Publications.

Chapter 45

Aspects of Integrative and Dialogical Co-operation between Therapeutic Pedagogues and Psychotherapists in Working with the Mentally Retarded

W. Reukauf
H.S. Herzka

Introduction

From a perusal of the programme for this congress, our attention was very much drawn to the fact that for the care of mentally retarded children, adolescents and their families today, a multitude of helpers from various professional fields are involved. On the one hand, such multifarious efforts can be seen to indicate a welcome interdisciplinary development. On the other hand, practice shows that concrete application of such diverse approaches yields dissent in both theory and methodology which, in turn, may jeopardize the very efforts being made to help. Using examples of co-operation between therapeutic pedagogues and psychotherapists, the following paper will show how integrative and dialogical approaches facilitate collaboration between experts from different professional streams.

As has been shown elsewhere (Reukauf, 1985b), the problem of "discordant helpers" is a much-observed phenomenon amongst members of the medical, pedagogical, psychological and sociological professions. A detailed study of the backgrounds in the development of these therapeutic schools of thought reveals some connections in history, social psychology, psychology of the personality, as well as in the theory of science. Such connections clarify both the historical growth of these schools of thought as well as the present inevitability of disagreements amongst them. This explains, in our opinion, how differing viewpoints amongst helpers arise, for we are dealing with representatives of professional groups which have their own specific history. Furthermore, all of these groups are subject to social psychological laws. Because the theories and methods which are used by people of the helping professions to understand and therapeutically influence people are contradictory, it is characteristic of "helpers" to tend towards quarrelling, also because of certain personality traits and training peculiarities.

Multiplicity of therapeutic approaches

With our modern-day boom in therapy, together with our inflation of methodologies, there exists a confusing multiplicity of therapeutic approaches which are called "integrative", but which mean something different in each case (Herzka & Reukauf, 1988). In our opinion, it is possible to distinguish three approaches: the eclectic, the integrative (in the narrower sense of the word), and the pluralistic (Reukauf, 1985b). With an eclectic approach, it is permissible to combine theories of different origins, but this is done in an often inadmissible manner, according to the motto "the end justifies the means", whereby the only thing that counts is effectivity, not, however, theoretical clarity. Characteristic of the integrative approach is the search for an all-embracing "homogenous theory", an intention which has proved illusory, for man is a far too complex creature to be covered by any one closed uniform theory. Finally, the solution offered by the pluralistic approach is to accept the contradictions inherent in existing therapeutic theories, and to view such contradictions as being the foundation of fruitful dialogue and contest between the different schools. Compared to the eclectic or to the all-encompassing amalgamation of integrative therapeutic procedures, it would seem that a combination of well-tried and coherent therapeutic methods has proved itself to be most effective, also in practical work with the mentally retarded.

Within pluralism's effort towards integration, the following presentation of a dialogical-complementary approach has special significance insofar as it lends pluralism structure and definition. In the history of western philosophy, dialogical thought can be traced back to antiquity. But it attained its present significance only in the 19th and 20th centuries. Dialogics was especially furthered by, among others, Martin Buber (Buber, 1962; Iben, 1988) and became what it is today through the work of the contemporary philosopher H.L.Goldschmidt of Zurich (Goldschmidt, 1976). H.S. Herzka, also of Zürich, who is a child psychiatrist and co-author of this paper, introduced dialogical thought into the arena of child psychiatry and has applied it to many problem areas (Herzka, 1970, 1986, 1989; Reukauf & Herzka, 1985).

Dialogical thought

Dialogics postulates that two thoughts (which cannot be thought simultaneously), or two endeavours (which cannot be realized simultaneously), or two ideas (which are exclusive and pertain to their own particular area), or, as in our following example, two ways of approaching a child, namely pedagogy and psychotherapy (each with its own basic concepts and laws), make a simultaneous whole (not one after the other, as in dialectics) which is of equal value (without one being superior to the other) and is unified. Dialogics, then, is thinking in bi-poles. There is a certain contradiction or tension between the poles. Contradiction and tension are viewed as a sign of vitality and wholeness, and are accepted as being of fundamental importance and always necessary. This paradigm of thinking is also the basis of the principle of complementarity of the physicist Niels Bohr (Bohr, 1985; Fischer, 1987).

Table 1
Pedagogics – Psychotherapy: A Theoretical Comparison

	Pedagogics	Psychotherapy*
Perception of goal	Educational goal	Therapeutic goal
Direction of goal	Prospective	Retrospective
Means	Role models, guidance, corrections	Therapeutic situation: Association and interpretation
"Content"	Reality > fantasy	Fantasy > reality
Relationship	Closeness > distance	Distance > closeness
Duration of relationship	Basically always, with relationship changes	Transitional, therapeutic hour
Mediating basic skills	Important	Peripheral
Psychic resistance	Often necessary	Most often to be resolved
Autonomy	Often primarily an outer autonomy	Primarily an inner autonomy

*We are referring here to a depth-psychology oriented therapy, a so-called "uncovering" therapy. Behavioural therapy has in many aspects other criteria for differentiation.

By contrasting pedagogical and therapeutic points of view (Table 1), dissimilar, but in a dialogical sense compatible, ways to achieve one's goals in the care of the mentally retarded shall be given theoretical elucidation. To begin with, it is known that the psycho-reactively sick child needs psychotherapy because he is sick, and he needs (therapeutic) pedagogics because he is a (retarded) child. Therefore, in our opinion it is appropriate to view (therapeutic) pedagogics and psychotherapy as being two equal means of influencing a child, each being subject to its own laws which fundamentally contradict each other but which only together make a whole. They stand together in a dialogical-complementary relationship. Both standpoints should be kept clearly separate. But only when the identity of each viewpoint has been defined, and only when both professional groups (the therapeutic pedagogues and the therapists) accept each other in all their differences is it possible, in our opinion, for co-operation, based upon a mutual effort to understand, to occur, including all contradictions and tensions inherently there. Such tensions, however, may not be offloaded onto the patient (Herzka, 1985).

Pedagogical goals and therapeutic goals

Some of the most important points in which pedagogics and child psychotherapy differ and simultaneously complement each other are set out in Table 1 and are briefly commented upon below (Herzka, 1980, 1985, 1986). In both cases, the perception of goals is different: the comprehensive educational goal of pedagogics is contrary to the transformational goal of therapy. Pedagogical goals such as "to adapt", or "to become independent" may simultaneously contradict therapeutic goals such as "not to repres aggression" or "to allow oneself to regress". From the time perspective, pedagogical goals are aimed towards the future and are, therefore, prospective. Therapy, on the other hand, is directed more at what a child has experienced up to the present time and is, therefore, mainly retrospective. The means available to educators include role models, guidance and, if necessary, behavioural correction. In the therapeutic situation, association and interpretation are the main means at one's disposal, whereby in psychotherapy for the mentally retarded non-verbal techniques are used with mutual attention focused upon facial expressions and body movements. With regard to content, whereas pedagogics is primarily concerned with the concrete situation of the child with his abilities and talents, as well as his interactional behaviour, the psychotherapist is mostly interested in the intrapsychic life of the child, in his fantasies and dreams. In his relationship to the patient, a psychotherapist must preserve some distance. He does not become as close to the child as an educator might. The duration of the relationship in pedagogics is unlimited. The child is educated and the mentally retarded child requires life-long education. From the outset, a therapeutic process is transitional, it has a time restriction. Separation is inherent in the first contact. In psychotherapy of the mentally retarded, instruction in basic skills, such as independence in dressing and eating, play a peripheral role. At most, it helps the child become more responsive, and prepares him for learning processes, whereas in education, the same learning processes are, in themselves, important. Also different is the manner in which psychological resistances are dealt with. In pedagogics, they are often necessary and are part of normal defence mechanisms in everyday life. In therapy, however, they must often be resolved or at least be put into question. According to pedagogics, autonomy is often achieved by an outer independence being won through practical experience in real-life situations. In psychotherapy, it is often the case that a patient is assisted in attaining a greater internal independence in unchanged external circumstances.

To summarize, we emphasize again that we have sketched two basically different attitudes, both of which must be taken into consideration to varying degrees by educators and therapists. This means that in his treatment of psychologically disturbed mentally retarded patients, the pedagogue often needs to adopt a therapeutic approach or at least he needs to consider therapeutic aspects along with pedagogical ones, and that the therapist must sometimes function as an educator, or must employ pedagogical principles.

The practice of co-operation between therapeutic pedagogues, psychotherapists and members of other professional groups shall be further illustrated below in a short case-presentation.

Case-Presentation "Jean-Pierre"

After having enjoyed a carefree childhood, this boy suffered severe skull and brain damage in a traffic accident which occurred when he was nine years old. After several weeks of coma, various brain operations were performed which restored Jean-Pierre's intellectual abilities to the extent that he was able to be enrolled in a therapeutic pedagogical school for educationally subnormal children with the diagnosis "imbecility through brain trauma". Later on, he was able to find a position within the professional world by working in the kitchen of a home for the mentally retarded. Because of recurrent depression, suicidal fantasies, feelings of inferiority, fears of not being accepted, disproportionate guilt complexes along with psychosomatic reactions, the then nineteen year old youth was registered for psychotherapeutic treatment with our child and youth psychiatric service.

From my very first encounter with Jean-Pierre, I was impressed by his well-developed perceptional abilities for interpersonal relationships as well as his large capacity to reflect upon things, both of which were perceivable behind his evident intellectual retardation. The most important therapeutic goals towards which I aimed were to increase his level of psychic endurance as well as his ability to introspect. I also aimed at helping him achieve a realistic evaluation of his own potential and supported him in his efforts to come to terms with his earlier and present problems.

The following themes have been extracted from our conversations: memories of his accident; hope that an operation could repair the damage done to him; the aspect of fate in such unfortunate accidents; acceptance of his own body; somatisations; social problems and sexual education; dealing with insults; professional competence and limitations; patronization; being in a home and remaining there.

All the above psychotherapeutic endeavours would have been in vain had it not been for the fact that from the outset, there was amongst the various personnel of the home (for example, the director, the house doctor, the nursing staff, the social worker and the head of the kitchen) and myself a co-operative and productive and, in the sense outlined above, a dialogical-complementary team work which was given expression in the many and sometimes very controversial discussions which took place. In our personal dealings with Jean-Pierre it was necessary, though often difficult, for all those who were involved with him to draw a clear line between "psychotherapeutic" and "other" discussions. In my opinion, Jean-Pierre benefitted from all the united but varied endeavours and attention which were focused upon him by all who were interested in his fate, and not simply because he underwent a counselling therapy with one of those individuals. The therapist had his own defined and special role to play, but it was a co-ordinated role, performed within a pedagogical-therapeutic social network (Reukauf, 1985b).

References

Bohr, N. (1985). Atomphysik und menschliche Erkenntnis. Aufsätze und Vorträge aus den Jahren 1930-1961. Braunschweig: Vieweg.

Buber, M. (1962). Werke, Bd. l: Schriften zur Philosophie. München: Kösel. Heidelberg: Lambert Schneider.

Fischer, E.P. (1987). Sowohl als auch. Denkerfahrungen der Naturwissenschaften. Hamburg/Zürich: Rasch und Röhring.

Goldschmidt, H.L. (1964). Dialogik – Philosophie auf dem Boden der Neuzeit. Frankfurt a.M.: Europäische Verlagsanstalt.

Goldschmidt, H.L. (1976). Freiheit für den Widerspruch. Schaffhausen: Novalis.

Herzka, H.S. (197Off.). Ansätze zu einer Anthropologie des Kindes I-III, V. Prax. Kinderpsychol. Kinderpsychiat. (I: 19, 16-18 (1970); 20, 253-257 (1971); III: 22, 250-253 (1973); V: 25, 28-31 (1976)).
Herzka, H.S. (1980). Kinderpsychiatrische und therapeutische Aspekte bei geistig Behinderten. In Th. Hagmann (Hrsg.), Beiträge zur Pädagogik Geistigbehinderter (S. 119-131). Luzern: Verlag der Schweizerischen Zentralstelle für Heilpädagogik.
Herzka, H.S. (1985). Die Dialogik therapeutischer und pädagogischer Ansätze. Schweiz. Heilpäd. Rundsch. 7 (11), 259-264.
Herzka, H.S. (1986). Kinderpsychopathologie – ein Lehrgang. (2. erg. Aufl.). Basel: Schwabe.
Herzka, H.S. (1989). Die neue Kindheit. Dialogische Entwicklung – autoritätskritische Erziehung. Basel: Schwabe.
Herzka, H.S. & Reukauf, W. (1988). Zur Methodenintegration in der Kinder- und Jugendpsychiatrie. In G. Klosinski (Hrsg.), Psychotherapeutische Zugänge zum Kind und zum Jugendlichen (S. 11-2O). Bern/Stuttgart/Toronto: H. Huber.
Iben, G. (Hrsg.). (1988). Das Dialogische in der Heilpädagogik. Mainz: Matthias-Grünewald-Verlag.
Reukauf, W. (1985a). Kinderpsychotherapien. Schulenbildung, Schulenstreit, Integration. (2. erg. Aufl.). Basel/Stuttgart: Schwabe.
Reukauf, W. (1985b). Zur Praxis der Kooperation zwischen Psychotherapeuten und Heilpädagogen aus psychologischer Sicht. Schweiz. Heilpäd. Rundsch. 7 (11), 265-268.
Reukauf, W. & Herzka, H.S. (1985). Problems of integration of different approaches in child psychotherapy. Mediterr. J. Soc. Psychiat. 66 (1-2), 182.

Došen, A., Van Gennep, A., Zwanikken, G.J. (Eds.) (1990). Treatment of Mental Illness and Behavioral Disorder in the Mentally Retarded. Proceedings of the International Congress, May 3rd & 4th, 1990, Amsterdam, the Netherlands. Leiden, the Netherlands: Logon Publications.

Chapter 46

Mental retardation, emotional and behavioural disorders and foster care: a useful combination?

J. Prins

Introduction

Professional care in the Netherlands is characterized by a strict differentiation of services based on a differentiation of problems. Psychiatric disorders, behavioural disorders, delinquency, mental and physical handicaps: every problem has its own care system. This differentiation of problems and care systems is satisfactory, as long as the questions for help can be covered by one care system. A child with complex problems on which it could receive help in several care systems, is in danger to be excluded. Such a child is often rejected by institutions, because it has some other problems the institution has insufficient expert knowledge of.

The William Schrikker Foundation (WSF) is a national specialized guardian and supervision board for the benefit of mentally and/or physically retarded children and adolescents. In addition it extends help on a voluntary basis, especially concerning foster home placement for retarded children. Foster care has several advantages:

- the child can profit from individual caring and education, which is important for its social and emotional development
- the child has a greater opportunity to become a member of the community
- the child gets acquainted with the daily pattern of home life.

The WSF is often confronted with the consequences of the present differentiation of care systems. In addition, since it is providing help for the mentally retarded, the WSF is faced with two more problems. The first problem relates to the fact that until recently, emotional and behavioural disorders of the mentally retarded have hardly received any attention. The question for help was too unilaterally defined as originating from a mental handicap; the answer was consequently aimed at the mental retardation. Possible other specific problems were not acknowledged as such.

A second problem the WSF is faced with, being part of the care of the mentally handicapped, is the care's institutionalized way of thinking. The need for a residential setting is decided merely on the grounds of a person's mental retardation. The specific questions for help of the retarded and its caretaker or parent are insufficiently checked before offering help. Foster care is consequently second choice.

The three problems mentioned above, that are differentiation of problems and care systems, ignorance or little acknowledgement of emotional and behavioural disorders of some mentally retarded children, and a institution-orientated care of the mentally retarded, have to be dealt with by WSF in its care for a specific group of pupils, who, besides being mentally retarded, suffer from emotional and behavioural disorders as well. Continuation or initiation of residential treatment is often not advisable for these children and they are often thought to be more helped by living in a family environment. Their foster parents are faced with a difficult task however. Experience has shown that problems occurring in raising such a child often require intensive supervision and support of the foster home.

When placing children with emotional and behavioural disorders in a foster home, Therapeutic Foster Care (TFC) is a possibility that is sometimes considered. When TFC is applied for, however, mentally retarded children are rejected on the grounds of their intellectual functioning. These children end up at the WSF, where the social workers, because of their high caseload (33 clients, in contrast with the TFC's caseload of 12 clients) are not able to offer the foster home the necessary intensive supervision. In addition, there are usually complex problems concerning the development of the child and concerning its original family, as well as pedagogical problems within the foster home. This complexity requires a profound involvement and a close cooperation of several disciplines.

The WSF therefore started an intensive supervision of these foster homes on an experimental base in 1988. This is the so called Project Intensive Foster care (PIF), which intends to develop a methodology which will offer more than a social worker can usually offer and which should increase the chance of success of the foster home placement. For this purpose PIF uses facilities which are more or less similar to those of the TFC, such as a decrease of the social worker's caseload to 15 pupils (which gives him more time to select, supervise and support the foster parents) and an increase in staff members for the benefit of multi-disciplinarity.

In principle, intensive supervision is temporary since the PIF tries to attain a situation where foster parents are sufficiently equipped to raise the child without the supervision.

The Department of Special Education of the Free University Amsterdam was asked to describe and evaluate the project. The research is financed by the Ministry of Welfare, Health and Culture.

This paper will successively discuss the research model, the preliminary research (already concluded), the development of methodology, results until now, ideas for the future, and a conclusion.

Research model

The aim of PIF is: enabling placement and education of mentally retarded children with emotional and behavioural problems in foster homes.

Corresponding questions are:

- Which policy (organizational, financial and staff) and methodical conditions could enable mentally retarded children with emotional and behavioural disorders to be permanently adopted by a foster home as an alternative for lengthy institutionalization?
- If these conditions prove to be practicable, what would be the best form for a structured continuation of this project?

These main questions will be answered by way of 4 research phases. Phase I relates to the preliminary analysis of the project's target group and the shortcomings of the present care for foster homes raising these children. Phase II will verify which methodical and policy conditions are necessary to realise an adequate education in a fosterhome. Phase III will analyse the results of the project and phase IV relates to the research into the future form of the project.

Preliminary research (phase I)

The preliminary research (Prins, Baartman & Janssen, 1989) has already been concluded. An extensive questionnaire has been put to the social workers of the WSF. The results illustrate their opinion of potential PIF-candidates, of present foster homes, of the specific problems concerning rearing of these children and of the shortcomings of their own interventions.

According to the social workers about 8% (38) of the WSF-pupils (463) were suitable for the PIF in 1988. A general tendency towards an increasing group of foster children with emotional and behavioural problems can be recognized in the figures of the WSF. An upward tendency can be observed concerning the percentage of children suitable for PIF (in 1986 6%; in 1987 7%; in 1988 8%). In addition it should be noted that these potential PIF-candidates are children who are already pupils of the WSF. It is very probable to assume that the number of children in need of intensive foster care is much larger. For there are children institutionalized at present who might be more adequately helped by PIF. However, their caretakers are not aware of the possibility of applying for the project.

The group of children at the WSF who are suitable for PIF and who are involved in the research, consists of a larger percentage of boys (59%) than girls (41%). Their age ranges from 9 months to 14 years, with an average of 7 years. 56% of these children are living in a foster home at present; however their foster parents need intensive supervision. The remainder is institutionalized. On average, the children have not been living with their original family for 3½ years, in fact half of their lives. The majority of the children have been subject to a measure of child-protection, such as placement under supervision, taking away of parental rights or deprivation of parental authority.

The children's level of intellectual functioning varies from borderline to mildly and moderately retarded, or they are developmentally delayed. In many cases there are physical handicaps, retarded motor- and speech/language development. This group of children actually is doubly handicapped, due to the fact that the majority (84%) suffers from emotional problems such as withdrawal (contact disorder), anxiety, show no emotions, lack the ability of differentiation in attachement, and form behavioural problems such as negativism, agressiveness, hyperkinesia and chaotic, stubborn and inaccessible behaviour.

The answer to the questions what the future would be without PIF shows clearly that without PIF there would be no alternative for institutionalization. The homes these children come from can usually be called multi-problem families. In raising this specific group of children, parental neglect played an important role, which is also the most important reason for a measure of child-protection.

The reason for foster parents to adopt a foster child usually relates to their social concern or unwanted childlessness. The choice of a mentally retarded child is often related to the (positive) experiences acquired with mental retardation in a job or within their family or acquaintances. Foster parents are prepared to spend a great deal of time in an (often difficult) upbringing. Most foster homes are characterized by a traditional assignment of tasks. The problems foster parents have raising these children are diverse and occur almost every day. Exhaustion and deception are very important. They often have insufficient specific educational competence, needed to raise these children. The part played by the child in creating these problems is in any case related to its emotional and behavioural disorders. The demand for help from the foster-parents is mainly in the field of educational expertise. Regular care fails in those cases, when, regarding the complex problems of the child:

- matching the child and the foster home requires special attention;
- psychiatric, child-psychological and special educational knowledge is required for an adequate supervision of the foster parents;

– time-consuming contacts between social workers and foster parents are necessary.

Methodology and results (phases II and III)

The multi-disciplined supervisory team, responsible for carrying out the professional care, consists of a social worker who visits the foster home every 3 weeks and is their sole contact, and of a psychiatrist/psychotherapist and pedagogue who give advice which the social worker can integrate in his actions.

The care proceedings can be distinguished in several phases, viz.: child selection, foster home selection, matching child and foster home, preparations for placement, formulation of supervisory plan, supervision, evaluation, decrease in contacts and conclusion of supervision. Each phase will be discussed shortly.

Child selection: The team decides, in consultation with the applicant, whether or not to include a child in the project. The applicant will provide the necessary information. If the child is included, a foster home has to be found within 9 months or the decision is to be reconsidered. In the period between May 1988 and February 1990 a total of 32 children were applied for at the project, of which 14 are now living in a foster home, 3 are on the waiting list and the intensive supervision of the foster homes of 2 children have already been succesfully concluded . 13 Children are rejected for reasons such as too little need or indications for intensive supervision and acceptance for Therapeutic Foster Care.

The problems of the accepted children and their adaptation level at present is in accordance with the description of the target group in the preliminary research. In addition, they are generally very limited in their possibilities for attachment and making contact. These children are mainly in need of a permanent caretaker, who can expect little in return, however. Starting point is that admission into PIF can contribute to the well-being of the child by offering permanent caretakers, structure and prevention or delay of institutionalization.

Foster home Selection: The project is largely dependent on the Recruitment Centres for foster care to find foster parents that are interested. The laboriousness of providing information and carrying out foster parent reviews may be clear from the fact that only 15 to 20 % of the families are found suitable for PIF. The remainder is rejected for reasons as personal problems, specific handicaps and family structure, and often they withdraw themselves. So it is of vital importance to publicize this kind of foster care through large advertisements and information sessions and meetings. In conclusion one can say that the number of foster homes is increasing slowly but steadily. A lack of foster homes during the first year of PIF led to a waiting list and a stagnation building up the case-load.

In order to decide whether or not a family is suitable for PIF and supervisable by the social worker, a review takes place consisting of 4 interviews. The review should also provide special attention areas for the supervision of the foster parents.

The PIF does not only select traditional families. It is the quality of the home that counts. But naturally, the family structure is one of the specific areas that are considered in matching. So far, foster parents do not seem to need specific professional skills, but they should be able to accept the child for what it is and should be willing to spend much time and care on its education.

Matching: During this phase it will be examined on the basis of which characteristics a foster home and child will match. Starting point is that the 'ideal foster home' can not be found. The question is whether the team can provide the kind of care which would account for a placement of this specific child in this specific home. In addition to indication and contra-indication, items for supervision are formulated.

There seems to be a tendency towards placement of the child as the youngest member of the foster family, to reduce possible competition with other children. Naturally the limited number of selected children and foster homes set limits to the possible matches.

Preparation for a foster home placement: An important condition for the success of a placement is a thorough preparation of the foster home and child. The social worker spends a great deal of time on this preparation. The exact planning of the introduction procedure, which is directed by the social worker, depends on the individuals concerned. The planning is dependent of the age of the child, its adaptation level (how much knowledge does the child have of things to come and to what extent is the child attracted to its present caretaker), culture of the present educational situation of the child, capacities and wishes of the foster parents. Each important step of the introduction procedure is evaluated with the social worker to make the necessary adjustments to planning and to enable him to supervise the foster parents' expectations and to sympathise.

If possible, the present most important caretaker is involved in the introduction at an early stage. This is important in order to give the foster parent a realistic view of what they will be faced with. It proves to be of vital significance to keep the expectations a family has of the child realistic (especially concerning his capacities for attachment and reciprocity). Foster parents should be fully aware of the sort of child they have chosen. They are told that by adopting a PIF-child, 'they will not have the children out of their hands for a long time'.

Formulation of the supervisory plan: When a child has been placed in a family, a supervisory plan is formulated which will act as a guideline for the supervisory discussions. The points for attention from the foster parent review and the child's demands are included in this plan. Hypotheses are formulated of possible blockades concerning the placement and the resulting aims and methods for supervision. This scheme can always be adjusted on the basis of new information.

Supervision: The social worker visits the foster family every 3 weeks. This frequency of visits enables trust, continuity and availability towards foster parents. In addition it creates a possibility for more influence, because the social worker can intervene more often and problems can be indicated at an early stage. An escalation of problems can thus be prevented. The education should be optimalised by decreasing the burden (by way of a day, weekend, holiday arrangement) as well as by increasing their resources. Concerning the foster parents' resources, their needs are the starting point, so they can hold on. When problems occur, the parents are supervised (curative) and they will be made more competent in view of future problems (preventive). The psycho-hygiene of the family should be guarded; one should not save the fosterchild, while sacrificing the other members of the family. This justifies the occasional sacrifice of the foster child.

The emphasis is not on treating the problems of the foster child. Starting point are the child's limitations, which should be acknowledged and accepted, and as long as they do not deteriorate the situation is satisfactory. Treatment raises expectations for normalisation and when treatment is suggested it is often disappointing, because recovery is not always the case. The family is the focus of care.

It is essential that the foster parents receive information concerning the foster child and that its adaptation level, emotionally as well as cognitive, is elucidated. Raising a foster child is different from raising one's own. A foster child has often missed out on normal experiences. This will be clear from many day-to-day occurrences: these occurrences should lead the supervision of the foster parents.

Evaluation: After 6 months and consequently each year, an evaluation of the foster home placement and the supervision will take place. This evaluation includes the view of the team and foster parents, as well as the view of an external assessor of the development of the child.

Up until now, the intensive supervision of 2 placements have been concluded, because there is no longer need for or indication of supervision. The foster parents are skilled enough to cope with the support on a regular basis. These intensive supervisions have taken about 1 1/2 year. This means that circulation is possible. The intensive supervision is generally experienced as a useful experience.

Decrease in contacts and conclusion of the supervision: When the PIF decides to end intensive supervision, there are extensive discussions with the applicant to hand over the supervision. The termination of a placement should be carefully supervised, especially the process of leaving.

The future of the project

On the basis of present results, tentative conclusions appear justifiable that there is a need for this form of foster care, that, however hard, it proves to be possible to find foster homes for these children and that PIF is successful in developing useful care. Expectations are that the WSF will need a capacity of about 50 places. In the long run, when this type of foster care gets widely known, the capacity might need to be much larger.

It is still unclear which way the care will have to be organized exactly. However, a number of conditions will have to be met, such as an increasing number of foster homes and a probable case-load of 12 for the social worker.

Conclusion

The title of this paper asks whether or not mental retardation, emotional and behaviourial disorders and foster care is a combination which can be usefully united in one care system. At this stage of the research, the question can not be answered definitely, but it appears to be a practicable care system.

Up till now, the facts show that PIF will have to deal with a very difficult group of children. Children whose development is slower or deviant present their care-takers with many questions. The foster parents must learn skills that makes them able to handle these children.

The methodology developed by PIF up till now appears to be helpful and useful. In addition, the research has clearly shown that the success of the project is dependent on policy and social aspects as well. There should be more attention for foster care as a possible setting for the mentally retarded. In view of the need for an increasing amount of foster homes, the public image of mentally retarded people should be improved, just as the recognition of and facilities for foster parents. Another big problem WSS is faced with, when terminating a placement, is to find a (temporary or permanent) place for the child in an institution because of the structural lack of space. The PIF can hardly account for asking people to adopt these difficult children in their families, while consequently not being able to ascertain a place for the child when continuation of the placement turns out to be impossible.

With PIF, the WSS hopes to have found a way to face a complex educational problem, by way of combining elements from various sections of professional care.

Reference

Prins, J., Baartman, H. & Janssen, W. (1989). Interimrapport I: Het vooronderzoek. Vrije Universiteit, Amsterdam.

Došen, A., Van Gennep, A., Zwanikken, G.J. (Eds.) (1990). Treatment of Mental Illness and Behavioral Disorder in the Mentally Retarded. Proceedings of the International Congress, May 3rd & 4th, 1990, Amsterdam, the Netherlands. Leiden, the Netherlands: Logon Publications.

Chapter 47

Psychotherapy with a retarded, schizo-affective women: an application of Prouty's Pre-Therapy

D. Van Werde

Introduction

Pre-Therapy (Prouty, 1976; Peters, 1986, Van Werde 1989, 1990) is an evolution in 'reflective' method, especially designed for the treatment of the dually diagnosed.

This paper describes the theory of Pre-Therapy and its application to a woman who was diagnosed as mild to moderately retarded and schizo-affective.

Psychological contact, the necessary condition of psychotherapy

Psychological contact as the first condition of a therapeutic relationship is necessitated by poor ego functioning, institutionalization and impaired communication. These factors interfere with relationship formation and experiential processing and therefore require a different methodology. Pre-Therapy represents an evolution in Client-Centered theory and method (Rogers, 1957; Gendlin, 1968). Its specific theoretical and clinical goal is to restore or develop 'psychological contact' with the withdrawn, isolated or 'out of contact' clients who are not accessible to psychotherapy or habilitation programming. Hence the prefix 'pre'-therapy.

Clients are generally referred or chosen for Pre-Therapy due to their combinations of retarded, schizophrenic, autistic or brain damaged features.

Pre-Therapy: a theory of psychological contact

Pre-Therapy centers on the concept of 'psychological contact', developing psychological contact with World, Self and Other (Merleau-Ponty, 1962).

Contact is theoretically described on three levels. First, it is a set of therapeutic techniques. The CONTACT REFLECTIONS, by which the therapist facilitates contact with the client. Secondly, it is a set of psychological functions necessary for therapy to occur, i.e. reality, affective and communicative contacts, the CONTACT FUNCTIONS. Thirdly, it is a set of 'outcome-behaviors' or CONTACT BEHAVIORS, i.e. the emergent behavioral manifestations of psychological contact which result in operationalisation for research.

1. Contact reflections

Rank (Rycklack, 1971) developed reflection as a linguistic technique to elaborate therapist cognitive understanding. Rogers (1966) further evolved reflection to concretize non-directiveness, empathy and unconditional positive regard, all elements in his relationship theory of therapy. Gendlin (o.c.) alternately described reflection as an experiential technique directed at facilitating the concrete process felt by the client. Prouty conceptualizes reflective technique as the method by which the therapist makes contact with the contact-impaired client.

There are five contact reflections:

The 'situational reflections' are directed toward the client's immediate environment, situation or milieu. The theoretical purpose of these SR is the development or restoration of psychological contact with the World (Reality Contact).

E.g. 'The wall is yellow', 'the phone's ringing', 'it's dark outside'

The 'facial reflections' are focused toward pre-expressive affect in the client's face. The theoretical purpose is contact with Self (Affective Contact).

E.g. 'You smile', 'Bruno looks sad', 'you laugh'

The 'word for word reflections' assist the client to experience himself as expressor and communicator. These WFW are pointed toward word fragments, isolated words, incomplete sentences, meaningful sounds and various incoherent expressions. The theoretical function is contact with the Other (Communicative Contact).

E.g. 'Bah !'; C: 'Ggst, house, mmt' T: 'house'.

The 'body reflections' are intended to assist the client in his body-sense. These BR are empathic literal or verbal descriptions of the various bizarre bodily expressions or body states of the client.

E.g. 'Your arm is up', 'you point at your nose'.

The utilization of previously successful reflections in order to facilitate the experiencing process is done by the 're-contact/reiterative reflection' (RR).

E.g. 'The phone rang and you smiled', 'I said hello and you closed your eyes'.

2. Contact functions

Contact functions are described on three levels of awareness.

'Reality contact' is defined as the literal awareness of people, places, things and events (World).

'Affective contact' is defined as the awareness of moods, feelings and emotions (Self).

'Communicative contact' is defined as the symbolization of reality awareness and affective awareness to Others.

These are the necessary pre-conditions of therapy. The sharing of a mutual here and now and the expression of felt emotions form the theoretical goals of Pre-Therapy.

3. Contact behaviors

As a result of the Contact Reflections and the facilitation of the Contact Functions, Contact Behaviors are the emergent behavioral manifestations of psychological reality, affective and communicative contact. As a consequence, the client is more accessible to psychotherapy or remedial programming (social, vocational, educational).

For quantitative data supporting the Pre-Therapy hypothesis, we refer to an overview of the pilot research by Leyssen and Roelens (1988).

For intensive case studies see Prouty in Došen and Menolascino (1990): Pre-Therapy with a depressed mentally retarded adult; Prouty and Kubiak (1988) for working with a catatonic schizophrenic of high intelligence, and Prouty (1990) for Pre-Therapy with a retarded with schizophrenic like symptoms.

Case illustrations

In the following vignettes, we would like to give you a flavour of how the Pre-Therapy way of reflecting the situation, the facial expressions, the body and the spoken words or sounds is done.

We present you a random session of an ongoing therapy with a dually diagnosed woman.

Ann is 22 years old. She has a dual diagnosis of mildly to moderately retarded and schizo-affective. She is staying at a State of Illinois residential facility and is receiving lithium treatment.

During an unexpected pregnancy, Ann began to exhibit psychotic episodes of excitement (yelling and screaming) and became self-abusive (cutting and biting). At that time, she was staying at her grandmother's who was taking care of Ann and Ann's mother, mentally retarded herself. The child was aborted. The grandmother got ill and died shortly after. Ann had to be admitted.

Pre-Therapy was indicated to work with patient's low-level an distorted mode of thinking, feeling and acting.

The session is after 4 months of therapy. You'll see how the Pre-Therapy reflections correspond with the patient's pre-expressive efforts to cope with her emotions concerning the given themes: the pregnancy (through playing with a toy duck), the removal and the death of her grandmother.

A few months after this session was recorded, therapy had to stop since Ann was transferred to another state facility.

The therapist (T) is Katherine Finke (Pre-Therapy Institute) and at that time a paraprofessional. The name of the client (C) is changed into "Ann".

T 111	(FR)	You have a little smile on your face.
T 112	(BR)	You move your head quick.
T 113	(BR)	You scratch yourself.
C 114		(sound)
T 115	(WFW)	You're making noises.
T 116	(RR)	You were real quiet. Before you were talking, now you're quiet and you're making noises.
T 117	(BR)	You gesture with your hand.
T 118	(SR)	You look at me.
T 119	(BR)	You point to your throat.
T 120	(FR)	You close your eyes.
T 121	(SR)	You look down at the duck, you're looking out the window.
T 122	(SR)	You look up and all around.
T 123	(FR)	Little smile on your face.
C 124		(sound)
T 125	(WFW)	You make a little whiny noise.
T 148	(FR, SR, RR)	You're laughing, you're flipping your duck's head and laughing.
C 149		(laughter)

T 150	(FR)	You laugh.
T 151	(SR)	You make the sign for baby.
T 152	(RR)	Last week we talked about a baby and you made the same sign.
T 153	(RR)	You told me about a baby last week.
T 154	(BR)	You hold your hand up like this.
T 155	(SR)	You look at me.
T 172	(FR)	You close your eyes.
T 174	(BR)	You scratch your nose.
T 175	(RR)	Before, you said you wanted to go for a ride.
T 180	(SR)	You're looking at the desk.
T 181	(BR)	You have a scratch on your neck, right here.
T 182	(RR)	You have a red scratch on your neck.
C 183		Ha, ha, ha, ha.
T 184	(FR)	You laugh, little laugh ...
T 185	(BR)	You put your head down.
T 186	(SR)	You touch your duck.
T 187	(BR)	You put your head way down.
T 188	(FR)	Ann's face looks sad.
T 189	(FR)	Your face looks sad.
T 190	(FR)	Your face looks sad, Ann.
C 211		(noise)
T 212	(WFW)	You make little noises.
C 213		(noise)
T 214	(WFW)	(T makes the same noise)
T 215	(RR)	Sometimes you talk to me, sometimes you make noises.
T 216	(SR)	You pet your little duck's head.
T 217	(BR)	(T does the same thing)
T 218	(RR)	Before when you were petting your duck, you made the sign for 'baby'.
T 219	(SR)	You hold the duck close to you.
C 220		(noise)
T 221	(WFW)	You make little noises.
T 222	(BR, SR)	You touch your nose and your duck.
T 223	(FR)	Your eyes look sad.
T 224	(SR)	You look out the window.
T 225	(BR)	You rub your nose.
T 226	(SR)	You pull little things out of your pocket and you throw them on the floor.
C 227		(laughter)

T 228	(FR)	You laugh.
C 229		I laugh, I wanna.
T 230	(SR)	You saw somebody outside the window.
T 231	(WFW)	I wanna.
C 232		What kind of place I going to?
T 233	(WFW)	What kind of place are you going to?
C 234		Uh hum.
T 235	(WFW)	Uh hum.
T 236	(FR)	Your forehead's all kind of wrinkled up.
T 237	(FR)	You look worried, your face looks all worried.
C 238		Uh Hum.
T 239	(RR)	What kind of place am I going to?
T 240	(FR)	Your eyes and face looks sad.
T 241	(BR)	You tough your forehead.
C 242		I feel so tired.
T 243	(WFW)	So tired.
T 244	(BR)	You rub your hair back.
T 245	(FR)	You look sad.
T 246	(FR)	Your face looks so sad.
T 247	(RR)	You ask, you wonder what kind of place you're going to.
C 248		I'm going to take all my stuffed animals and leave my clothes behind.
T 249	(WFW)	You're going to take all your stuffed animals and leave your clothes behind.
C 250		My mama and grandma don't want my clothes.
T 251	(WFW)	Your mama and grandma don't want your clothes.
C 252		They do.
T 253	(WFW)	They do.
C 254		Uh Hum.
T 255	(WFW)	Uh Hum.

C 358		(laughter)
T 359	(FR)	You laugh.
T 360	(BR)	You rock back and forth.
C 361		Will you help pack and move my things?
T 362	(WFW)	Help me pack and move my things?
T 363	(SR)	You look at me.
T 364	(SR)	You're looking at me. You're asking me a question.
T 365	(RR)	Help you pack and move your things.
C 366		I want to move them now.
T 367	(WFW)	You want to move them now.
C 368		I want to move them out and never come visit.
T 369	(WFW)	You want to move out and never come visit.

C 370		(laughter)
C 371		I am.
T 372	(RR)	You say that strongly: I want to move out and never come visit.
C 373		I want my prisoners to take me out.
T 374	(WFW)	You want your prisoners to take you out.
C 375		Yeah.
T 376	(WFW)	Yeah.
T 377	(BR)	You're rocking.
T 378	(RR, SR)	You rock and I rock.
C 379		(singing and humming)
T 380	(WFW)	You sing.
C 381		(singing) I'd like to go far away.
T 382	(WFW)	You want to go far away.
C 383		(singing) I want to take my mom and my grandma ...
T 384	(WFW)	You'll take your mom and your grandma too.
T 385	(RR)	There ain't no love in the whole town.
C 386		(singing) I like to go far away (humming)
T 387	(WFW)	You'd like to go far away.
T 388	(FR)	Your eyes look sad when you say it.
C 389		(singing)
T 390	(BR, SR)	We're both rocking
C 391		(singing)
T 392	(SR)	You're looking at me.
C 393		BOOM (laughter)
T 394	(WFW)	BOOM That was a quick ending to that song. (they laugh together)
T 460	(BR, RR)	You touch your forehead where I touched it before.
T 461	(BR)	Right there.
C 462		I want my grandma alive.
T 463	(WFW)	You want your grandma alive.
C 464		Great grandma.
T 465	(WFW)	Great grandma.
C 466		Yeah.
T 467	(WFW)	Yeah.
C 468		She's in heaven with God.
T 469	(WFW)	She's in heaven with God.
T 470	(RR)	You want her alive.
T 471	(FR)	You close your eyes.
T 472	(FR)	Your face looks sad.
T 473	(RR, FR)	Ann, your face looks sad and your eyes look sad.

C 474		I want something to eat.
T 475	(WFW)	You want something to eat.
T 476	(FR)	You make a face.

Discussion

In the fragment, the different kinds of reflection are used. You can see how 'playing' with these 'techniques' assist the patient in her private struggle for contacting reality, affect and communication. You see how the patient is met. It shows how this non-directive way of empathic reflection deals with a confused, contradictory, stereo-typed and acted-out way of experiencing. The patient has plenty of opportunity to express herself, even if the level is low. The therapist shows a lot of trust in the patient. There is no interference with her process, her tempo is respected, no questions that could distract her are asked, no interpretations are given. It's building a relationship, it's being with the unfolding experiencing. It helps to bring back together pieces of shattered communication.

When we look closely at the fragment and with her biographical data in mind (that at the moment of the session were unknown to the therapist!) we could say that the general theme is 'loss'. The patient circles around her duck – what later becomes her baby that was aborted – then talks about leaving, going for a ride, moving and ends with really contacting her being tired (C 242) and her mourning for the deceased grandmother (C 462/4/6/8).

We see that patient and therapist had a long way to go to reach that kind of contact. It shows how through the use of the five kinds of empathic response at patient's level of concreteness and periodically adequate language, contact with emotions and reality is reached.

References

Gendlin, E.T. (1968). The experiential responce. In A. Hammer (Ed.), *Use of interpretation in treatment* (pp. 208–228). New York: Grune and Stratton.

Leyssen, M. & Roelens, L. (1988). Herstel van contactfuncties by zwaar gestoorde patiënten door middel van Prouty's Pre-Therapie. *Tijdschrift Klinische Psychologie*, 18, 21–24.

Merleau-Ponty, M. (1962). *Phenomenology of perception*. New York: Routledge and Kegan Paul.

Peters, H. (1986). Prouty's pre-therapie methode en de behandeling van hallucinaties: een verslag. *Ruit*, 26–34.

Prouty, G. (1976). Pre-Therapy, a method of treating pre-expressive psychotic and retarded patients. *Psychotherapy, Theory, Research and Practice*, 13, 290–294.
Prouty, G. & M. Cronwall (1990). Psychotherapy with a depressed mentally retarded adult: an application of Pre-Therapy. In Došen, A. & F. Menolascino, *Depression in mentally retarded children & adults*. Leiden: Logon Publ.
Prouty, G. & M.A. Kubiak (1988). The development of communicative contact with a catatonic schizophrenic. *Journal of Communication Therapy*, 4(1), 13–20.
Prouty, G. (1990). Pre-Therapy: A theoretical evolution in the person-centered/experiential psychotherapy of schizophrenia and retardation. In Lietaer, G., J. Rombauts & R. Van Balen (Eds.), *Client-Centered and Experiential Psychotherapy in the nineties* (pp. 645–658). Leuven Univ. Press.
Rogers, C. (1957). The necessary and sufficient conditions of therapeutic personality change. *Journal of Consulting Psychology*, 21, 95–103.
Rogers, C. (1966). Client-centered therapy. In S. Arieti (Ed.), *American handbook of psychiatry* (Vol. 3, pp. 183–200. New York: Basic Books.
Rychlack, J. (1971). *Introduction to personality and psychotherapy*. Boston: Houghton Mifflin.
Van Werde, D. (1989). Restauratie van het psychologisch contact bij acute psychose: een toepassing van Prouty's Pre-Therapie. *Tijdschrift voor Psychotherapie*, 15(5), 271–279.
Van Werde, D. (1990). De Pre-Therapie van Prouty: Psychotherapie met de pre-expressieve zwakzinnige cliënt. In Došen, A. & D.A. Flikweert (Eds.), *Zorg voor geestelijke gezondheid bij zwakzinnigen* (pp. 126–132). Groningen, Stichting Kinderstudies.

Došen, A., Van Gennep, A., Zwanikken, G.J. (Eds.) (1990). Treatment of Mental Illness and Behavioral Disorder in the Mentally Retarded. Proceedings of the International Congress, May 3rd & 4th, 1990, Amsterdam, the Netherlands. Leiden, the Netherlands: Logon Publications.

Chapter 48

Diagnostic and treatment issues for adults in community care

N. Bouras
C. Drummond

Introduction

The resettlement of adults with a mental handicap from long stay institutions to community has started a new era in the delivery of services. One case is the closure of Darenth Park Hospital which was one of the oldest institutions in Britain built in 1878. There were over 2000 residents at one time on the site, living in more than 40 wards. The hospital closed almost 2 years ago following a closure process lasting for about 15 years. (Korman and Glennerster, 1990).

Alternative community services were developed by the different Health Districts to receive back their residents. In our case a plan was developed over a period of five years based on the philosophical principles that people with a mental handicap: participate fully in a range of activities alongside people without disabilities; that they are enabled to make choices and decisions for themselves; and that people will have different needs and therefore the service will respond flexibly to meet them.

The setting

The plan was supported by an expert psychiatry of mental handicap service. The primary tasks were clinical, and multi-agency advisory/supportive. The clinical role involves mainly psychiatric assessment, treatment for adults with diagnosable mental illness, monitoring of psychotropic medication, contribution to the clinical management of epilepsy and liaison with other doctors.

The multi-agency advisory/support role includes, therapeutic intervention and multi-disciplinary work in the clinical management of behaviour problems and challenging needs; contribution within a multi-disciplinary forum to support relatives and care staff; participation in training initiative and skills transference to staff as well as generating ideas for improving the service.

Place and Mode of Working

(1) Community visits (homes, hostels, day centres)
(2) Outpatient clinics
(3) Clinical meetings with the community multidiscipline team
(4) Special meetings with social services, direct care staff, hospital staff, general practitioners, family and other community agencies.

All referred clients receive a detailed assessment. The assessment is followed by the documentation of any intervention plan, targeting specific goals in symptom or function. The active intervention is followed by supportive phase during which the changes or modification are seen to be established and a gradual withdrawal of the provided expert service occurs. Then progress is reviewed at regular follow-up intervals.

The two applied therapeutic interventions are Home-based and Admission-Treatment.

Home-based Intervention

This intervention occurs in the clients' normal living environment, which is important because this is where the identified behaviour is occurring and also the people with whom the client interacts are important agents for producing change. The treatment plan is individually devised and remains flexible, to be responsive to changing situation demands.

Admission and Treatment Intervention

Less frequently admission might be needed, either because a more complex and detailed assessment is required, or the intervention cannot be carried out in normal living environment. Two inpatient beds are available for this purpose in a designated general psychiatric ward.

The following plan is applied with each admission:
(1) The length of stay and disposition are established before admission.
(2) The nursing staff are informed and prepared on the expecting client.
(3) A complete diagnostic assessment is carried out.
(4) Treatment plan is developed which might include behaviour monitoring and modification, individual care plan, and medication.
(5) A reinforcement independent functioning programme is devised as required.

(6) Gradual transfer of client is arranged and continuation of treatment intervention to the usual living environment.

In both interventions the existing resources and skills from either the specialist or generic services and agencies might be used.

Evaluation method

The present study is concerned with the assessment of the behaviour and psychiatric needs of the 74 people with a mental handicap, recently resettled to community facilities within their own geographical area. The majority of the clients (76%) were resettled to ordinary houses, 10% in hostels and 14% in a long stay large residential, of a small type institution facility. All residents were assessed prior to their resettlement and one year after. Details of their personal and clinical characteristics were recorded on the "Assessment and Information Profile Rating Scale" (Bouras and Drummond 1989). This is a multi-dimensional assessment procedure covering social and demographic characteristics, family information, medical history, skills assessment, behavioural problems, psychiatric assessment, problem oriented list and clinical management decisions.

Results

Of the 74 assessed clients in the institution 3 had died a year later. Two were elderly and the third suffered from myeloma prior to his resettlement. Of the remaining 71 residents 44 were men and 27 women. The mean age was 46.1 (SD ±17.9) years.

The majority of the people had severe mental retardation (46%), while 23% had a moderate degree and 31% mild.

Behaviour Problems

Behaviour Problems, as rated by the scale we used (Kushlick et al 1973) were present in 30 residents before and 28 after the relocation. The difference was not statistically significant (x = 0.13). We found also no difference in the mean scores of frequency or severity of behaviour problems.

Psychiatric Diagnosis

Psychiatric assessment was performed on all residents one year after their resettlement and diagnosis was based on ICD-9 clinical criteria. (Insert Table A here).

Table 1 shows that the number of clients with a psychiatric diagnosis was slightly increased from 14 (20%) before relocation to 17 (24%) after but the difference was not statistically significant.

Only 3 clients had to be admitted to a psychiatric unit for treatment. One suffered from depression, one for personality disorder and severe disturbed behaviour problems and one for schizophrenia. Similar low admission rate was found in our community study where 21 clients out of 260 referrals required inpatient treatment. (Bouras and Drummond 1989).

Table 1
Psychiatric Diagnosis

	Before (n=71) N	After (n=71) N
Adjustment Reaction	2	4
Depression	1	2
Schizophrenia/ Paranoid Psychosis	4	4
Personality Disorder	7	7
No Psychiatric Diagnosis	57	54

Comments

A psychiatrist providing a service to adults with a mental handicap living in the community faces many challenges. These focus around the provision of clinical service to people who are living in 'ordinary' staff supported houses. Some times the philosophy of the service might conflict with the 'medical model' which views a person to have a disorder of such a nature or degree that different expectations of the person apply, while the individual shows evidence in their behaviour or speech of this disorder. The challenge for the psychiatrist is to bridge together the two conflicting aspects and transform them to successful therapeutic intervention.

The de-institutionalisation movement has dramatically altered the environment experienced by the clients and staff. The old institutions were normally hospitals with qualified nurses in charge of wards and psychiatrists providing general medical as well as psychiatric care. In the community the clients live in ordinary houses scattered throughout the district. Tremendous responsibility is placed on untrained members of staff at times.

The role of the staff in maintaining people with mental handicap in community houses is vital and crucial. It has been a gratifying experience for clinical psychiatrists to work very closely and intensively with unqualified care workers, called "support workers". The following factors have been identified from our experience as important.

a) Recognising the Problem

Diagnosis of psychiatric disorders depends on taking a full psychiatric history with particular emphasis on the mental state as observed during the interview. This method presents difficulties if the person examined has little or no verbal communication skills. A certain level of functioning must be present before the presence of thought disorder or perceptual abnormalities can be determined.

Therefore it is important to get more information from a reliable witness and good historian who can indicate the usual level of function and identify behaviour which may have altered recently. Recent changes in client's life might have also been noticed. Several factors affect the reliability and validity of the provided information such as the personal experience of the witness and the acceptance that psychiatric disorders may not always be the result of environmental factors.

b) Communication

The importance of staff communication and in particular disagreement on hospital in-patients has been well documented for psychiatric inpatients. (Bouras et al 1982). Staff disagreement could be open or covert but in either instance the effect on clients is detrimental. This issue becomes equally of a problem when people with mental handicap live in community staffed house.

c) Commitment

Commitment to the philosophy of service is a necessary component for all human services and in particular for people with learning disabilities. Commitment however should be balanced with reality because there is a risk of "burn-out" as staff are faced with difficult long term challenges.

Conclusion

As we have shown often the client does not have a psychiatric illness but is showing emotional and behavioural disturbance. Initial reports from the implementation of the descripted service plan, suggest that ordinary housing did provide a more effective service model than either larger residential facilities such as hostels and hospitals (Joyce 1990). There appears, however, to be a number of complex factors important in the production of good quality outcomes. These factors might have much more to do with the organisation and management of the setting than the characteristics of the clients living in a particular type of setting (Ibid).

These important issues should be taken into consideration in developing community services for people with mental handicap together with economic appraisal indicating that the cost of "small units" is higher than hospital care (Glennerster 1990).

With the current rapid developments of care for people with a mental handicap, it is important to provide informed experience with which to advise others and to encourage some form of evaluation to be built into the establishment of new services. This report has illustrated some generally applicable experience of the behaviour and psychiatric needs of adults resettled from institutional care to community facilities and could contribute to a process evaluation of quality of care.

References

Bouras, N. and Drummond C., (1989). Community Psychiatric Service in Mental Handicap : Health Trend. 21, 72.

Bouras, N., Trauer, T., Watson, J.P. (1982). Ward Environment and Disturbed Behaviour. Psychological Medicine 12, 309-319.

Glennerster, H., (1990). The costs of hospital closure : reproviding services for the residents of Darenth Park Hospital. Psychiatric Bulletin, 14, 140-143.

Joyce, T., (1990). Does ordinary housing work? Mental Handicap Research (in press).

Korman, N. and Glennerster, H., (1990). Hospital Closure : A Political and Economic Study: Open University Press. Milton Keynes.

Kushlick, A., Blunden, R., Cox, G. (1973). A Method of rating Behaviour Characteristics for use in large scale surveys in mental handicap. Psychological Medicine, 3, 466-478.

Došen, A., Van Gennep, A., Zwanikken, G.J. (Eds.) (1990). Treatment of Mental Illness and Behavioral Disorder in the Mentally Retarded. Proceedings of the International Congress, May 3rd & 4th, 1990, Amsterdam, the Netherlands. Leiden, the Netherlands: Logon Publications.

Chapter 49

A network of services for the mental health care of the mildly and moderately retarded in South-East Noord-Brabant (the Netherlands)

J.J.M.Gielen

Frequencies of prevalence

On behalf of the planning of provisions for Health Care, all 12 provinces in the Netherlands (± 14.000.000 inhabitants) are divided into so-called health regions. The province of Noord-Brabant is subdivided into four health regions, one of which is the region South-East with 651.326 inhabitants (1990).

Studies (I.V.A., 1988) have given estimates of prevalence of mental retardation in the Dutch population, within the category of age 5-70 (see Figure 1).

Figure 1
Estimation of mental retardation within the Dutch population (I.V.A., 1988)

level of retardation	ratios		numbers	
	male	female	male	female
mild and moderate retardation	4.7 0/00	3.1 0/00	30.087	19.437
severe and profound retardation	4.1 0/00	3.4 0/00	26.222	22.072
			56.309	41.509
total number			97.818	

The I.V.A. report has also given estimates of minimum and maximum numbers of mentally handicapped persons in the Dutch population (4 to 70 years of age). In another study (R.O.Z., 1990) these ratios have been transposed to the population of South-East Noord-Brabant (see figure 2).

Figure 2
Estimation of mental retardation in the population of South-East Noord-Brabant (R.O.Z.,1990)

level of retardation	ratios		numbers	
	min.	max.	min.	max.
mild and moderate retardation	3.7 0/00	4.1 0/00	2.104	2.332
severe and profound retardation	3.6 0/00	3.9 0/00	2.048	2.218
total			4.152	4.550

Estimates of prevalency of mental illness in the non-retarded population range from 7% to 10%, while within the population of the mentally retarded estimates range from 24% for the retarded staying within their families up to 40-50% for the institutionalized population (Došen, 1985). Applying these ratios to the population of mentally retarded, we roughly estimate that within Sout-East Noord-Brabant about 1553 tot 1691 patients with mental retardation also suffer from mental illness.

About half of them – 800 persons – are mildly and moderately retarded. This group is the subject of this paper.

A model of coöperation

At a national congress on mental health care for the mentally handicapped persons, one year ago, various Dutch experts in the field of the mentally ill – mentally retarded (Došen, 1990; Stark, 1990; Lucieer, 1990) argued the need for models of cooperation and forms of organization for an adequate treatment of the mentally handicapped with mental and behavioral disorders. The question is not that there does not exist knowledge about mental illness, on the contrary: there is much individual practical experience within the group of psychologists, physicians, social workers, staff members etc. The problem however is lack of both organization and cooperation between services and institutions, as well as lack of bringing together experiences and exchange of knowledge between workers.

Lack of organization and cooperation between institutions is especially a problem for the mentally retarded with behavioral and mental disorders who are intellectually or socially capable to live in small group homes in society or with their own families. In the last decade this group has increasingly become a problem because neither the general institutions for the mentally retarded nor the psychiatric hospitals were actually equipped for this care. Within their families and within the community-based group homes their behaviors couldn't be tolerated, and for psychiatry they generally couldn't follow the ruling therapeutic climate. In the meantime, the Dutch government had selected 5 specialized centres with a total of 168 places. They received additional financial means for the treatment of the very severely disturbed for 3 years at most. The aim of treatment was to enable the return to the original milieu. However, the limited level of treatment facilities and lack of coordination of expertise frustrated the attempt to offer a perspective of return to a normalized form of living to the group of mildly and moderately retarded. As a consequence, special care units within the institutions for the mentally retarded kept filling up of.

In 1988 all organizations and institutions in South-East Noord-Brabant who give care to the mildly and moderately mentally retarded, be it inpatient care or outpatient care, have entered into an agreement to cooperate in the treatment of the mentally retarded with behavioral or mental disorders. The participants are:

- a general psychiatric hospital
- a general institution for the mentally handicapped
- an institution for mildly retarded children up to age of 18-21
- 2 organizations for specialized social work within the field of mental retardation
- organizations for the community based living groups
- a specialized centre for the treatment of the very behaviorally disturbed mentally handicapped.

All participant have underlined some essential principles which are seen as hallmarks for the optimalization of the mental health care within the region Sout-East Noord-Brabant.

These principles are:

1. Collective responsibility

The notion of collective responsibility is the keyword for adequate functioning of the lien of cooperation. All participants are aware that the treatment of mentally handicapped must not be pushed off to one or two institutions or centres. Such a ward or centre would get filled in less than no time with the risk of ghetto-formation. No other institutions would be prepared or equipped to admit such patient after treatment. Such a course of action would conflict with the basic client-centered attitude, where the mentally retarded with mental or behavioral problems is seen as a human being with own needs, wishes and goals of life and the right to live in normalized conditions as much as possible. Besides, concentrating the mentally ill – mentally retarded in one or two inpatient centres would not stimulate the necessary dissemination of knowledge and change of attitude within other institutions within such a region. Replacement would heighten the risk of recidivism, with no continuity of care and treatment.

Finally, it must be stressed that all participants have agreed on commitment for exertion. That is, any problem with a behaviorally or mentally disordered patient must be solved between all participants.

2. Committee for indication and assignment of care

All participants have expressed the collective responsibility by starting a committee with the task of assessing problems that have been reporterd and assigning care for this problem to each of the participating institutions. Chairman of the committee is also chairman of the so-called committee for coordination of care, that tests the indications for mental retardation and assigns the admissions of all mentally retarded in the whole region. The committee plays a very important role in the bringing together of expertise and enhancement of knowledge of direct caregivers, staff members, etc. Examples are: discussions about case reports, collective meetings for study and thematic topics, exchange of experience between caregivers, etc.

3. Network of services

The regional coordination and cooperation has made it possible that a network of services has become available for the mental health care of the dually diagnosed. Of course there is a group of mildly mentally retarded who live independently or within their families, who can use the services of the general psychiatric hospitals or the outpatient mental health care for the non-handicapped population. Mildly retarded children who often stay at home can use the services of the observation centres for children, child psychiatric services or specialized centres within the care for the mildly retarded children.

Examples of services within the region South-East Noord-Brabant are: acute admission in crisis situations, intensive 24-hour care, outpatient forms of psychotherapy, 8-hour day-care, specialized care in community based group homes, specialized knowledge for intensified observation and treatment, and additional support for diagnosis and treatment in services in the region.

Participant in the network is also a specialized centre for the very severely mentally or behaviorally disordered. A child psychiatrist, specialized in the mental health care of the mentally retarded, is with to this centre and gives his expertise to all participating services in the region. For the region, the centre has the function of breeding place in the development of knowledge on issues of diagnosis and treatment. Patients from the region are sent to this centre in case of questions about specialized observation and treatment. The centre has scientific connections with the university. Services in the region South-East Noord Brabant can hand over their data, observation materials and other information for the purpose of scientific research. In addition to ambulant forms of psychotherapy, the centre offers to the region a team that can give support concerning diagnosis and treatment.

This network of services, this continuum of possibilities for treatment gets its significancy and activity, only if the participants come to adequate tuning by means of good deliberation and consultation, and if the needs of the mentally handicapped persons are taken as the primary focus of care.

4. Continuity of treatment and care

In the collective cooperation, all participants attach great importance to continuity of treatment. Actually, from the patient's point of view one must prevent that the mentally retarded person is confronted with a totally different approach when he/she is going to move to another institution. This requires from therapists, experts and staff members an exchange of their ideas and basic theories about mental illness in the mentally retarded, and ideas about therapeutic approaches as well. Meetings of collegues, multidiscipline meetings, discussions of case reports, etc. are good means to achieve more homogeneity in basic concepts. The point of view to be pursued in the regional cooperation is the developmental-dynamic approach (Došen, 1988). Stressing the need for continuity of treatment, participants have agreed on the idea that in case of transferring a patient from one institution to another, nurses and direct caregivers must be exchanged, and do their duty according to the duty-rota of the other team. They also participate in each others team discussions after the transfer of the patient. In case of questions about how to deal with the patient, consultations are possible.

5. Unification of basic concepts

For the sake of continuity in diagnoses and treatment, all participants acknowledge that there must be an optimal agreement concerning the way mental problems should be approached theoretically as well as practically. As mentioned before, the developmental dynamic approach seems to offer good perspectives for the mental health care in the region. Of course, one cannot expect an immediate change of viewpoints and assumptions on which diagnoses and treatment are based in the regional institutions. For some categories of patients, probably of higher cognitive levels and with more classical-psychiatrically coloured symptomatology, phenomenological-etiological diagnostics suffice as starting points for diagnosis and treatment. However, the usual diagnostic categories generally fall short of dealing with the diversity of clinical aspects, especially with the more severely handicapped.

Another objective of treatment within the regional cooperation is that the patient keeps the perspective on placement in a setting which fits best his/her possibilities. This attitude may be seen as an underlying assumption of the developmental approach where disorders are faced with hopeful expectation.

Whether or not a placement has a chance of succes depends largely on the level of respect and acceptance with which the mentally handicapped is encountered. Exchange of direct caregivers, transfer of complete information, possibilities of experts, etc. are measures that can reduce the risk of relapse considerably. However, a proportion of patients will hardly succeed in maintaining themselves in a community based group home and will have to remain for a considerable length of time in the relatively protective circumstances of the inpatient care, using the activity facilities of the institution.

6. Specific attitude

The care for the mentally handicapped person with mental or behavioral problems requires a specific attitude. This attitude is characterized by ful acceptance of the mentally retarded with his/her problems, and does not focus on a therapeutic climate or structure that aims to curtail, suppress, etc., but wants to understand the mentally handicapped person from his/her own system of giving sense to his/her life. It is a client-centered approach that tries to explore the meaning of the patient's behaviour in terms of his/her story of life. It takes into account the wishes and goals the patient sets in his/her life. Sometimes, manifestations of behaviour, often indicated as a behaviour disorder, can be interpreted as a crisis, as a signal that the situation in which the patient lives in is not in concordance with his/her initial goals or system that gives sense to life. The question to be answered is: how can we give help to this mentally handicapped person in order to give him/her back his/her sense of life, that makes him/her recognize him/herself again and restores the happiness of his/her life.

This approach assumes that the observer is able to leave behind for a moment his schemes of diagnosing, probably his premature opinions, while he is invited to give words to what the handicapped person cannot express verbally. Anamnestic information, analysis of video tapes, verbal information of members of the family and important others, all form important sources in the understanding of the patient's story of life. However, it is not the objective completeness of this information that we must strive for. It is rather the empathic understanding of the meaning of life events, social context, etc. for the patient and how this historical context has influenced his/her values, strivings and construct of life.

This enquiry serves the interests of the patient. It may prevent that the patient is approached by the diagnostician with a rigid point of view, as an overall explanation of different kinds of behavioral or mental problems. It may prevent that the patient is approached by direct caregivers with rules and limitations as an overall therapeutic model suited for all patients. When the patient is moved to another institution, new caregivers are challenged to understand the patient with his/her unique strivings and goals for life.

7. Consultation and expertise

Participants have agreed that expertise should be available for all services for the care of the mentally ill – mentally retarded. Experts from participating institutions are prepared to help solve questions and problems concerning patients elsewhere. Within these institutions the notion has been established that a specialized psychiatrist can contribute significantly to the level of the mental health of the dually diagnosed. By written agreement, the psychiatrist who is with the specialized centre for the severely disordered gives his services to all participating institutions in the region for several hours a week. Within these organizations he is a member of a multi-discipline team, which enables him to continuously follow the progress of treatment defined in a broad sense. He can be very helpful in the transfer of knowledge concerning mental problems in mentally handicapped, the establishment of the optimal therapeutic conditions, etc.

8. Coordination

A regional network with services for the dually diagnosed does not work without adequate coordination and initiation. Participants have agreed that one participant has the responsibility of coordination for the whole region. the coordinating institution has the task to take initiatives for the development of policy for mental health care in the region, to arrange meetings, coordinate courses and education, to call in expertise, etc. It gives the facilities to the committee for indication and assignment. Moreover, the regional cooperation has at its disposal an office with the task of registration of indications for the regional services, planning of meetings, taking of minutes, etc.

Conclusion

Until now, the cooperation of services in the region South-East Noord-Brabant have served mainly the needs of the mildly and moderately mentally handicapped. This is partly because of the practical reason that the network services were initially set up for the mildly and moderately retarded. Extending the target group at this moment to the more severely handicapped would be a too large burden on the cooperation. Besides, cooperation between organizations and institutions only works if these organizations themselves feel the need to cooperate. There is of course much knowledge and expertise among the workers who take care of the mental health of the more severely handicapped. However, this expertise should be exchanged more systematically and scientifically. The mental health care for this group should also be organized under the conditions of coordination and agreements between organizations. The cooperation of services in South-East Noord-Brabant may serve as an example of how forms of cooperation can be achieved. This may have stimulating effects on other workers in the field of the mental health care in the Netherlands, who also try to find ways to cooperate.

References

Došen, A.(1988), *The Developmental Approach to the diagnosis of psychiatric disorders among mentally retarded adults.* World Psychiatric Association Regional Symposium, Washington D.C.

Došen, A.(1985), Zwakzinnig kind met psychische stoornis; een weinig bekend gebied. *Tijdschrift Orthoped. Kinderpsych.*, (10), 26-34.

Došen, A.(1990), Psychische en gedragsstoornissen bij Zwakzinnigen en de behoefte aan vormen van speciale zorg voor de geestelijke gezondheid bij deze populatie. In: A. Došen en D.H. Flikweert (red.), *Zorg voor geestelijke gezondheid bij zwakzinnigen.* Stichting Kinderstudies en N.G.B.Z., Groningen/Holland.

Instituut voor Sociaal-Wetenschappelijk Onderzoek (I.V.A.) (1988), *Frequentie-onderzoek geestelijk gehandicapten 1986.* I.V.A., Katholieke Universiteit Brabant, Tilburg.

Lucieer, W.J.(1990), Gedragsgestoordheid bij Geestelijk Gehandicapten: een visie bij de Inspectie. In: A. Došen en D.A. Flikweert (red.), *Zorg voor Geestelijke Gezondheid bij Zwakzinnigen.* Stichting Kinderstudies en N.G.B.Z., Groningen/Holland.

Regionaal Overleg Zorg voor geestelijk gehandicapten Zuid-Oost Noord-Brabant (1990), *Beleidskader zorg voor geestelijk gehandicapten Regio Zuid-Oost Brabant.* R.O.Z. Zuid-Oost Brabant, Eindhoven.

Stark, F.T.P.G. (1990), Regionaal Hulpverleningstraject voor licht geestelijk gehandicapten met gedragsproblematiek. In: A. Došen en D.A. Flikweert (red.), *Zorg voor geestelijke gezondheid bij zwakzinnigen.* Stichting Kinderstudies en N.G.B.Z., Groningen/Holland.